MITA

Mobile Internet Technical Architecture

Visions and Implementations

IT Press

Published by
Edita Publishing Inc.
IT Press
P.O.BOX 760
FIN-00043 EDITA
FINLAND

Distributor information:

For information about distribution, please visit our Web site
at **http://www.itpress.biz/distributors**

ISBN 951-826-670-0

Printed by Gummerus Inc., Finland.

This document is an approved part of Nokia Mobile Internet Technical Architecture release.

Nokia Mobile Internet Technical Architecture, aims to provide seamless interoperability between all interaction modes, any network environment and, with any type of access. The ultimate objective of the initiative is to create a user-friendly Mobile Internet experience for everyone.

In developing a clear technical architecture for the Mobile Internet, Nokia aims to limit the complexity of the inherently technical environment; consumers do not want to worry about the underlying technologies.

An open solution benefits all; profitable business scenarios call for interoperability, short development cycles, large volumes and, most of all, global reach. Unless there is a commonly accepted architectural solution, markets will be fragmented as well as requiring separate parameters, and the total volume will be much smaller than in a single global market.

Nokia Mobile Internet Technical Architecture (MITA) is defined by Nokia Mobile Software unit. Any comments concerning this document can be sent to mita.feedback@nokia.com. Please visit the official MITA Web site at: www.nokia.com/mita

Table of Contents

Mobile Internet Technical Architecture 25

Marko Suoknuuti

Modeling the Technical Architecture 36

MITA Concept Models 45

MITA Implementation Model 53

III VISIONS 59

Introduction to MITA Specifications 61

Marko Suoknuuti, Juha Lampela

Architecture Specifications 61

Key System Specifications 65

Mobile Internet Interfaces 233

Juha Hietasarka

Quality of Service 245

Kalevi Kilkki, Jussi Ruutu

Hui Huang, Jian Ma

Pekka Pessi, Jari Selin, Mikko Lönnfors

Acknowledgements

The past two years have been an exciting time with the challenges of the Mobile Internet and its defining Technical Architecture. We have seen the summit of the Internet boom and lately faced a more demanding period in the mobile industry. In the interim, the definition of the Nokia Mobile Internet Technical Architecture has matured to a complete release in the form of this book series.

I would like to thank the people involved in this effort:

o   All the contributors and teams for their remarkable efforts in creating the content

o   The Editors' Board: Jyrki Kivimäki, Juha Lampela, Hanna Passoja-Martikainen, Sari Päivärinta, Krister Rask and Jussi Ruutu for their excellent work in keeping the book process on schedule and in shape

o   Sami Inkinen and Mikko Terho for their support and guidance en route to the complete release

o   Jani Ilkka, Juha Kaski and the rest of the IT Press team for doing an outstanding job with the publishing process

o   Nely Keinänen, Anna Shefl and Michael Jääskeläinen for doing a great job with the language revision and proofreading large amounts of technical material on a very strict schedule

o   Eija Kauppinen and her team at Indivisual for numerous high-quality illustrations

And finally:

o   My wife, Helena, for her understanding and support, especially in the last few months when the book process has occupied my time

Marko Suoknuuti
Chair of the Editors' Board

The Authors/Contributors:

Antti Vähä-Sipilä	Jari Urpalainen	Matti Kangas
Asko Komsi	Jarno Rajahalme	Mika Lepistö
David Banjo	Jian Ma	Mikko Lukkaroinen
Fan Yang	Juha Hietasarka	Mikko Lönnfors
Frank Dawson	Juha Kokkonen	Mikko Terho
Gabor Marton	Juha Lampela	Mitri Abou-Rizk
Guido Grassel	Jukka Alakontiola	Murali Punaganti
Hannu Flinck	Jukka Saunamäki	N. Asokan
Hao Wang	Jussi Ruutu	Olli Rantapuska
Harri Paloheimo	Justin Ridge	Ossi Korhonen
Heikki Riittinen	Jyrki Stenvall	Pekka Kuismanen
Holger Hussmann	Kai Nyman	Pekka Pessi
Hui Huang	Kalevi Kilkki	Petri Asunmaa
Jan-Erik Ekberg	Kari Oinonen	Sami Virtanen
Janet Cerniglia	Lauri Paatero	Sari Päivärinta
Janne Kilpeläinen	Margareta Björksten	Stephane Coulombe
Janne Uusilehto	Marko Heikkilä	Teemu Jalava
Janne Ylälehto	Marko Kokko	Tero Koskivirta
Jari Kinnunen	Marko Suoknuuti	Timo Koskiahde
Jari Malinen	Markus Isomäki	Toni Sormunen
Jari Mustajärvi	Martti Mela	Viktor Varsa
Jari Selin		

I PROLOGUE

o Prologue

Prologue

The next few years will see the convergence of mobile communications and the Internet resulting in new services, new business models and new business opportunities.

The Internet has become an everyday source of information, entertainment and other services for millions of people around the world. In our vision, the Internet will become mobile and content will go wireless, as voice communication has done. The future is no longer about the Internet but about services on the mobile Internet. This is a new environment, called the Mobile World, where the evolution paths of Mobile communications and the Internet have converged. The Mobile World provides innovative services for consumers, and the development of these services is driven by consumer behavior.

The Mobile World can be perceived as a holistic, evolving environment of the future, but also as an environment on a personal level that enables people to shape their Mobile World through personalized communication services. In the Mobile World, delivering targeted, timely information and services is essential.

The key to commercial success in the Mobile World depends on three main factors:

o   Understanding consumer needs, lifestyles and attitudes, and consequently being able to provide a matching combination of service portfolios and products,

o   Readiness of the business system to enable service consumption, and

o   Being able to match technical architectures to evolving consumer needs and to the evolution of business systems.

Those who deliver product categories and platforms with the right services and technologies will be the victors in the Mobile World.

The winning technical architecture in the Mobile World will enable seamless interoperability between key applications, network environments and the user identity/addressing system, limit the complexity of the technical environment supporting services so that consumers do not need to be concerned with the underlying technologies, support open technologies, standards and relevant initiatives which support and facilitate the deployment of global technologies and services, and stimulate market growth.

The Nokia solution addressing these demands is the Mobile Internet Technical Architecture (MITA). For the players in the field, MITA is the essential framework for creating user-friendly Mobile World experiences. It is an architecture which comprehensively enables networks to be driven by services. MITA addresses relevant technologies and standardization forums for the Mobile Internet, the current solutions and developer environments provided by Nokia, specifies design principles and technology visions for the Mobile Internet, and describes reference implementations.

Mobile Internet services need to address consumer needs, as this provides a healthy starting point for creating business. Consumers will be introduced to new, exciting services, but their concerns related to privacy issues and the secure use of services must be taken into account. To ensure the take-off and use of Mobile Internet services, the technical solutions must be geared towards minimizing underlying system complexity, be it application behavior or multiple access management. The Visions section outlines requirements for the key building blocks of the Mobile Internet Technical Architecture.

MITA work involves a strong emphasis on reference implementations. These are needed to validate new concepts, to gain experience and to smoothen the way for products based on the latest technologies. They will also serve as a basis for open source distributions which will benefit the developer community. Implementations section introduces the MITA Reference Implementation Environment, which consists of reference terminals and networks. This environment includes many of the latest technologies integrated on the same platform. After the overview, various reference implementations will be described.

Long term MITA technical visions and technology evolution scenarios are complemented with a Systems Software Architecture (SWA) that specifies a near term application and service architecture for the Mobile Internet. It has been a contribution of Nokia to open global standardization of mobile services (e.g., Open Mobile Alliance).

The Mobile World is evolving as we speak. New consumer needs are arising, and innovation on the Internet is taking place at an accelerating pace. Thus, it is clear that technical architectures also need to be continuously developed. Nokia invites all parties of the Mobile Internet to join and contribute to the development of the Mobile World. For this purpose, we would greatly appreciate input from our readers.

Mikko Terho
Senior Vice President

II INTRODUCTION

o The Mobile World

o Mobile Internet Technical Architecture

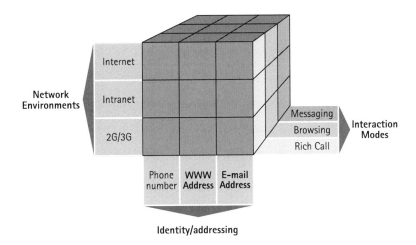

The Mobile World

The next few years will see the convergence of mobile communications and the Internet resulting in various new technologies, new business models and business opportunities.

The Mobile Internet is not simply the Internet of today accessed from a mobile device. We will not spend our time browsing Internet pages for content as we do today, although this will still be possible. Instead, we will use applications to access content, make transactions, do business, link up with friends and family, play games, watch videos, and listen to and download music. More importantly, we will use the Mobile Internet to help control our lives and give us more time to do the things we enjoy.

We are moving towards a Web-based business model where mobility and the Internet are unified. This will not happen overnight and will require new competencies from all parties involved in the industry. Understanding mobility and the unique characteristics of mobile business will be vital in building the networks and services of the future. Success in the Mobile World will be about speed: speed of application and mobile device development for refined consumer segments, speed of new service creation, and speed of cost-optimized network development and roll-out. It will be about the control of services and content residing in your own hands.

From a consumer's perspective, the most tangible element is the mobile device, which provides access to all of these services. To ensure the success of services in the Mobile World, they must be highly user-friendly. Actually, the user should be able to ignore the underlying technologies and purely enjoy the richness of the supplied services, regardless of the access method.

Along with the continually growing importance of mobile devices as life management tools, the Mobile World will become much more than a source for a quick weather information update. The Mobile Internet is not a fixed entity, yet it is starting to formulate its existence with the services and applications to be linked to it. Hence, as the business and technical environments develop, the available architectures will need to match them accordingly.

In the Mobile World, delivering targeted, timely information and services is essential. Consumer behavior drives the development of these applications and services. The key to commercial success lies in understanding consumers, their lifestyles and attitudes, and in creating the product-service combinations which match their wants and needs. Those who deliver winning product categories and platforms with the right technologies will succeed in the Mobile World.

The Nokia solution to cover these demands is the Mobile Internet Technical Architecture (MITA). For the players in the field, MITA is the essential framework for creating user-friendly Mobile World experiences. MITA supports network evolution to the Mobile Internet for both voice and data and is an architecture which comprehensively enables networks to be driven by services. The main target of MITA is to provide seamless interoperation in the consumption of content in all networks and create open and non-fragmented markets with maximum access to all.

Introduction

Nokia is proceeding towards a vision of the Mobile World. In this vision, the majority of all personal communication will be wireless - be it in the form of phone calls, messaging, browsing or images.

The perception of the Internet has been technology focused, i.e., it has been assumed that people wish to access the Internet and huge amounts of data while on the move. Yet, what people will do is something very different. To begin with, in the Mobile World, the Internet will become practically invisible as people are not concerned about "accessing the Internet" but about using services and their favorite applications. A special focus will be on consuming information and producing information to share with others. The consumption will apply to mobile brands, products, information, and advertising.

Consumers want value for money, ease of use, and a diverse choice of personally relevant services. Without an open solution, they are forced into a confusing and fragmented world of proprietary services and terminals. Therefore, the aim will be to limit the complexity of the technical environment so that consumers can enjoy services without worrying about the underlying technologies. As a result, a unified architecture will benefit all users in the Mobile World.

Mobile World Challenge

The Mobile World vision assumes that consumers will use different types of devices for connecting to multiple sets of services via various access networks. These services should be reachable in a unified way regardless of the access technology or mobile device. Naturally, there will always be slight differences between user experiences. However, it is expected that these will be made as transparent as possible.

The above requirements describe technical challenges, which need to be solved before the objectives of the Mobile World can be completely achieved. Interaction Modes, Identity and Network environments are the main elements that the industry needs for constructing an environment for tackling the Mobile World vision. This environment can be described as the Mobile World challenge.

Also, from the MITA perspective, this setting presents those areas that require close consideration in order to achieve a fully functional technical architecture for the Mobile World.

Interaction Modes

Today, consumers have the possibility of making phone calls, exchanging short messages, e-mail or images, and browsing data on the Internet. It is assumed that these communication modes are a baseline for services in the Mobile World. However, the convergence of communication technologies into IP-based solutions enables new services and extensions into baseline communication services.

The Mobile World Challenge addresses this evolution by classifying consumers' communication needs into three types of interaction modes to simplify the definition of basic requirements for applications, terminals, and service provisioning technology.

Messaging

Messaging is non real-time, client-server based communication in which an intermediary server is involved in the communication sequence. The intermediary server stores and/or processes messages before they are delivered to the destination. The intermediary server can be based on store and forward (e.g., Short Message Service and Multimedia Messaging Service), store and retrieve (e.g., e-mail) or even store and push functionality. The intermediary server may also provide queuing services.

Browsing

Browsing is nearly real-time one-way or two-way communication between a source and the destination. It includes one-way audio and video streaming. Differing from Rich Call, Browsing has no delay limitations for communication. In third generation networks, Browsing will be based on an evolution from today's Wireless Application Protocol (WAP) based browsing to graphics and multimedia-enriched browsing.

Rich Call

The Rich Call interaction mode maps to communication using a two-way real-time component. The real-time requirements mean that there are limitations for end-to-end and round-trip delays, and for jitter. Rich Call refers to voice and video calls in their simplest form, and in more complicated cases, concurrent communication (e.g., file transfer is combined with a real-time communication element).

Network Environments

The Internet boom started around the mid 1990s. Since then, an increasing number of corporations have connected their Intranets to the Internet, and a growing number of consumers use Internet services. Similarly, consumers have found attractive mobile services for use in their daily lives.

These three Network environments: mobile networks, the Internet and Intranets are the environments where most of the user interaction will take place in the Mobile World. Moreover, these different environments need to work seamlessly together and enable evolution towards unified service networks.

Identity

Today, each communication mode and its applications have specific addressing mechanisms (e.g., phone calls require numbers, messaging uses e-mail addresses). Luckily, applications have evolved and enable address books for mapping technical addresses to formats which are easier for consumers to manage (e.g., names).

An effective addressing system is vital for handling and simplifying the multitude of e-mail addresses, phone numbers and Web addresses of individuals and organizations. This will be even more true in the future, as the ways of communicating will expand and individuals will be using several different types of devices. The consumer should be faced with as few differences as possible between the addressing methods.

These Mobile World challenges are illustrated in the figure below, which models the interworking scenarios of networks, identities and interaction modes. It is a simple diagnostic framework for highlighting the issues involved in interworking between the layers on the Mobile Internet.

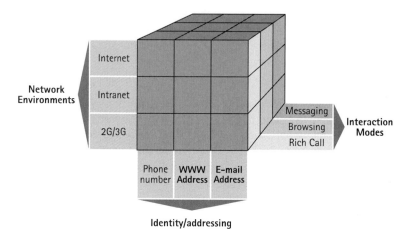

Mobile World Challenge

Mobile Internet Technical Architecture

To make the Mobile World a reality, correct technology choices are required if a technical architecture capable of supporting the myriad of services is to be built. For this reason, Nokia created MITA as a methodology to model the new environment and to understand the inherent technical issues in building the optimal technical architecture. Nokia is using this approach to assist players in the field in making the right technology choices to deliver the optimal consumer experience.

Openness and interoperability are central elements in the MITA approach. Situational analysis is not biased toward any network environment - fixed or mobile - and this maximizes inclusivity; Nokia recognizes the importance of collaboration in this new business environment and MITA gives all the players equally open access to the emerging architecture so that the ultimate goal - a world in which subscribers can utilize the seamless functionality of all Mobile Internet related applications and services - is achieved with the active participation of the whole industry. To achieve this goal, a mobile service market must be created, which offers more business for all companies involved, and provides better and a larger number of services for consumers.

Because all the elements have been taken into consideration, the outcome is highly beneficial to all parties including consumers, carriers, application developers, service providers, infrastructure providers, etc. Only through an open approach from all key players can the industry ensure a seamless user experience and rich service offering on a global scale. At the same time, this approach ensures open competition and rapid growth of the Mobile Internet market.

MITA Objectives

The primary objective is to provide a user-friendly Mobile Internet experience, with browsing, messaging and rich calls working seamlessly in any network environment and with any type of access. Hiding different addressing mechanisms and minimizing the impact of different access technologies from the consumer improves usability. These essential aspects of a user-friendly mobile entity are collected into the following figure presenting the scope of MITA.

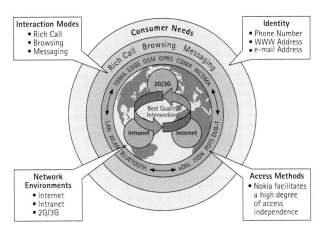

Scope of the Mobile Internet Technical Architecture

In order to lay a solid foundation for the evolution path towards future MITA compliant solutions, the development of current solutions must consider future needs. This backward compatibility will provide valuable building blocks for the Mobile Internet, which will evolve into something much more versatile than it is today. Rapid development is already seen and we can only estimate the future impact of a comprehensive technical architecture for the Mobile Internet.

To ensure far-reaching accessibility, Nokia supports open interfaces bringing new options for the Mobile Internet. Therefore, the Internet itself will not be changed but utilized in more versatile ways, while mobility has a principal role. The value of the Mobile Internet will increase if users are able to access services independent of location and network environment. The Mobile Internet itself will not be a tightly set entity and, hence, the preferred business and technical architectures will need continual revision as the industry and technologies advance.

MITA Work Phases

When the first analysis of the technical architecture was completed, we concluded that following the typical design path (i.e., begin with existing technologies and R&D activities and search for the optimal roadmap towards the Mobile World environment in gradual steps) is not the optimal route to the best technical choices. Because of this, we studied other alternatives, concluding that by following the development cycle in reverse, we could identify new and potentially revolutionary issues on time and take the actions needed to tackle them as a part of normal evolutionary roadmaps.

Based on the above conclusion, MITA work follows three primary phases:

1. **Set targets**
2. **Align with environment**
3. **Influence roadmaps**

The first phase studies current products and technologies, reviews Nokia roadmaps and the products and technologies that are emerging within a 3 year time frame and compares them to problems in the Mobile World and MITA targets. An outcome of this phase is a technical vision which provides direction for the technical architecture and gives it its first model.

In the second phase, the technical architecture model is aligned with the existing R&D roadmaps at Nokia and the activities in standardization bodies. The result is a more detailed technical architecture and an initial implementation view.

In the third phase, the implementation view is finalized and the required R&D activities are addressed for product development.

Every phase has a different relationship with the time frame, as illustrated in the next figure. The first phase addresses MITA on long-term issues, the second phase shifts the focus to mid-term aspects and the third phase completes MITA work with short-term roadmaps, product development plans and reference implementations.

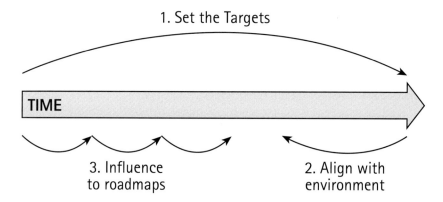

MITA work phases

MITA has already completed the first phase and the key results have been collected in these MITA books. Second phase work has begun with updated work items. The following figure updates the MITA work process for the second phase.

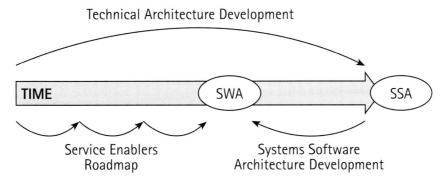

MITA work items in the second phase

The main task in the second phase is to develop a Systems Software Architecture (SWA) for Service Enabler implementations. Another task is to develop a technical architecture into the Subsystem Architecture (SSA), which describes MITA Subsystems and Mobile Internet Interfaces in more detail. The third task is to update technical visions with the latest research results.

MITA Methodology

At the core of the MITA approach is a neutral methodology to help the constituents of the Mobile World understand the critical technical issues in the Mobile Internet. This is achieved through abstract models which describe a conceptual framework for the Mobile Internet environment in progressively more detail and highlight the challenges of interworking between them. MITA tools consist of:

o   Architecture modeling principles

o   Architecture concept models

o   Architecture implementation models

o   Architecture specifications

o   Reference implementations

Collectively, the MITA tools are used to provide a consistent, unbiased situational analysis and a direction for making technology decisions. And, as the approach is technology neutral, it is flexible and ensures that a consistent approach is applied as new technologies evolve.

Architecture Modeling Principles

The technical architecture modeling is based on principles which should enable the creation of a future-proof end-to-end architecture with high possibilities for the modularity of components in the technical architecture.

II

Introduction

The principles for modeling can be listed as follows:

o   The architecture divides into independent subsystems while fulfilling business needs

o   The architecture is open, modular, and hierarchical, utilizing a layered approach

o   The architecture can tolerate varying rates of technological change in individual components. Change in one component should not render the whole architecture useless.

The above principles dictate that layered models are applied to element design, network modeling, and identity structuring. A generic content delivery model is defined for a specification of Interaction Modes and related subsystems. In a similar way, access independent requirements are collected into and specified in a model of an Access Independent Interface.

Architecture Concept Models

For the architecture, there are two approaches worth closer examination. From a business architecture viewpoint, there is the Mobile Internet Business Architecture (MIBA) and MITA can be used as the concept model for a more technical approach.

As a concept model, MIBA defines the interaction between different architecture elements. In the MIBA model, the terminal segment provides the consumer with access to services, the network segment provides terminals with connectivity to service networks, and the server segment provides content and services for consumers.

Within each segment (i.e., content, connection and consumption) the MITA approach models each interacting entity as an element that can be described as consisting of three abstract layers: Application, Mobile Internet, and Platform.

Describing MITA elements in terms of constituent layers enables us to identify the interfaces required for interworking between entities in each segment. Interworking is based on protocols implemented on the Mobile Internet layer and protocol-enabled content exchange between applications on the Application layer.

By mapping the MITA element to the MIBA concept model, a conceptual end-to-end view of MITA is achieved. The MITA end-to-end view is a high-level reference model for more detailed technical architecture design. All architecture elements in MITA can be derived from the same baseline MITA element.

Architecture Implementation Models

The MITA Subsystem Architecture introduces an implementation view of the technical architecture. It is another viewpoint into the technical architecture, encapsulating a group of functionalities into independent, well-isolated subsystems.

In general, a primary requirement is that an implementation of any subsystem can be replaced with another implementation, requiring no or only a minimum amount of modifications to other subsystems or applications utilizing the services of the replaced subsystem. In a similar way, the implementation technology of a subsystem may be completely changed without influencing other related subsystems. The modular MITA implementation model enables a flexible evolution of product implementations according to MITA specifications.

Architecture Specifications

Technical architecture work is divided into MITA specifications, to create technical work items of manageable scope and to enable comparison with other models on the specification level. The MITA specifications are divided into three groups:

o   Architecture specifications

o   Key system specifications

o   Architecture frameworks

The architecture specifications are specifications that have a more permanent nature, whereas the key system specifications represent issues where understanding end-to-end system aspects prior to technology selections is important. The third set of specifications includes frameworks for complicated issues (e.g., security or Mobile Internet Interfaces).

Reference Implementations

Technical architecture development has multiple parallel tracks: reviews of existing products and solutions, analyses of the current actions in standardization, reviews and studies of the latest research results, conceptual modeling actions, and the production of technical visions and specifications. However, these tracks as such do not make any practical implementations or references.

A combination of the Mobile Domain and the Web Domain is by no means without challenges. The resulting environment will contain many relatively complicated components. Without thorough prototyping, an adequate result could be hard to obtain. The experiences and competences obtained from prototyping can be fed quickly back to other parts of architecture development, for example, to protocol developers, which saves development time and requires less work to reach the targets.

However, it is not simply a question of prototyping individual components, e.g., protocols. An equally essential part of prototyping is the integration of various parts to the overall system. While the careful definition of interfaces between various layers can make integration easier, real, hands-on experience is one of the keys to success. This is because reference implementations provide a bridge between the technology visions and the real world, a world that is sometimes full of technical limitations and complicated dependencies. What works in theory may not work well in practice, as additional components affect the overall performance of the system. For example, two technologies can, in a tightly integrated environment, interact in a manner that was not foreseen by the developers of the individual technologies. Essentially, these side effects are the price of increased complexity in future communication systems.

Thus, any far-reaching process, such as MITA work, must be able to face the facts and be able to make the correct conclusions at the right time. Implementations are the right tool for this. They serve as a reality check and as insurance against unexpected problems.

For these reasons, MITA work includes a strong effort to produce so-called MITA Reference Implementations. These do not form a complete MITA system, but are a summary of key technologies needed to build the Mobile World. Note that MITA reference implementations are a continuous development process that adopts new technologies when they are ready to be prototyped.

Compliance with MITA Principles

As described in the previous sections, the evolution towards the Mobile World brings new requirements and various challenges. For product and solution developers, MITA is a framework for building product and solution architectures, as illustrated in the following figure.

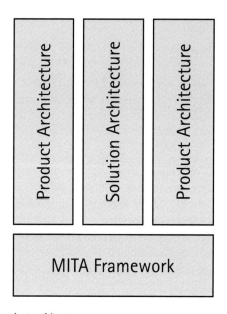

MITA Framework and product architectures

When applying the MITA Framework and methodology to product and solution implementations, three key criteria must be adhered to for compliance with MITA:

o   Providing multiple access capable solutions

o   Securing the highest quality interworking between networks

o   Securing the best interworking between multiple addresses and identities

The above criteria are a very high-level set of principles guiding developers up an evolution path to the Mobile World.

Providing Multiple Access Capable Solutions

Services should not be tied to access methods. If this were the case, new access methods would render the architecture useless. Therefore, a high degree of access independence is a key driver for the technical architecture. Multiple Access Capable solutions are required in order to achieve the global reachability of individuals as well as global access to content.

Securing the Highest Quality Interworking Between Networks

There will also be separate Network environments of mobile networks, the Internet and Intranets. The interworking of these is yet another factor to ensure seamless end-to-end services. These Network environments will be where most user interaction will take place in the Mobile World. To ensure smooth communication between these environments for the consumers, fluent interworking on the technical level is required.

Securing the Best Interworking Between Multiple Addresses and Identities

The reality of multiple access services will require handling multiple identities and addresses that have, historically, been closely tied to networks or applications. A MITA compliant solution recognizes this issue and proposes the best possible way to overcome the challenge.

The dissection of applications should be done in such a way that network requirements are identified, and decoupled from application specific requirements. Requirements for similar applications are grouped under the three Interaction Modes (i.e., Rich Call, Browsing and Messaging). It is important to consider the differences between Network environments, and how to enable applications to seamlessly work between any of the environments, i.e., to ensure service interoperability.

Applications and the Technical Architecture

Nokia classifies applications into four main categories: content, communication, productivity, and business solutions. Example services for each classification category are shown in the following table.

Category	Services
Content	News, Banking, Finance, Local Services, Buy and Sell, Travel, Music, TV, Lifestyle, Fun, Games, Astrology, Dating
Communication	Messaging, e-mail, Fax, Rich call
Productivity	Organizers, Personal Assistants, Tools
Business	Intranet and Extranet access, Information management, Enterprise Communication, Virtual private networks, Telematics

For instance, a game can be downloaded to a terminal from the net and played independently. Here the Interaction Mode is Browsing and the Network environment is the Internet. If the game is played interactively between several people who send messages while playing and, for example, solving game related tasks, then the Interaction Mode is Messaging and the Network environment is the Mobile network, possibly also interaction with the Internet. Finally, if the game is played in an on-line interactive environment, the situation is a Rich Call Interaction Mode in the Mobile network. These game situations highlight the fact that applications must be able to interact freely in all different Interaction Modes and over all Network environments.

In applying the MITA approach to application development, it becomes clear that applications which have been implemented directly on the Platform layer functions while having integrated Mobile Internet layer functions are unacceptable. MITA compatible applications follow the modular implementation model keeping functions between the MITA layers separated.

Mobile Internet Business Architecture

To be able to create a winning solution for the Mobile Internet Business Architecture, Nokia has identified the drivers behind it as well as both the short and long term ramifications which we need to focus on.

Clearly, we cannot overlook the maintenance of profitability, so we prefer solutions which facilitate increases in business revenue. In order to do this, we need to identify the key constituents in the value chain, along with their potential. Hence, consumers, developers and content providers all have to be linked to service providers who in turn link them into the synergy of Consumption, Connection and Content, as illustrated in the following figure.

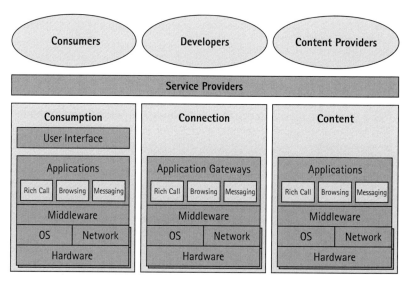

The Mobile Internet Business Architecture

The model contains the key constituencies on the top row, while a simplified architecture with three segments, Consumption, Connection and Content, is presented on the bottom. The key constituencies in the MIBA are consumers, developers, content providers and service providers. The consumer constituency covers both consumers and corporate users, while the service provider constituency covers all types of service providers, i.e., mobile service providers, Internet service providers, application service providers, or in some cases, companies acting as service providers for their own corporate users.

The consumption segment refers to consumers who will be accessing the content provided by a variety of content providers on the content segment. The connection segment (e.g., mobile network) provides a connection between these two segments, and the service providers will manage the connectivity network.

Once all these segments have reached seamless interoperability, all the constituencies will also reach their objectives. Consumers are looking for cost effective and sophisticated services within trusted and reliable coverage areas. Developers will be seeking big volumes and continuity. For content providers, the key issues will be cost efficiency and reachability on a massive scale. Furthermore, service providers are in the business to maintain and maximize their user base and to collect subscription and transaction fees to generate profits.

Middleware Benefits

Middleware solutions provide services for consumers by bringing together software solutions from application vendors and carriers. When the middleware architecture is based on MITA methodology, the following benefits are gained:

1. Support for different network access types from wide area mobile networks to alternate methods. This allows carriers and service providers to build intelligence into their services today and enable their evolution to future technologies.

2. The interfaces are based on open industry standards. Carriers can easily integrate the middleware to their current systems regardless of their network configuration. They can also easily manage their application portfolio. Service providers can provide content using the same standard interface and ensure that applications can utilize their content.

3. Application developers can develop their application to utilize the intelligence of middleware enhancing the features with interoperation capability. This will enhance the consumers experience and make users more willing to use services while on the move, through the Mobile Internet.

Other benefits of middleware for consumers include:

o **Single login** - user logs in once and all services become available

o **Terminal identification through the Mobile Internet layer** - Users will always receive content optimized for their terminal.

o **Preferences** - the user can choose areas of interest and only relevant options will shown (e.g., favorite restaurants, music).

o **Navigation support** - the user can use easy navigation

MITA Deliverables – End-to-End Solutions

It would be impossible to create winning solutions unless extensive end-to-end views guide the design of the technical architecture. These end-to-end views aim to cover all aspects of "Voice goes mobile," "Content goes mobile" and even "Servers become smart" so that overall functionality will be guaranteed.

The architecture elements requiring an end-to-end view are the interaction modes, network interconnectivity, key system elements and access methods. As we are in the middle of the development path towards the Mobile World, coexistent multiple views are already a reality and some new views will be added for completeness.

As the next wave of growth in the Mobile World is expected to come from mobile services, Nokia is actively working with open global standardization of mobile services. The mobile service industry has established a new forum to drive these mobile service standards, it is called Open Mobile Alliance (OMA).

Working within various standardization bodies, the mobile industry will cooperate to create non-fragmented, interoperable mobile services across markets, carries and mobile devices by identifying, endorsing and implementing open standards.

In order for Nokia to ensure the future compliance of these end-to-end views, we already have numerous solutions that fill the MITA model comprehensively and form the foundation for future applications and services. The following table lists many of these solutions and quite clearly illustrates the overall view that has carefully been taken into consideration when aiming to provide optimized creation and delivery of services.

Segment	Services
Consumption	Entertainment phones, Imaging phones, Voice/Messaging phones, Mediaphones, Communicators, Home Multimedia Terminals
Connect	Virtual Private Network solutions, Security appliances, Broadband gateways, Wireless broadband systems, Fixed broadband, xDSL, Wireless LAN, Mobile connection and control servers, Multi-technology radio access networks, Mobility gateways
Content	Mobile commerce, Content applications, Messaging and Community applications, Application developer community, Mobile entertainment services, Mobile Internet services middleware, Connectivity servers , Charging and billing solutions, Advanced call related services, Location services middleware

Conclusions

Nokia is developing a comprehensive technical architecture for the Mobile Internet. The Mobile Internet Technical Architecture aims to provide seamless interoperability between all interaction modes, any network environment and with any type of access. The ultimate objective of MITA is to create a user-friendly Mobile Internet experience for everyone. It will be done:

o   by identifying the relevant interaction modes,

o   by defining the key technologies required to support them, and

o   by driving industry participation to develop a common Mobile Internet platform.

In developing a comprehensive technical architecture for the Mobile Internet, Nokia aims to limit the complexity of the inherently technical environment, as users do not want to worry about the underlying technologies. Nokia sees three key elements as fundamental to the Mobile Internet Technical Architecture: Identity, Interaction Modes and Network environments. Bringing these together and managing the challenges they pose is at the core of MITA and will ensure high-quality and seamless interoperability in end-to-end services.

An open solution benefits all; profitable business scenarios call for interoperability, short development cycles, large volumes and, most of all, global reach. Unless there is a commonly accepted architectural solution, markets will become fragmented as well as require separate parameters, and the total volume will be much smaller than in a single global market.

Mobile Internet Technical Architecture

In order to master the end-to-end quality of future services, it is important to manage the three segments of the Mobile Internet Business Architecture and the key constituents in the value chain, as well as to identify their potential need. Hence, consumers, developers and content providers all have to be linked to service providers. A synergy of Consumption, Connection and Content segments is provided for the linked constituents via offerings from the service providers. The complexity of related technologies must simultaneously be hidden from the consumer. In short, from an engineering perspective, the main challenge of the Mobile World is how to manage and hide technical complexity.

Nokia is defining the technical architecture for the Mobile World. In the definition work, the ultimate objective is to provide a user-friendly Mobile Internet experience, where browsing, messaging and rich calls work seamlessly in any network environment and with any type of access or service. The next figure highlights topics that are important factors in building a user-friendly Mobile World. These are also the main tasks in the definition of the technical architecture.

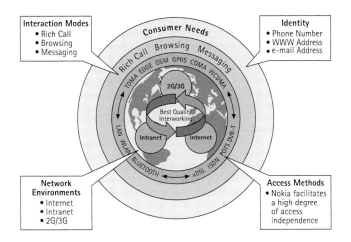

Scope of the Mobile Internet Technical Architecture

In presenting the technical architecture in this way, our goal is to drive for:

o   Multiple identities in all solutions

o   Dissection of the applications in such a way that network requirements are identified, and decoupled from consumer and application-specific requirements.

o   The network requirements for similar applications are grouped under the Interaction modes.

  o A multiple access capability in the creation of applications and solutions

  o Consideration of differences between Network environments, and how to enable applications to seamlessly work between any of the environments.

Identity

Identity is vital from the consumer's point of view. One characteristic of the Mobile World is the explosion of the scale and ways of communicating. Individuals who now own one mobile device or PC will use several devices of different types in the future. This means that an effective addressing system is required to handle and simplify the multitude of e-mail addresses, phone numbers, and Web addresses for individuals and organizations. It also means that the well-served coupling between a service provider subscription, user identity and an addressing method is facing a challenge of separation.

The address methods listed above are already widely used by consumers. The technical architecture needs to provide solutions, such as directory services that enable the interchangeability of address methods. The aim is to expose the consumer to as few differences between the addressing/identity methods as possible: compare the current mobile devices with a phone book where addressing is abstracted to a person's name. This means that clear and well-defined layers for naming, numbering and addressing are needed for simplifying addressing methods on different network layers.

It is assumed that many layers of addressing will grow on top of these technical addressing methods, establishing a new consumer-friendly layer for addressing, for example, addressing for location-based services using time, location and consumer relationship with the target service provider as elements of addressing: "All customers in the vicinity of a shopping mall in Market Street, at lunchtime." Issues such as consumer privacy and preferences, or security requirements, will be taken into account in the implementation of these systems. In a similar way, the number of entities to be addressed is growing with new services and their needs (e.g., addressing of content, services and information).

Network Environments

Despite the fact that different networks work seamlessly together, the separate network domains of wide-area mobile networks, the Internet and Intranets will remain. Although, from an aerial perspective, all networks seem to converge into a single IP network, the networks inherently have some characteristics that differ from each other. Therefore, securing high quality interworking between the networks is needed for seamless end-to-end services. Each of the access networks has its own characteristics and requirements. For example, in the case of mobile networks, effective radio resource control management is needed and in a corporate Intranet, security can be provided with Virtual Private Network (VPN) technology.

Mobile networks, the Internet and Intranets are the Network environments where most user interaction will take place in the Mobile World. Different service providers control these environments, and their design is driven by different requirements. Fluent communication over these environments requires good interworking on the technical level.

From an overall perspective, it looks like there is only one unified network based on IP technology, but in practice, there are many technical challenges to be solved before a seamless service experience can be provided. A few examples of the challenges are:

o   Addressing and routing between access networks (e.g., network address translations and routing between IPv4 and IPv6 networks)

o   User authentication, authorization and billing

o   User and service roaming between access networks and Network environments

o   Security issues (e.g., firewalls, VPNs and policies)

o   Quality of service and its connection to other control issues (e.g., network policies, billing and traffic control)

The Mobile Internet Technical Architecture divides the above complexity into four hierarchical network perspectives:

o   Network domains

o   Network environments

o   Access networks

o   Access technologies

At the strategic architecture level, there are two domains: the Web domain and the Mobile domain. At the technical architecture level, there are three Network environments: Mobile networks, the Internet and Intranets and a number of Access networks:

o   Mobile access networks (e.g., Global System for Mobile Communications (GSM) network and Wideband Code Division Multiple Access (WCDMA) network)

o   Fixed access networks (e.g., Public Switched Telephone Network (PSTN) and any Digital Subscription Line (xDSL) network)

o   Corporate access networks (e.g., Local Area Network (LAN), Wireless Local Area Network (WLAN) and xDSL network)

o   Home, ad-hoc and other private networks (e.g., Bluetooth and WLAN)

The relationship between these network perspectives is illustrated in the next figure.

II

Introduction

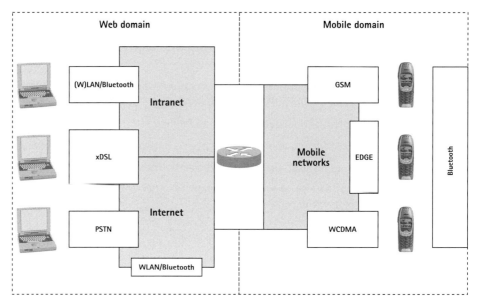

MITA Network perspectives

While seamless interworking between different network environments is emerging, convergence between the same services, regardless of service providers, will advance addressing harmonization requirements for service technologies. It is assumed that this will be a starting point for the creation of new unified service networks (e.g., Web service, rich call, presence and reachability, distributed directories and content delivery) as illustrated in the next figure.

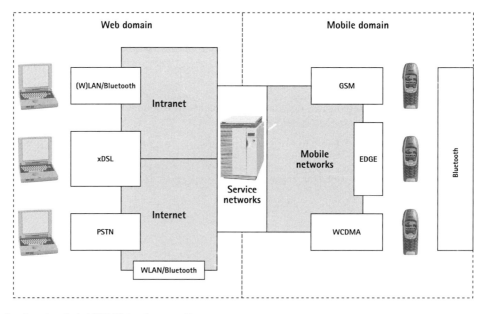

Service networks in MITA Network perspectives

Multiple Access Capability

Services need to function with multiple access methods. Regardless of the efforts to create global standards for network access, there will always be alternative methods for accessing services. Differences, such as wide and local area mobility versus fixed access technologies, remain. The concept of the global reachability of individuals and global access to content requires multi-access systems.

A high degree of access independence is a key driver for the technical architecture. In end-to-end solutions the emphasis in the technical architecture is to provide the best possible service based on the characteristics of the access technology (e.g., available bandwidth, connection setup time, network delay and symmetric/asymmetric performance). Services and their implementation should not be tied to any specific access technology. Otherwise, reusing the existing service base could not be done with a new access technology.

Interaction Modes

Interaction modes are not very well utilized in the current networks and their communication applications. In most current communication applications, the user interface, communication modes and network technologies are vertically integrated, providing one complete application for specific communication needs. Examples of communication applications are:

o   Phone, Short Message Service (SMS), Multimedia Messaging Service (MMS) and browsing clients on mobile networks

o   E-mail, Web browsing, streaming and instant messaging clients on the Internet

o   File access and database transaction clients on Intranets

This vertical integration means that implementations of current communication applications are not freely and easily usable in new applications.

In the Mobile Internet Technical Architecture, Interaction modes consist of characteristics and attributes related to requirements for end-to-end content transport and processing of and expectations for network service characteristics (e.g., Quality of Service (QoS), security, privacy).

It is assumed that a small number of Interaction modes cover the needs of most communication applications in the Mobile World. Based on this assumption, one primary objective in MITA is to find a minimum set of application and network independent Interaction modes. So far, three Interaction modes have been identified: Rich Call, Browsing and Messaging. The primary characteristics and attributes of the Interaction modes are listed in the next table and some examples of applications and their mapping to the Interaction modes are presented in the second table.

II

Introduction

Table: Characteristics and Attributes of Interaction Modes

Interaction mode	Characteristics and Attributes
Rich Call	End-to-end delay minimization is a critical attribute. This addresses requirements for both end-point internal processes and delivery network service expectations. A two-way interactive element is always present in Rich Call. It may use parallel multimode communication (e.g., audio and video). The delivery model is synchronous, and sessions are connection-oriented.
Browsing	Near real-time one-way or two-way communication and one-way real-time communication. The content creation process, delivery network, intermediary end-point(s), or processes in the receiving end-point cause more delays than the Rich Call Interaction mode limits allow (e.g., delayed playback in a consumer process). The delivery model allows both synchronous and asynchronous deliveries. The session may be connection-oriented or connectionless.
Messaging	Non real-time communication with at least one intermediary end-point. The intermediary end-point(s) enable store-and-forward, store-and-retrieve, and store-and-push communication models. Delivery is always asynchronous and the session is connectionless from end-to-end. However, peer-to-peer sessions may be connection-oriented (e.g., retrieve sessions from receiving end-point to the intermediary server).

Table: Application Examples for Interaction Modes

Interaction mode	Application Examples
Rich Call	Voice and video calls, concurrent communication (e.g., file transfer is combined with the real-time communication element), networked interactive games, real-time two-way chat or messaging, real-time streaming with upstream control (e.g., video surveillance with remote camera control), real-time multi-user games with multiparty call, or point-to-point and multipoint conferencing.
Browsing	Audio and video streaming, IP broadcasting from broadcasting server to receiving end-points, one-way multicasting between a local content delivery server and receiving end-points, one-way push applications, games utilizing browsing technology, or viewing and interacting with multimedia content.
Messaging	Short message service, multimedia messaging service, e-mail, instant messaging via intermediary proxy, play-by-e-mail games (e.g., e-mail chess).

The classification of Interaction modes simplifies technology development as it helps to define the basic requirements of applications, terminals and service provisioning technology.

Building solid support for the above Interaction modes in the End-to-end architecture enables fast introduction of new applications with similar characteristics and requirements. One application can also utilize multiple Interaction modes in communication at the same time.

There will also be commonalities and common services utilized by all Interaction modes. Such services include profiles and settings, which are handled system-wide. From a consumer viewpoint, these must be user friendly, requiring a minimum amount of setup, but still providing settings that are more elaborate for advanced consumers.

End-to-End Views

The scope of MITA according to the previously described definitions is quite wide and allows multiple starting points for specification work. One key target in MITA is that specification work turns company wide visions and strategies into a technical architecture that can be used as a concept model for further actions. It guides MITA development to investigation of a strategic architecture in Nokia. The strategic architecture addresses three primary end-to-end views:

o   Connecting people

o   Content goes wireless

o   Servers become smart

The above end-to-end views are starting points for MITA use cases, technical specifications and service scenarios.

Connecting People View

The *Connecting people view* is the most familiar view, from a Mobile domain standpoint. In this view, the end-points of the communication are both mobile devices. In the Mobile domain, voice communication is a typical connection type. In the Web domain, person-to-person, and specifically, peer-to-peer communication is already taking new forms. Some scenarios for communication alternatives in this view are illustrated in the next figure.

II

Introduction

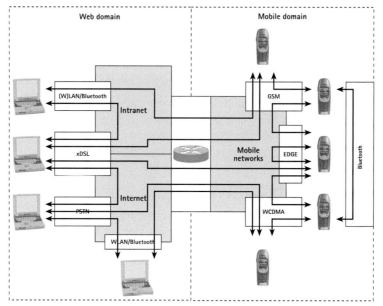

Examples for the Connecting people view

Content Goes Wireless View

The *Content goes wireless view* takes into account the current state of the Web domain, where content is located on a server, and combines this with the mobility of mobile networks in the Mobile domain. Thus, a client in a mobile device accesses the content on servers in either the Web or Mobile domain. The end-points of the communication are a terminal and a server. A few scenarios for the communication alternatives in this view are illustrated in the next figure.

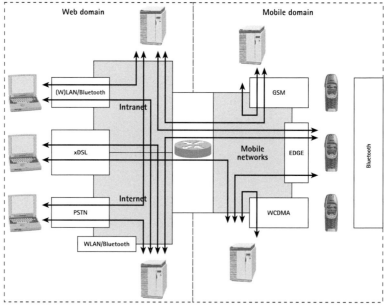

Examples for the Content goes wireless view

Servers Become Smart View

The *Servers become smart view* looks forward to and anticipates the gradual evolution of the Web domain, and the technologies utilized in the servers. In this view, the end-points of communications are actually servers. The servers communicate with each other directly to accomplish tasks that do not necessarily involve terminals. A few scenarios for the communication alternatives in this view are illustrated in the next figure.

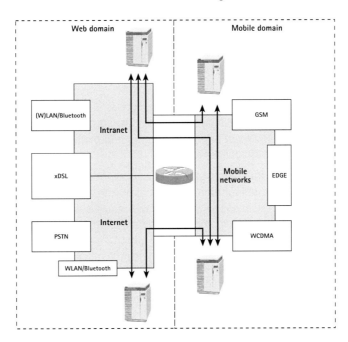

Examples for the Servers become smart view

Services and the Technical Architecture

It would be impossible to create winning solutions unless extensive End-to-end views guide the design of the technical architecture. These MITA End-to-end views aim to cover all aspects so that overall functionality will be guaranteed.

In order for Nokia to ensure the future compliance of these End-to-end views, we already have numerous solutions that fill the MITA model comprehensively and form a foundation for future applications and services. To map these solutions to the MITA model, definitions for customer service and applications have been created:

o   An application is a piece of software which enables a service for a consumer

o   An application together with the content related to it create a service, which becomes a consumer service once it has direct value to the consumer (i.e., service usage is chargeable)

The main application categories are content, communication, productivity and business solutions. These categories are classified as follows:

o   **Content** - Information: news, banking and financial services, local services (city guide), buy and sell and travel. Entertainment: music, TV, lifestyle, fun, games, astrology and dating

o   **Communication** - Instant messaging, e-mail, fax, rich call

o   **Productivity** - Organizers, personal assistant, tools

o   **Business solutions** - Intranet and extranet access, information management, telematics, enterprise communication services and virtual private networks

In addition to the above main application categories, there are special application groups. For example, applications like Personal Information Management (PIM) with support functions (e.g., management, synchronization or printing), group information services and profile management can consist of a group of applications.

The technical architecture needs to support service creation for the applications listed above. However, rigidly integrated solutions should not be created so that the applications and services can be isolated from the networks and platforms underneath. This approach is illustrated in the next figure, where the main application categories do not directly map to category specific protocol stacks having support for only one identity, one access technology and one network environment. Instead, the main application categories share Interaction modes and Key system functionalities.

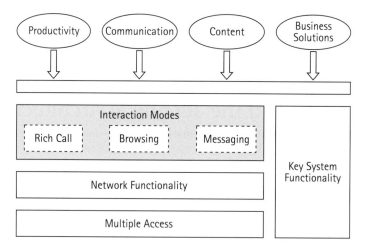

Mapping applications to the technical architecture

The previous figure shows how the applications do not directly mandate transport requirements to network functionality, but rather the application content processing and transport requirements are first mapped to the Interaction modes, and the most suitable one is selected. The applications are then implemented on interfaces provided by the selected Interaction modes, independent of network functionality. Basically, this mapping decouples the network functionality and the implementation of applications. This approach can be highlighted with two examples:

1. **Chat**: Chat may be utilized as a productivity or a content/information application. In the content/information category, there may be different requirements concerning authorization or billing. In the productivity category, security aspects may be of the highest importance. Regardless of the category, the underlying technical architecture should not need changes.

2. **Games**: Consider the transport requirements of the following game types: a real-time multi-player game with multiparty call, a game utilizing Wireless Application Protocol (WAP) technology, or a play-by-mail type of game (utilizing SMS or e-mail). Dissecting these games to their transport requirements and mapping the requirements to the Interaction modes decouples the tight vertical integration.

The implementation of applications on top of the Interaction mode interfaces aims for best in class content processing and transport capabilities for all applications with similar requirements, as in Rich Call, Browsing and Messaging. This decoupling allows parallel application development as well as enhancing and improving Interaction mode implementation. In some cases, it may not be possible or even desirable to avoid vertical (and horizontal) binding. However, most such binding cases can be handled in the scope of the Key system specifications.

The Mobile Internet Technical Architecture aims to avoid technical solutions which translate to vertically tightly-integrated stacks targeted too narrowly to specific use cases, or groupings thereof. If applications are mapped directly to network functionality, this may potentially create rigid silos where functionality designed specifically for one type of application will not be readily available for other types of applications, as illustrated in the next figure. In the worst case, these rigid silos cause multiple implementations of similar network functionality with slightly differing features.

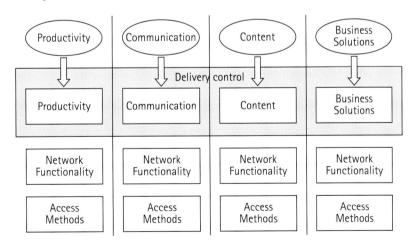

Strong application grouping

The Interaction modes presented enable a single implementation of network features for multiple applications and even for multiple platforms, thus reducing the needed code space, improving the reliability of the implementation and reducing the amount of maintained source codes.

Modeling the Technical Architecture

At the core of the MITA approach is a neutral methodology to help us understand the critical technical issues in the Mobile Internet. This is achieved through abstract models that describe a conceptual framework for the Mobile Internet environment in progressively more detail and highlight the challenges of interworking between them. The MITA tools consist of:

o   Architecture modeling principles

o   Architecture concept models

o   Architecture implementation models

o   Architecture specifications

o   Reference implementations

Collectively, the MITA tools are used to provide a consistent, unbiased situational analysis and a direction for making technology decisions. And, as the approach is technology neutral, it is flexible and ensures that a consistent approach is applied as new technologies evolve.

As the modeling of the technical architecture is done from a technical implementation perspective, fine granularity is required in the model. At the same time, the emphasis moves from business and general architectural principles to layering, to interfaces between the layers and to protocols that enable interaction between entities.

Principles for Technical Architecture Modeling

Technical architecture modeling is based on principles, which should enable the creation of a future-proof end-to-end architecture with high possibilities for modularity in the constituencies of the technical architecture.

The principles for modeling can be listed as follows:

o   The architecture divides into independent sub-architectures while fulfilling business needs

o   The architecture is open, modular and hierarchical

o   The architecture can tolerate varying rates of technological change in individual components. Change in one component should not render the whole architecture useless

The above principles imply that layered models need to be applied to element design, the network model and the identity structure. A generic content delivery model is defined for a specification of Interaction modes and related subsystems. In a similar way, multiple access capability requirements are collected into and specified in the Access Independent Interface (AII).

Layered Element Model

Both, the business and the technical architecture require that a model of the technical architecture meets the principles and assumptions discussed above. In generic technical architecture modeling, one way to achieve these objectives is to divide an element of the technical architecture into layers: application, middleware and platform, as shown in the next figure.

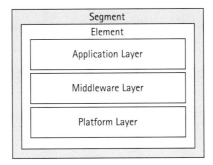

The layered element model

The Application layer contains User Interfaces (UIs), application logics and related support functions. The Middleware layer isolates the Application and Platform layers, allowing the same applications to run on multiple platforms and provides tools for developers to implement new services in a solid execution environment. The Platform layer consists of operating system specific software modules and hardware.

Full separation of these layers requires that the interfaces between the Application and Middleware layers and the interfaces between the Middleware and Platform layers be well defined. Typically, these interfaces are provided to developers in the form of Application Programming Interfaces (APIs).

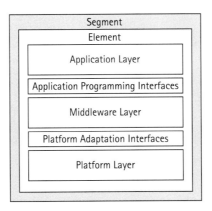

The layered element with APIs

It is assumed in the previous sections that communication modes are a baseline for services on the Mobile Internet. The convergence of communication technologies enables new services and extensions into baseline communication services. The Interaction modes simplify the definition of basic content processing and related protocol requirements for applications, terminals and service provisioning technology. Hence, interaction between two instances of technical architecture elements is based on protocols implemented on the Middleware layer and on exchanged application or service contents on the Application layer, as shown in the next figure.

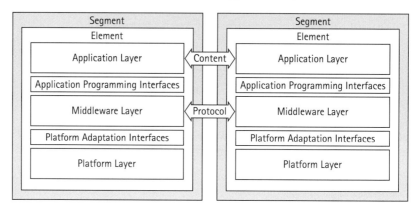

Interaction between Layered elements

The division into the element layers and the interaction model between elements are important for the Mobile Internet Technical Architecture. The division enables the identification of internal interfaces between the layers in an element and the identification of external interfaces between elements.

Layered Network Model

Typically, network protocols and network architectures are presented based on layered models. Two well-known layered models are the Open Systems Interconnection (OSI) model for generic network architectures and the Department of Defense (DoD) model for the Internet. Both of these models can be adapted to the requirements of MITA; however, the Mobile Internet evolution is a driver leading MITA modeling closer to the native Internet model. Therefore, the Mobile Internet Technical Architecture follows the principles of the DoD model with slight modifications. MITA has combined the host-to-host and internetwork layers of the DoD model into one Connectivity layer. Session management protocols are also included on the Connectivity layer. The MITA layered network model is illustrated in the next figure.

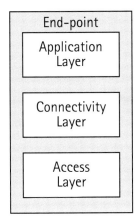

Network layers in a general MITA end-point

In this model, the Access layer includes network hardware and link level device drivers in the operating system. The Connectivity layer includes routing, transport and session management protocols, and the Application layer includes application protocols. Mapping to the OSI model means that the Access layer covers OSI layers 1 and 2, the Connectivity layer covers OSI layers 3, 4 and 5, and the Application layer covers OSI layers 6 and 7. This mapping is also illustrated in the next figure.

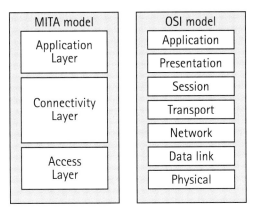

Mapping the MITA layered network model to OSI layers

In a similar way, following the Internet end-to-end architecture model, a general end-point-to-end-point interconnection model can be presented, as shown in the next figure.

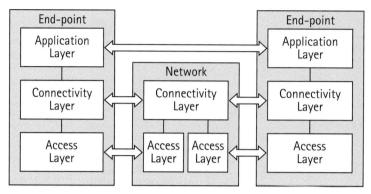

An end-point-to-end-point interconnection model for MITA

This model simplifies mapping entities to Network and End-point categories. Entities in the Network category terminate the Access layer protocols and relay Application layer protocols transparently, whereas processing the Connectivity layer protocols depends on the entity functions. Entities in the End-point category terminate all protocols.

When comparing this mapping to MITA, it means that entities in the terminal segment will belong to the End-point category as mobile devices. In a similar way, entities in the server segment will also belong to the End-point category as application and service servers, whereas entities in the network segment belong to the Network category and are further divided, according their primary functions, either to routing and transport entities, or to connectivity control and content intermediary entities. When more detailed categorizations are made, a separation of user, control and management planes must be taken into account and the implications of the planes for the model and the categories must be identified.

To complete the principles of MITA network modeling, the control plane entities need to be investigated one step further. The above layered network model and mapping it to MITA segments indicates that there are a number of control plane network entities that can be identified as belonging to the control plane server category. Therefore, in the Mobile Internet Technical Architecture, the control plane servers are classified into the following categories for clarity:

o   Access servers (e.g., Radio Access Network (RAN) servers)

o   IP network servers (e.g., Authentication, Authorization and Accounting (AAA), Domain Name System (DNS) or Dynamic Host Configuration Protocol (DHCP) servers)

o   Connectivity servers and gateways (e.g., Home Location Register (HLR) server, session management servers or PSTN gateways)

o   Application servers (e.g., rich call, Web or e-mail servers)

o   Service servers (e.g., presence and reachability, content delivery or directory servers)

Layered Identities Model

An effective addressing system is vital for handling and simplifying the multitude of e-mail addresses, phone numbers and Web addresses of individuals and organizations. Indeed, this need will become even more pressing in the future, as ways of communicating expand, with individuals using several different types of devices. Hence, the third layered model for the Mobile Internet Technical Architecture categorizes identities and addressing methods. Each of the previous network layers has individual addressing methods and identities. Therefore at least three Identity layers are required:

o   Access Identity layer

o   Connectivity Identity layer

o   Application Identity layer

Luckily, applications have evolved and enable address books for mapping technical addresses to formats that are easier for consumers to manage (e.g., names). This introduces an additional Identity layer above the Application Identity layer where identities are in the most convenient format for consumers. In MITA, this consumer friendly layer is called the Human Identity layer. In summary, all four Identity layers are illustrated in the next figure.

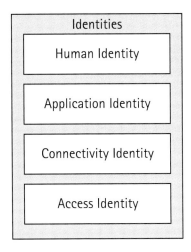

Identity layers in MITA

These Identity layers address requirements for translation services between presentation formats on the different Identity layers, as shown in the next figure. The following address translations are used in the MITA model:

o   Translation from a Human Identity to an Application identity through search engines

o   Translation from an Application identity to a Connectivity identity through directory and presence services

o   Translation from a Connectivity identity to an Access identity through address resolution and local directories

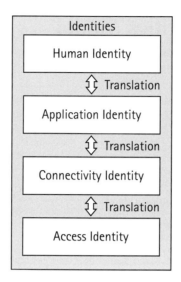

MITA Address translations

One of the objectives of MITA is that the technical architecture should ensure fluent interworking on the technical level between the different Network environments. In principle, this enables smooth communication between these environments for the consumer. In order to ensure such smooth communication, there need to be relationships between network layers and Identity layers. A mapping between these MITA layers is shown in the next figure.

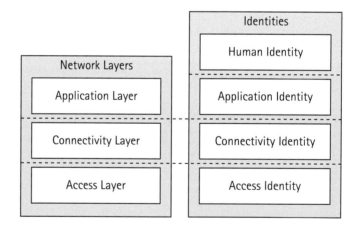

Relationship between Network and Identity layers

Another MITA objective related to identities is to enable mobile subscribers to use interoperable mobile services across service providers, carriers, access technologies and mobile devices. This challenging objective requires that different subscriptions and related business models are tackled well in the MITA models. It also means that the identity model should allow different kinds of subscription models. There are two primary models in mapping identities and subscriptions:

o   A Unified subscription model providing one subscription for both the Application and the Connectivity layers with one combined identity.

o   A Separate subscription model enabling at least one Connectivity layer subscription with its own identity and one or many Application layer subscriptions with their own identities.

The unified subscription model is illustrated in the next figure.

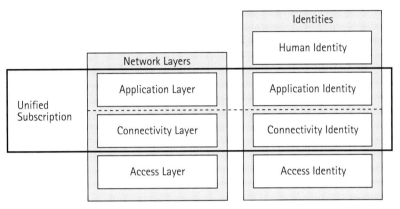

Unified subscription model

The Separate subscriptions model is illustrated in the next figure.

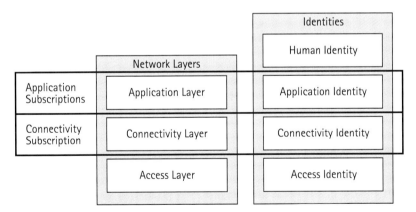

Separate application and connectivity subscriptions model

Content Delivery Model

A generic model for all content delivery scenarios is provided for technical architecture needs, as shown in the next figure. It consists of two network end-points: a source and a sink. The source end-point provides content for the sink end-point, which consumes the content. Between the source and the sink, the content is delivered over delivery networks. Both end-points have three processes. In the source end-point, the processes are content creation, content delivery control and network sending, and in the sink end-point they are network receiving, content delivery control and content consumption.

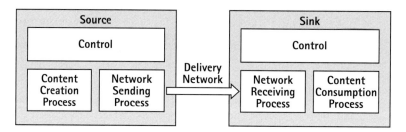

MITA content delivery model

In some scenarios, content may be delivered between the source and the sink via a third end-point or a group of end-points, called intermediary end-points, as shown in the next figure. In the simplest case, the intermediary end-point only receives the content from the source end-point and forwards it to the sink end-point. In a more complicated scenario, the intermediary end-point processes the content (e.g., reformatting or adapting the content) before sending it forward.

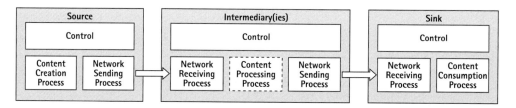

Intermediary end-point in the MITA content delivery model

Access Independent Interface

The MITA architecture makes the user plane as independent as possible from the underlying access technology. MITA defines an Access Independent Interface to shield the network protocols from the actual access technology. The interface prevents the consumer from any access technology specific control interaction with the access layer when using different access technologies. Three system entities are related to the AII definition as illustrated in the next figure: the link layer driver, the protocols for transport and a process for access independent mobility management.

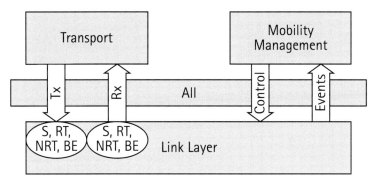

Access Independent Interface functions

Four main groups of AII functions are addressed in the previous figure: sending functions (Tx), receiving functions (Rx), access control functions (Control) and access layer events (Events). The primary objective of AII definitions is to enable the seamless usage of multiple wireless access networks simultaneously. It addresses many issues for deeper investigation (e.g., access independent mobility management, location of handover logic (e.g., link vs. network layer), and algorithms and methods to select a wireless link for a session from a set of available links). In a similar way QoS classes need to be defined and investigated. In the current model, four classes are identified: Signaling (S), Real-Time (RT), Non-Real-Time (NRT) and Best Effort (BE) classes as illustrated in the figure above.

MITA Concept Models

The principles for technical architecture modeling presented in the previous chapters are initially applied to the entities of the Mobile Internet Business Architecture. Then, the fundamentals of the Mobile Internet Technical Architecture are mapped to these principles and concept models for both MIBA and MITA are formed.

MIBA Concept Model

The principles of technical architecture modeling presented a layered element model. In that model, the Middleware layer isolates the Application and Platform layers allowing the same applications to run on multiple platforms and provides tools for developers to implement new services on a solid execution environment. In the Mobile Internet era, service interworking and a seamless service experience are major sources for added value to consumers. Both of these increase the importance of Middleware solutions. Hence, in the Mobile Internet Technical Architecture, the middleware layer has been named the Mobile Internet layer, as illustrated in the next figure.

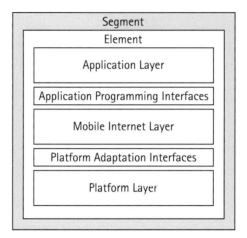

Mobile Internet Layer in the MITA Element

The above three element layers are applied to each of the MIBA segments and their elements. Interaction between the elements is provided with protocols and content delivery within the payloads of the protocols. An outcome of this approach is shown in the next figure. In this MIBA model, the terminal segment provides access to services, the network segment provides for terminal connectivity to service networks, and the server segment provides content and services for the consumers.

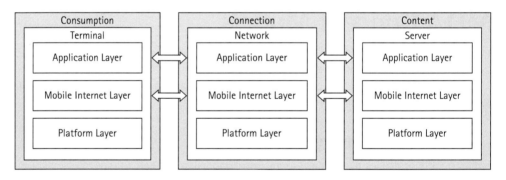

End-to-end view of the Mobile Internet Business Architecture

In some technical architecture models, the application layer is further divided into application and content layers. In the Mobile Internet Technical Architecture, content has been seen as information, which may have multiple presentation formats and is handled in the content processing functions of the Mobile Internet layer. Hence, content is not presented on its own layer.

MITA Concept Model

The basic model for the Mobile Internet Technical Architecture is achieved by applying the principles and assumptions set forth in the previous sections to the generic model of the technical architecture.

Interaction modes have been supported for dividing the Application layer into two sublayers - one for the applications and their logic, and the other consisting of support functionality for the Interaction modes, as illustrated in the next figure. There are groups of enablers that support applications on the Application layer. For example, contact database functionality would be considered to be a supporting enabler for phone and e-mail clients.

Applications access the supporting enablers through Application Programming Interfaces. In application development, lower layer interfaces of the MITA Element (e.g., Network interface functions or functions in Software Development Kit (SDK) libraries) can also be accessed when necessary. The supporting enablers on the Application layer access the Mobile Internet layer functionality below them through the Application Development Interfaces (ADIs).

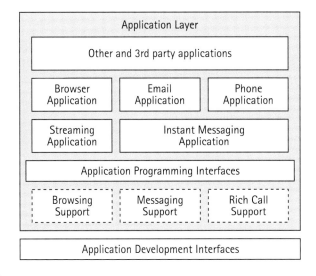

MITA Application layer

The Mobile Internet layer is divided into two functional stacks:

o   Operating System (OS) and Platform support stack, providing local support for applications (e.g., application framework functions, execution environment and UI support)

o   Internet Protocols stack, providing Mobile Internet protocols above the link layer functionality for Interaction mode support and applications

The architecture of the Mobile Internet layer is illustrated in the next figure.

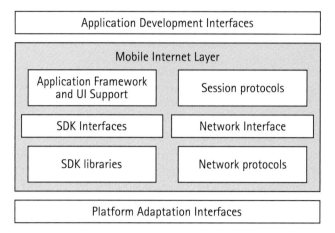

MITA Mobile Internet layer

The Platform layer consists of operating system core modules, device drivers and platform hardware, as shown in the next figure. Platform Adaptation Interfaces (PAIs) are located between the Platform layer and the Mobile Internet layer, as illustrated in the previous figure and the next figure. In the Mobile Internet Technical Architecture the generic PAIs consist of the following primary interfaces:

o   Platform interfaces enabling access to local resources

o   The Access Independent Interface enabling access to network resources

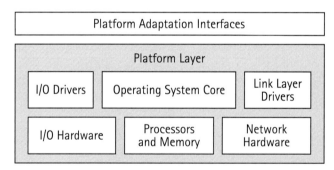

MITA Platform layer

Network functionality maps primarily to the Internet protocol stack of the Mobile Internet layer (e.g., TCP/IP and General Packet Radio Service (GPRS)), but also partly to the device drivers (link layer) and to the network related hardware (physical layer) of the Platform layer. Operating system functionality maps partly to the platform support (including SDK libraries) of the Mobile Internet layer, and partly to the OS core and the hardware drivers of the Platform layer.

As these components are combined, a basic model for an element of the Mobile Internet Technical Architecture emerges, as illustrated in the next figure.

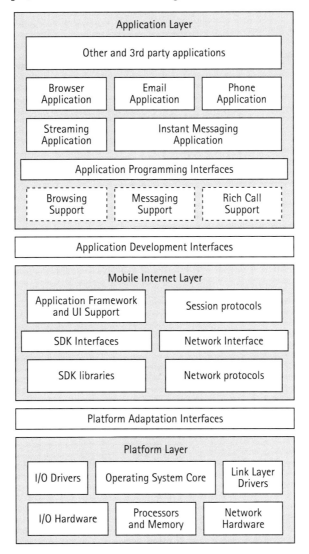

A MITA element

The conceptual MITA end-to-end view is achieved by mapping the MITA element to the presented MIBA end-to-end view. An outcome of the mapping is illustrated in the next figure.

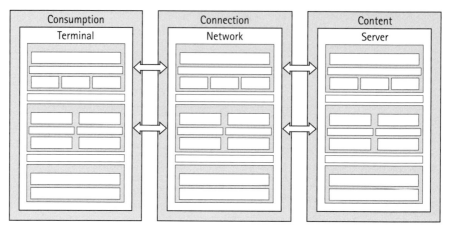

MITA end-to-end view

The MITA end-to-end view is a high-level reference model for more detailed technical architecture design. It shows that in principle, all elements of MITA can be derived from the same baseline conceptual MITA element. When the characteristics and requirements of different Network environments are noted, the above MITA end-to-end view extends to the MITA end-to-end matrix as illustrated in the next figure.

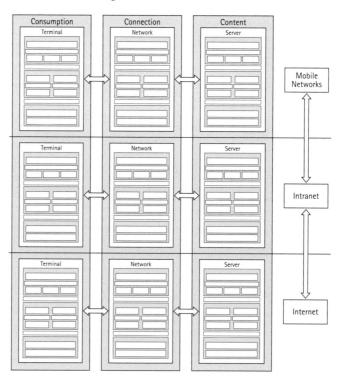

The MITA end-to-end matrix

MITA Network Model

A MITA network model maps the end-point-to-end-point interconnection model in MITA to the end-to-end views in the Nokia strategic architecture. The following three examples describe the outcomes of the mapping. In the Connecting people view, both end-points of the interconnection model are mobile devices as illustrated in the next figure.

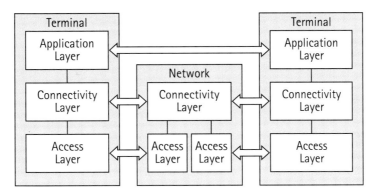

MITA network model for the Connecting people view

In a similar way, the Content goes wireless view is achieved when another end-point is replaced, from a terminal to a server as the client-server model assumes. This network interconnection scenario is shown in the next figure.

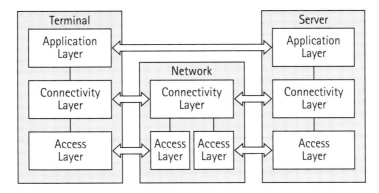

MITA network model for the Content goes wireless view

Finally, the Servers become smart view is achieved when both end-points are servers as illustrated in the next figure.

II

Introduction

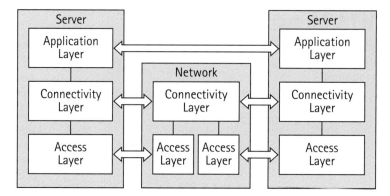

MITA network model for the Servers become smart view

The above conceptual MITA network model and its three interconnection scenarios develop into a complete network model when they are applied to real use cases. In the following example, the MITA network model is applied to a Rich Call Interaction mode where two mobile devices in different carrier domains communicate in a Rich Call session. The next figure illustrates a network model for the control plane of the Rich Call session.

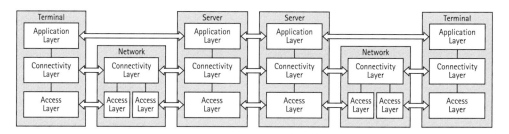

End-to-end control plane in the Rich Call session

In most Rich Call sessions, the control plane and user plane do not follow the same sequence of end-points. Typically, the control plane is routed via the domain servers, whereas the user plane is optimized for peer-to-peer communication due to high end-to-end delay and jitter requirements. The user plane is illustrated in the next figure of the Rich Call session.

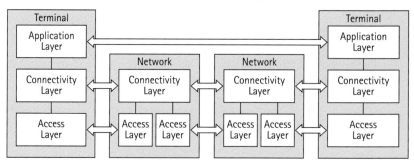

End-to-end user plane in Rich Call

These mappings and examples indicate that the MITA network model is applicable to all end-to-end views in the Nokia strategic architecture and can be used as a starting point for creating MITA use cases and service scenarios. The complete MITA network model is achieved when the above end-to-end views are completed with network architectures for the Application, Connectivity and Access layers.

MITA Implementation Model

The concept model for the Mobile Internet Technical Architecture consists of three functional layers presented in the previous sections. These layers were further divided into high-level functionalities: applications, Interaction mode support, Internet protocols stack, OS and platform support stack and Platform layer elements. The interfaces presented isolate these functionalities on a logical level.

The primary targets of the Mobile Internet Technical Architecture require extending its modularity one step further by introducing an implementation view of the technical architecture, called the MITA Subsystem Architecture (SSA).

Subsystems in MITA

The Subsystem Architecture is another viewpoint into the technical architecture, encapsulating a group of functionalities into independent, well-isolated subsystems.

A primary requirement is that an implementation of any subsystem can be replaced with another implementation with no or only a minimum amount of modifications to other subsystems or applications utilizing the services of the replaced subsystem. In a similar way, the implementation technology of a subsystem may be completely changed without influencing other related subsystems. The next figure illustrates an outcome of the above requirements, which is that subsystems must have clear, well-defined interfaces:

o   A support interface for other subsystems or applications that utilize the services of the present subsystem

o   The implementation of the subsystem is based on adaptation interfaces provided by other subsystems and/or the SDK libraries of the platform

o   An optional protocol interface, which allows interaction with other subsystems over the network

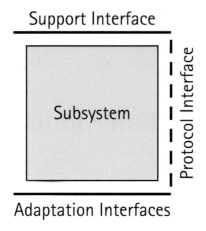

Subsystem interfaces

In the MITA Subsystem Architecture, two instances of MITA elements may be interconnected with an interoperable protocol interface on both elements, as illustrated in the next figure.

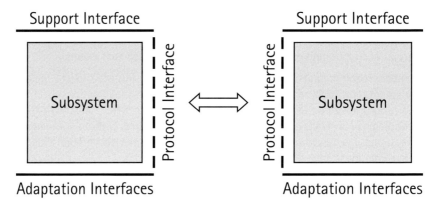

Interconnected subsystems

Categorization of MITA Subsystems

The MITA Subsystems are categorized into two groups:

o   Intra-Element subsystems encapsulate functionality within one MITA element

o   Inter-Element subsystems encapsulate interconnecting functionality over a network

A few examples of MITA Subsystems are illustrated in the next figure.

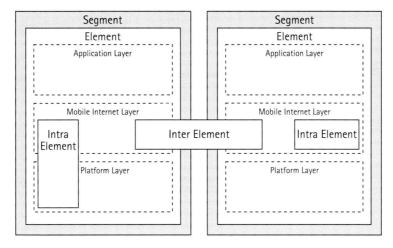

Examples of MITA Subsystem types

These subsystem categories can be used in building more complicated subsystem topologies, (e.g., client-to-server, server-to-server, or peer-to-peer communication scenarios). For example, a basic model for the generic content delivery model related subsystems in the terminal-to-terminal communication case is illustrated in the next figure.

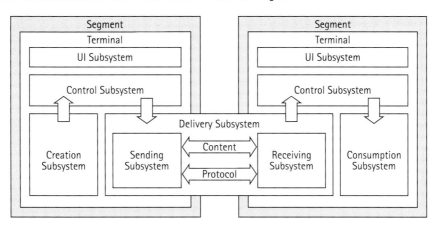

Content delivery subsystems for terminal-to-terminal communication

In a similar way, the generic content delivery model can be used for the server-to-terminal communication case, as shown in the next figure.

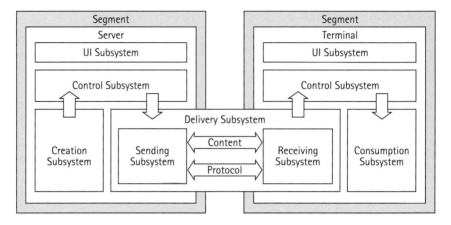

Content delivery subsystems for server-to-terminal communication

Finally, the content delivery model is applied to the server-to-server communication case in the next figure.

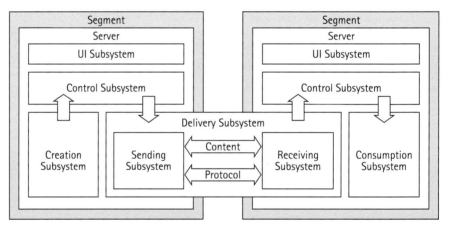

Content delivery subsystems for server-to-server communication

As the previous figures indicate, the same set of well isolated and defined subsystems can be used for multiple application scenarios. In many cases, this decreases the amount of specification and implementation efforts.

Modular MITA Element

One essential requirement for the success of the MITA model is that an implementation of MITA Elements is based on the MITA Subsystem Architecture and the basic requirements for MITA Subsystems presented above are met.

A typical approach to build a subsystem architecture is a bottom-up model enabling the separation of application and middleware software from platforms first and then building common software functionalities on top of these baseline subsystems.

The final outcome of this subsystem architecture approach is a design of a MITA element, which has well-defined software interfaces and a modular software architecture. The next figure shows the basic architecture of a modular MITA element.

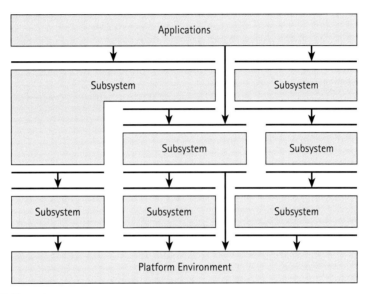

Modular MITA Element

III VISIONS

Introduction to MITA Specifications

Technical architecture work is divided into MITA specifications, to achieve technical teams of manageable scope and enable comparison to other models on a specification level. MITA specifications are divided into three groups:

o   Architecture specifications

o   Key system specifications

o   Architecture frameworks

The Architecture specifications are more permanent in nature, whereas the Key system specifications represent issues where understanding end-to-end system aspects prior to technology selections is important. The third set of specifications includes Architecture frameworks for broader system level issues.

Architecture Specifications

The architecture specifications are more permanent baseline specifications of MITA, covering the structure of the MITA element as illustrated in the next figure.

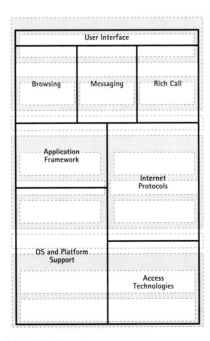

Architecture specifications and the MITA element

UI and Application Framework in MITA

The User Interface (UI) and Application Framework deal with issues related to the user interface and applications. A UI that is simple and easy to understand and use is seen as critical for the successful delivery of Mobile Internet services to the consumer. The importance of applications and their smooth and consistent interaction with the user interface is increasing, as application functionality increases. This becomes crucial when the size of mobile devices limits the display size and the number of user control mechanisms.

In the MITA era, various applications can be active simultaneously, thus providing the consumer with the possibilities to use multiple services at any time. This makes the use of services more convenient and flexible, but also imposes new challenges to introduce these solutions in a user-friendly way. Convenience and flexibility can be further improved by supporting application functionality, which allows seamless communication between applications to exchange any information needed to benefit the consumer.

As applications become downloadable and installable, security becomes increasingly important. Mobile Internet era devices will contain more and more personal and trusted information and functionality and the consumer must have confidence in the behavior of new applications to be downloaded; otherwise, consumer acceptance of new services may be reduced.

It is expected that a combination of revolutionary and evolutionary thinking is needed in order to create UI guidelines for the MITA era. We believe that these targets are best met by focusing the effort on a carefully selected (limited) set of UI styles and mapping the application functionality to the physical UI in an understandable and consistent way, thus minimizing the consumer learning curve and expediting the adoption of new applications and services.

Rich Call in MITA

Rich call is one of the three Interaction modes in MITA. Rich call covers applications which have as their cornerstone a real-time two-way communication component enriched with presence information, text, graphics, images and sounds before, during and after a call. Applications in this category are characterized by having demanding requirements for the underlying transport mechanisms and their integrity due to the real-time nature of the service. Typical applications in the Rich Call category are voice call and conference, video call and conference and real-time interactive games.

Rich call requires consistent behavior over various access networks and Network environments. The access network may impose some constraints over the Interaction mode, but it is desirable that the specific applications can scale their behavior to take this into account. The Network environments and their interworking are also required to be able to interconnect Rich call users residing in various types of networks.

Browsing in MITA

The Browsing Interaction mode covers applications which are interactive by nature, characterized by an interaction between a consumer and services in fixed or mobile servers and, in many cases, nearly real-time:

o   Online browsing (e.g., Markup style browsing interaction, interaction through executable programs and peer-to-peer browsing) o   Off-line browsing (e.g., Push of content to device, using the same markup languages and executables, but the interaction is limited to local servers and services)

Processed content may be displayable or metadata:

o   Displayable content includes various formats (e.g., text, graphics, animation and sound).

o   Metadata is not directly displayed, but can be used to expand the user experience by giving it a larger scope.

Browsing represents an interactive content consumption and manipulation experience. Initially, the consumer consumes content in an interactive manner, but the experience will soon expand into manipulation of the content (true interactive applications).

The browsing environment, and the browser in particular, will play a significant role as a platform, as the host of a browsing paradigm. The browser is enabled with Extensible Markup Language (XML), and can thus offer XML services to other applications. The concepts of embedded links and metadata in markup documents translate very well into any XML content or content that can be translated into an XML representation, be it contacts, calendar or generic data.

One of the key roles of the browser, as the most important component of browsing, is to serve as a platform for enhanced functionality to be used by other applications. This functionality may include multiple technologies, such as animation services, audio services, and video services. In order to flexibly offer this kind of functionality, dynamic installations and the configuration of software (for example plug-ins) become important.

Messaging in MITA

The Messaging Interaction mode covers applications which provide two-way, asynchronous delivery of content. For example, Short Message Service (SMS), Multimedia Messaging Service (MMS) and e-mail involve a separation between the submittal of content and the delivery to the recipient.

Emerging technologies (e.g., Session Initiation Protocol (SIP) and XML) and applications (e.g., news, chat and Internet Relay Chat (IRC)) address challenges to traditional messaging technologies (e.g., SMS and e-mail) causing new interworking requirements. In a similar way, interworking between MITA applications (e.g., click-to-call and click-to-chat) and the management and processing of the static and dynamic message content and attachments in various conditions address requirements for messaging subsystems.

Internet Protocols in MITA

The underlying fundamentals for the success of IP networking include architectural and technical simplicity, openness, and scalability. The open end-to-end architecture has enabled the efficient development of new services and applications, and fast deployment of them on the Internet. The IP protocols are being extended to globally support user, terminal, and service mobility, which will enable new useful services and applications for all Internet users. As an outcome of the extension, some existing Internet protocols may need modification to meet the new requirements.

III

Visions

The Internet protocols specification introduces the MITA Internet protocols architecture; it explains the functions and roles of the protocol stack layers and places the protocol layers in the layered MITA network model. This section also introduces the major Internet protocols implementing the protocol functionalities.

Operating Systems and Platform Support in MITA

As an entity, MITA is not about Operating Systems (OS); it is, however, about how operating systems and applications can co-operate with each other to provide a rich consumer experience in a consistent manner. MITA sets certain requirements on the underlying operating systems and support functionality provided by the operating system to the upper layers, such as, SDK libraries, application protocols, and network protocols.

In many cases, the underlying operating system libraries set the base for architectural paradigms. For example, the Linux operating system and Linux libraries and APIs are good examples of the procedural programming style. On the other hand, the Symbian operating system and Symbian OS libraries provide pure object-oriented interfaces. It should be noted that programming languages (e.g., C, C++ and Java) and programming paradigms are separate issues. However, in most cases, procedural programming environments have been extended with high functionality object-oriented designs.

MITA does not define a preferred operating system. Operating system selection is a business decision, not an architectural issue. However, the operating system should always be compatible with MITA requirements. These requirements are set by the upper layers and are collected into this specification for easy access. On one hand, this also means that MITA is independent of operating systems and programming paradigms. On the other hand, it means that the implementation of MITA in different platforms may vary according to platform capabilities.

Another part of the OS and platform support specification are issues related to baseline development environments, and the principles presented for operating systems also apply to them. This specification collects the generic requirements.

Multiple Access in MITA

A typical mobile device consumer is primarily interested in applications and services, while the actual access technology should be as transparent as possible and should not require any technical understanding, when using an application or subscribing to a service. Still, this transparency should not limit potential applications, as all of them might not work in an acceptable way over all access technologies. These technologies have different technical characteristics (e.g., available bandwidth, connection setup time, network delay and symmetric/asymmetric performance), which impact the consumer experience, i.e., the technologies differ in multiple attributes (e.g., data rates, QoS, handover capabilities, latencies).

The Access Technologies Specification defines the elements needed to allow access from a mobile device to an IP network. Due to the differing functionality of the various access technologies, the platform layer varies between different forms of access. The Access Independent

Interface is supposed to shield the Mobile Internet Layer from the underlying technology, but access specific functionality is required within the network protocols in order to facilitate some access-specific functionality.

Key System Specifications

The Key systems are end-to-end and cross-organizational building blocks of the Mobile Internet Technical Architecture.

Naming, Numbering and Addressing in MITA

Naming, Numbering and Addressing (NNA) concentrates on the names and addresses of individual people or devices and how names and addresses appear on the user interface. The consumer favored nickname information is translated into globally unique names and finally to routable addresses. The translations between globally unique names and the related directory infrastructure belong to the Naming, Numbering, and Addressing specification. The implications and requirements of the NNA environment (e.g., anonymous addressing and regulator aspects) are also studied in the specification.

Naming, Numbering, and Addressing provides one unified translation infrastructure for Rich call, Messaging and Browsing services. Interaction with presence services enables networked and dynamic resolution of naming layer addresses. On the mobile device, Naming, Numbering, and Addressing functionalities are located in the address book subsystem. However, it should be noted that the NNA services are not limited to the address resolution requirements of the rich call service, for any application may utilize these services.

Presence in MITA

Presence deals with the issues of providing dynamic information about the status and availability of consumers and mobile devices. Presence is a key system for a number of specifications. The messaging specification utilizes presence services to enable instant messaging between consumers.

It should be noted that one consumer could have multiple application level identities. How to manage these and how to dynamically associate those to the current Connectivity layer identities are issues which link the presence specification to the reachability specification.

Reachability in MITA

The reachability of devices and people deals with the issues related to the question of how a device or a person is reached through the Web and Mobile domains. A communication network is not a single network with seamless IP connectivity. A communication network consists of networks, such as IPv4 Internet, IPv4 intranets, IPv6 Internet, carrier IPv6 based mobile networks and Public Switched Telephone Network (PSTN). There are also different types of gateways (e.g., Network Address Translation (NAT), firewall or Session Initiation Protocol (SIP) entities) between networks. Seamless person-to-person and device-to-device connectivity over these fragmented networks is the scope of the Reachability Specification.

III

Visions

Access Independent Connectivity in MITA

The Access Independent Connectivity (AIC) specification deals with seamless access to personal services in all Network environments independently of their location and connectivity/access providers. The primary focus of the AIC specification is to provide continuous connectivity for interconnected MITA end-points. The Access Independent Connectivity specification provides access independent mobility management for the Connectivity layer.

Typically, mobility management is involved in connections between a device and a network. This statement is also valid for the AIC Specification. In MITA, mobility management has been divided between the AIC specification and the Access Technologies specification. The Reachability, Service Discovery, and Presence Specifications also deal with mobility issues.

Service Discovery in MITA

Service discovery consists of three types of discovery methods:

o   Service discovery on ad-hoc networks

o   Service discovery on the Internet

o   A special type of service discovery is provided by the presence and virtual community navigation layer

The Service Discovery specification covers the Connectivity and Application layer service discovery technologies. The access layer-related service discovery technologies are covered in the Access Technologies specification.

The Service Discovery specification addresses requirements for the Access Independent Interface. When the AIC Subsystem identifies a need to change into a new access network domain, after proper authentication, the service discovery service for the Connectivity layer should be activated. In a similar way, the service discovery service provides control and event triggering interfaces for the Application layer subsystems and applications.

Location in MITA

The Location specification defines software and protocol interfaces for location services. In practice, this refers to interfaces receiving location information for applications and to applications that utilize location-based information. A goal in MITA is to define a mobile location services architecture and interfaces, which are able to deliver location information to applications regardless of the positioning technology and of the division of functionality between devices, networks and servers. The same architecture must be flexible for several business models. In other words, a simple business model should not dictate it.

Location information is also an important element in many other MITA specifications. For example, location can be used to automatically update a user's presence and reachability information, and it can also be utilized in service discovery for local services.

The mobile location services architecture in MITA actually consists of several different architectures, where the positioning infrastructures are different but location interfaces to applications and middleware, in between, should be the same.

Device Management and Data Synchronization in MITA

Device management, including both bootstrap and continuous device management, is very important. A good and correct configuration is a prerequisite for any application to actually be functional. Furthermore, it is to be expected that the complexity of mobile devices will increase with the addition of new and more powerful applications. At the same time, these increasingly complex devices will move into mass-market environments and it is not reasonable to assume that all the consumers will be willing to configure their applications manually. Thus, the need for device management will only increase.

It is highly likely that there will be multiple device management providers. Typically, each provider has access to a subset of the parameter space. For example, there might be different management entities for the device's look-and-feel, for the browsing environment and for the messaging environment. The managing entities, for the above three, could be the device manufacturer, service provider, and the company of the consumer, respectively.

Device management offers services to applications (e.g., provides them with configuration data). Similarly, device management also has its own user interface, for example, to allow the user to control and interact with the management process.

In MITA, data synchronization will cover at least the following issues:

o   Distributed applications and databases

o   Linkage between presence and contacts/calendar

o   Personal Information Management (PIM) related issues (e.g., contacts, calendar, to do lists)

o   Controlled content download and management, using smart messages or a device management mechanism

Content Formats in MITA

A content format refers to a convention of packaging content. Agreements must be made on content formats in order to build the necessary interoperability between various machines, devices and applications. Given the limitations of the processing environment in mobile devices, we have to select a certain reasonably small set of content formats to be promoted and supported in Mobile Internet offerings. Content formats are to be agreed on in the areas of audio, still images and vector graphics, video and general-purpose documents.

Content Adaptation in MITA

Content adaptation refers to the manipulation of content to make it suitable for specific machines, devices and applications. Although agreement on common content formats is the desirable solution, market segmentation, devices of different generations or categories with varying capabilities (e.g., processing power, display resolution, memory and bandwidth), and the unavoidable introduction of new formats are all true obstacles for interoperability. Content adaptation strives to fill the interoperability gaps as devices and content formats evolve. Examples of content adaptation include: image format conversion and the resolution reduction of images and video. Content adaptation can also modify content modality to suit the consumer's environment. For instance, text-to-speech technologies can be useful for retrieving text messages while driving a car.

Operation Support Systems in MITA

The Operation Support Systems (OSS) specification deals with the Mobile Internet management and support architecture. The functionality of the OSS architecture is divided into management layers:

o   Network management

o   Service management

o   Subscription management

o   Subscriber accounting and identity management

By combining the management layers with the possible business players, two frameworks could be constructed:

o   Management framework

o   Policy framework

Privacy in MITA

Privacy is not an add-on feature. All aspects of a system have to be designed to fulfill the inherent need for privacy. Privacy in MITA covers all relevant principles, solutions and technologies related to consumer privacy on the Mobile Internet.

Nokia is concerned about the emerging privacy threats. As the awareness of the Mobile Internet and privacy issues increases among the consumers, the pressure to maintain and build trust rises among all players. Companies need to address the privacy concerns seriously. Trust, once lost, is very hard to regain. Privacy, once lost, cannot be repaired.

Architecture Frameworks

Part of the MITA work deals with issues which are complicated to solve without having common and unified models. These issues are structured under common frameworks, before a more detailed technical architecture is built. Current such frameworks include directories, security, Mobile Internet Interfaces and Quality of Service (QoS).

Directories in MITA

Directories are network repositories for information about people, places and things. There are numerous instances of directories in the Mobile domain. For example, in GSM technologies the Home Location Register (HLR) is a directory of information about subscribers. Directories consist of three basic components:

o   Schema

o   Access method

o   Directory store

Information in a directory, whether it represents data about a person or a device, is structured in a particular way. The characteristic defining the selection of information that is stored about people, places and things is called a schema. There is also a need to represent directory information when it is transferred around the Mobile domain. Exchange formats provide a standard exchange scheme for such purposes. Significant MITA schemes include those that represent the mobile person object and the mobile device object. Other auxiliary schemes define managed mobile services for these basic objects.

Information in a directory is accessed using a directory access protocol. Directory access protocols provide methods for creating, modifying, searching and deleting entries. The administrators of a directory service can also utilize restricted administrator access methods to create new directory object types. There are a number of directory access methods that are needed for Mobile domain directories.

Information in a directory is maintained and managed similarly to information within a database. In fact, a directory is a specialized database application. Within the Mobile domain, there are numerous directory stores, each being used to capture information about a particular feature of the mobile person object or the mobile device.

Additional components in the MITA directory specification include the use of directory synchronization to keep the numerous mobile directory stores updated with each other. Directories contain critical mobile assets including security information about consumers.

Security in MITA

Security is about safety and trust. Safety is considerably easier to manage than trust, and without safety, it is hard to create trust between unseen entities. It is important to understand that security addresses requirements on all entities of the Mobile Internet Technical Architecture. Security is required when calling someone or making an electronic monetary transaction with browser security functionality or features protecting consumer information from being revealed or being altered during transmission. Similar security requirements also apply to server-to-server transactions.

III

Visions

MITA security objectives are:

o   **Integrity**
o   **Confidentiality**
o   **Availability**
o   **Authentication**
o   **Authorization**

Integrity deals with the prevention of erroneous modification of information. Authorized users are probably the biggest cause of errors, omissions and the alteration of data. Storing incorrect data within the system can be as bad as losing data. Malicious attackers can also modify, delete or corrupt information that is vital to the correct operation of business functions.

Confidentiality deals with the prevention of unauthorized disclosure of third party information. This can happen as a result of poor security measures or information leaks by personnel. An example of poor security measures would be to allow anonymous access to sensitive information.

Availability deals with the prevention of unauthorized withholding of information or resources. This does not apply just to personnel withholding information. Information should be as freely available as possible to authorized users.

Authentication deals with the process of verifying that users are who they claim to be when logging onto a system. Generally, the use of user names and passwords accomplishes this. More sophisticated is the use of smart cards and biometric authentication. The process of authentication does not grant the user access rights to resources - this is achieved through the authorization process.

Authorization deals with the process of allowing only authorized users access to sensitive information, protected services or resources and controlled actions. An authorization process uses the appropriate security authority to determine whether a user should have access to resources.

Mobile Internet Interfaces in MITA

Mobile Internet Interfaces are fundamental elements of the Mobile Internet Technical Architecture. Elsewhere in this book, both the layered model of a MITA element and the fundamentals of the MITA subsystem architecture were presented. These models identified many interfaces. Some of them are software interfaces within a MITA element and others are protocol interfaces between interconnected MITA elements.

Mobile Internet Interfaces are a group of open interfaces provided by Nokia for both software developers and system integrators, so that they can implement MITA compliant applications and systems. It should be noted that Mobile Internet Interfaces live longer than product generations and have similar features over product and server categories. Open software interfaces in the Mobile Internet Technical Architecture are called Mobile Internet Software Interfaces (MSI) and open protocol interfaces are called Mobile Internet Protocol Interfaces (MPI).

MSIs are divided into Application Programming Interfaces and System Software Interfaces (SSI). In a similar way, MPIs are divided into two parts: Protocol Data Units (PDU), including protocol payload definitions, and content formats, describing presentation formats for the content.

In the Mobile Internet Technical Architecture, all MITA elements have Mobile Internet Interfaces. In terminals, most of the open interfaces are software interfaces for application developers, whereas in servers, the open interfaces are both software and protocol interfaces enabling fast and rich service implementation by system integrators and developers. In network elements, Mobile Internet Interfaces are mainly protocol interfaces enabling different MITA end-to-end views.

Quality of Service in MITA

The QoS is an important topic that requires a common and unified model. QoS in MITA is approached by defining the basic objectives for a QoS system on four levels:

o   Support the mission of the service provider or carrier

o   Serve the principal needs of consumers

o   Meet the quantity and quality requirements of applications

o   Transmit as many packets as possible

The fundamental assumption is that when defining the actions of a network, a hierarchical structure is formed where the first objective is the most important and the last objective is the least important. For instance, when the needs of different customers are conflicting, we have to look at the upper level in the hierarchy (i.e., the mission of service provider) instead of a lower level (i.e., the applications requirements) in order to solve the conflict. From this perspective, QoS is more about the mission of the service provider, that is, typically business, than the fulfillment of the special requirements of applications. In order to meet the objectives set for QoS, the carrier has to proceed in phases that include defining the fundamental mission, designing the service model, building an appropriate network, and using suitable QoS mechanisms.

The Mobile Internet will consist of several different networking technologies, network environments and services. In some parts of the Mobile Internet, the Quality of Service mechanisms and principles may be based on an approach that is not suitable for other parts of the network. For example, radio technologies often support a natural flow or connection-oriented QoS while the legacy Internet has been designed for packet-based approaches. This implies that the only reasonable way to provide real end-to-end QoS must be based on a common measure, and fulfilling the business goals of carriers is exactly this measure.

PART 3.1

Application Layer

- o Browsing

- o Messaging

- o Rich Call

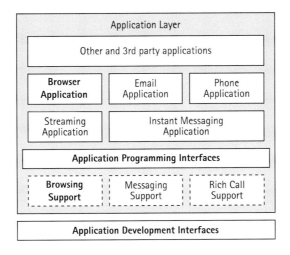

Browsing

This chapter studies browsing from the mobility point of view, and looks into its role in the Mobile World where millions of mobile devices are used to access a wide variety of different mobile services every day.

Introduction

A mobile browser is an application in a mobile device whose main function is to show content on its display and, based on the request generated by the consumer interaction with the displayed content or the programmed features of the content itself, fetch new content from the location specified by the request.

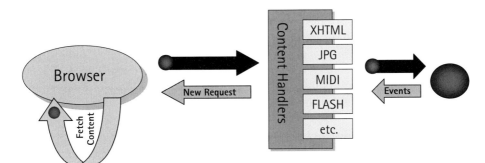

Main parts of the Mobile Browser

More specifically, the browser consists of the two main parts: Content Access and Content Handling. Content access is based on Mobile Internet protocols and, at its highest layers, supports HyperText Transfer Protocol (HTTP) requests and Uniform Resource Identifier (URI) addressing of content. Content handling is based on plug-in architecture where the browser, by default, supports a set of content handlers (e.g., markup pages, images, streaming media), but the architecture allows the extension of it either statically (requires recompilation) or dynamically (installation of new handlers can be done during run-time). Markup-based page description languages (e.g., Extensible HyperText Markup Language (XHTML)) form the backbone of the services but other types of content can also be supported (e.g., most of the content is downloaded as a whole to the mobile device before its use but also one way streaming type of content can be supported (audio and video streaming)).

In a Personal Computer (PC) based browsing environment, the Web browser has become a more and more dominant part of the operating environment. The reason is that the PC environment, by nature, is very suitable for it (e.g., lots of computing power, large screen, support for colors, keyboard and mouse based operation, and high speed networking). Mobile devices, on the other hand, do not and cannot have all of the features available on a PC. In addition, most mobile devices have been designed primarily to support their two main Interaction modes: Rich Calls (real-time communication) or messaging (non real-time communication). This does not mean that mobile browsing is secondary to these other Interaction modes. Instead it provides the mobile device a new and complementary near real-time Interaction mode and several enabling technologies to provide, for example, the following features:

o **Access to Services**: The mobile browser can be used to access markup based services or to, for example, download and install Java applications to the mobile device. Markup language based services and Java applications can be seen as complementary technologies for providing mobile services to the consumers.

o **Content delivery platform**: The browser can function as the search and delivery platform for content that the consumer wants to download to his or hers mobile device or even to external devices. One example of this is the download of now popular ringing tones, screen savers and Java applications for the installation into the mobile device. In the future, people can use the same platform to access, for example, their slide presentations of latest sales figures to be used for business purposes.

o **Visualization of content**: The core of the browser handles XHTML and other supported content types. This means that the mobile device already has quite a powerful engine to display XHTML and other content types even if they are not being provided through the browser. For example, E mail, Multimedia Messaging Service (MMS), and Java can use this engine to enhance their capabilities to handle many types of content. Thus, the browser is not just a separate entity anymore but many of its core technologies have become common enablers that can be used by the whole mobile application environment.

Since the mobile device is used more and more for accessing data services in addition to the regular rich call and messaging services, the browser environment and its core technologies are going to be some of the key elements in the development of the new General Packet Radio Service (GPRS) and third generation services.

Consumer Perspective

From the consumer point of view, the browser offers them one way to access services in the mobile network. Use of these services requires that the consumer understands a few basic browsing concepts: a browser, a page, an address and a link. The browser is an application in a mobile device used to access mobile services in the form of pages. A page is an entity that can contain, for example, text, images and interactive elements presented in a page type layout. Each page can also contain links that define alternative paths that can be used to move from one page to another. Each page has an address (identifier) and links use this addressing mechanism to point to other pages. The consumer can physically enter or select a link on a page and move to a new page. This move to a new page may also be a byproduct of consumer interaction with the interactive elements on the page.

What is typically not visible to consumers is the fact that the root of the browsing system relies on pages described in one of the available markup languages (e.g., XHTML) HyperText Markup Language (HTML) or Wireless Markup Language (WML)). Pages can even contain non-visual passive (e.g., meta data) and active elements (e.g., scripting) that help to make each of the pages easier to locate, faster to access, better to view and more secure to use. All that detail is not and should not really be relevant for the consumers. In most of the cases the technology is irrelevant and what counts is the service. Browsing is first and foremost an enabling technology to provide services to consumers and its benefits for the consumer are:

o   Simple concept to understand - A service is a collection of various interactive pages that together constitute the service user interface.

o   Simple to add new services - No need to install applications for each new service. All that is needed is the address of the new service and the consumer can start using it.

o   Consistent interaction model - Use of a wide variety of different services is easy due to the consistent use of standard user interface elements.

o   Visually rich - The user interface for the services can use different content types in various layouts depending on the capabilities of the mobile devices. This is a significant improvement from the previous pure text or voice based services.

The following sections look at the special requirements of mobile browsing and how they affect the development of mobile services.

Mobile Service Delivery Chain

The high-level mobile browsing end-to-end architecture and the main functions of its different entities are presented in the following figure:

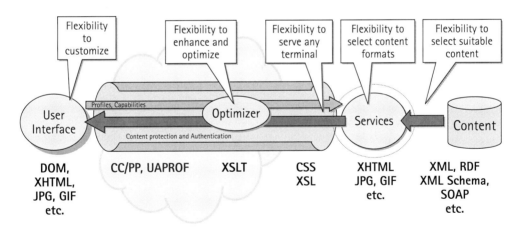

Mobile Browsing End-to-End delivery chain

As can be seen from the previous figure, one of the main issues in the mobile browsing delivery chain is flexibility. The whole chain from the mobile device to the content must provide a flexible channel to deliver the services to the consumer in most optimal (network resources and mobile device resources) and user friendly way.

The role of the User Interface entity is to provide the tools for the services creators to come up with highly usable service user interfaces for a wide variety of mobile services. The mobile device contains a set of user agents responsible to interpret the various content formats used by the services. The browser is the main user agent responsible for handling markup content. The browser can support various other content types as long as the corresponding content handlers are available in the mobile device. In some cases, the mobile devices are capable of extending their content handling capabilities by the use of dynamically downloadable content handler plug-ins.

Due to many reasons, consumers are and will be using a wide variety of different kinds of mobile devices. The consequence of this is that information about the characteristics of the mobile device and its user preferences is needed for an optimal use of services. Customer profiles and device capabilities serve a key role in providing this information to the elements in the end-to-end chain. This information can be used by the intermediate network elements (optimization) and the services to provide the most suitable content in the most optimal way to the consumer. HTTP headers, Composite Capability / Preference Profiles (CC/PP) and User Agent Profiles (UAProf) are the main technologies that can be used to describe and deliver this information.

The role of the Optimizer entity is to take the content being delivered to or from the mobile device and optimize it to best suit the needs of the consumer and the supported features of the mobile device. This can happen on the protocol layers (selection of the optimal delivery protocol) or in the application layer (e.g., filtering and conversion of content, and caching of content.). Proxy technologies and Extensible Stylesheet Language Transformations (XSLT) together with the information of customer profiles and device capabilities are some examples of technologies that can be used to optimize the delivery of content between the mobile device and the server.

Services are provided by servers that access content and turn it into suitable content formats presentable on a mobile device. Profile information together with Extensible Stylesheet Language (XSL) / Cascading Style Sheets (CSS) can be used to help the services to access content in its many formats and deliver it to the mobile device in the most suitable way.

Content is the data needed to construct a service. Content can be stored in local or distributed databases, it can be pieces of information accessible from the Internet, it can be data that can be provided by other network brokers or servers by using Simple Object Access Protocol (SOAP), Common Object Request Broker Architecture (CORBA) and Remote Method Invocation (RMI).

Whatever the access method, content can be represented in a wide variety of formats (e.g., Resource Description Framework (RDF), various Extensible Markup Language (XML) formats, image formats and database tables). The important thing is that the service can access the content and turn it into formats that can be represented on a wide variety of different mobile devices.

Finally, one of the key features of the delivery chain is its capability to provide tools for secure use of services. Especially in cases where the consumer is using the browser to provide valuable personal information to the services, the end-to-end architecture must provide all necessary tools to make the whole delivery chain secure. This includes, for example, content protection and authentication of the participants (the consumer and the service provider) to verify that the information is exchanged only between the right parties.

Discovery and Consumption

In principle, use of mobile services can be categorized to consist of two main activities: Discovery and Consumption. Before the consumer can use any of the available services they have to be discovered. There are several ways this can be accomplished today:

o   **Portals**: Portals are services that provide information about other services. They provide branded collections of links to a variety of services.

o   **Bookmarks**: Typically located in the mobile device itself. They can be used to collect links to services that are of interest to the consumer.

o   **Search engines**: Making searches among a large set of services to find out the ones that closely match with the consumer's criteria.

o   **Other**: Addresses to services can also be provided by documents, messages and other non-technical sources (e.g., magazines, advertisements, and letters) in which case the consumer must be able to type in the address manually.

The nature of consumption of discovered services can take many forms. This is simply because the browsing architecture has been designed to be generic and extensible. Consumption can mean studying of articles, books, news stories, presentations, advertisements or buying goods and services from Web based retailers or ticket offices. Banks and financial institutions can provide their services to mobile consumers as well as federal, state and local community officials (e.g. taxation, benefits, rules and laws, and community services). Mobile browsing can also be used to access services that typically have been provided by special applications (e.g., messaging, chatting, bulleting boards, news groups, and games).

From Web Services to Mobile Services

All the previously mentioned services are common to most of the Internet users today. They use the latest markup and visualization technologies to create visually and functionally rich interfaces to services that are provided by high performance servers, delivered by fast networks and accessed by PCs. Unfortunately, the same services as such do not work in the Mobile domain.

III Visions

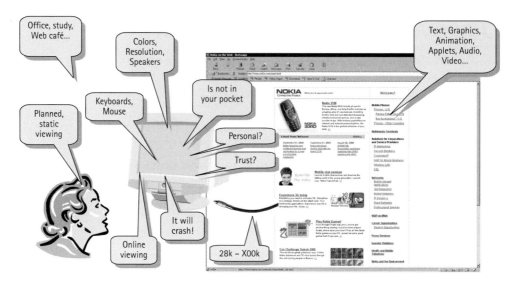

Browsing in the PC Environment

As can be seen from the figure above, many of the Web-based services are designed with the assumption that the whole service delivery chain is advanced enough (e.g., supports the use of large content types, large sized Web pages, and mouse based interaction). The fact is that many of these assumptions cannot be supported in the Mobile domain today or even in the near future. New services created for the consumer, or old Web services tailored to suit the need of the consumers, have to be designed to optimally use the mobile environment, the operating situation, the form factor and the available technologies.

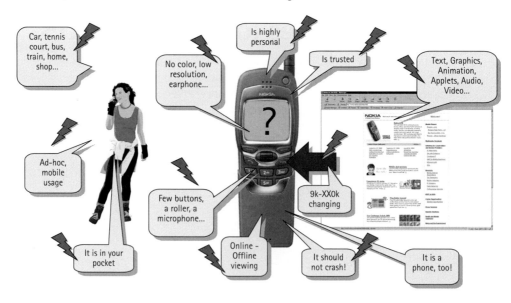

Challenges of Mobile Browsing

This does not mean that it is somehow technically more difficult or even impossible to provide services to the Mobile domain. On the contrary, the technologies that can be used in the Mobile domain are the same as in the Web domain, with the exception that certain features are not needed there and the mobile environment provides new features not available on the PC. Thus, the technical creation of the services has not changed but what has changed is the fact that the consumers are different and they require different services, the operating environment is different, the form factor is different and the mobile network provides less bandwidth but, in compensation, provides access to consumers at any time anywhere. The challenges are many but the rewards for succeeding are big: already today there are more mobile phone users than PC users in the world.

Framework for Mobile Services

There are several factors that have to be considered when providing services tailored for consumers. The first one relates to the way the mobile browser is used. The consumers tend to use the mobile browser to access certain services that are of interest to them at any particular time and the tendency is not to just look what is out there. There are several reasons supporting this. One is the fact that the limitations with the input devices make activities requiring lots of interaction hard. Another one is the size of the screen that does not provide access to the same amount and variety of information as available on the PC. Also, the situation in which the mobile device is used many times does not support long sessions of Web browsing. The use of the mobile browser is, thus, very service and consumer's immediate need oriented and the services should be developed with that in mind.

The screen size of a mobile device creates a challenge to content providers. The smaller the screen the less space the content provider has to present the information to the consumer. By increasing the resolution we can show more on the small screen but the readability of the content does not improve. Usage of larger than the display size pages with scrolling is not a good solution either because the aim is to limit the amount of scrolling that the customer has to do. Thus, services should be developed in such a way that they optimize the use of screen space, the amount of content, and the amount of interaction needed by the consumer to perform a useful operation.

Mobile devices, especially in the cost effective category, do not provide much space for content. Thus, to offer services in an environment like this, the amount of content used for providing a service must be minimized. In addition, large amounts of content can prolong the time it takes to download it and has a negative effect on the service response times.

Currently, one hand operation is the most common way to use mobile services. In addition, the person using the mobile device may be on the move. Requiring the consumer to select from a long list of alternatives, to scroll through many pages of information or to jump through a large set of links to find the right one has a negative effect on usability. Thus, the less the consumers have to provide unnecessary input the more satisfied they will be with the service.

Wireless bandwidth is not free. Mobile networks will probably always provide less bandwidth with higher cost than the fixed network. In addition, consumers are mostly long time mobile device users who are accustomed to pay for mobile services and are acutely aware of prices. The cost of using a network-based service must be counted in when deciding what kinds of services the mobile browser is good for. Long browsing sessions with no aim just to study "what is out there" may not be common in the Mobile domain. The right approach is to use the network resources sparingly and make the service quick to use and small in size.

Already today several types of mobile services are being used by people of different ages with different levels of education. This implies that usability and the ease of use are of highest importance when providing services for the wide variety of consumers. The consumer should not need any knowledge about any of the underlying technologies and the provisioning of the services must be such that even novices can start using them in no time.

Finally, design with the consumer's main goal in mind when they use the service. Think about what is important, essential and leave everything else out or at least do not clutter the main pages of the service with unnecessary data. Put extra information into separate areas of the service.

Mobile Browsing Extensions

The mobile browser provides the base for the creation of mobile services. However, new technologies and features are constantly being integrated into the mobile devices and in many cases the mobile browser has to be extended to support them. These extensions create a basis for the creation of new and more advanced mobile services of the future.

Location

Location is one of the key attributes of a mobile device. As such it is also one of the attributes that need to be well guarded and only given to the hands of those services that the consumer trusts to use it properly. Location information can be direct (current location of a device) or indirect (location of a restaurant) and it can be provided by the customer, mobile device or the mobile network. Location can also be presented by exact world coordinates or by less precise but in many cases more meaningful systems (e.g., street addresses, postal codes, and shop names). Special location services can turn these addresses into world coordinates with varying precision. Location can also indicate such things as time, speed, altitude, direction and heading.

Location information can be used with a multitude of services that are aimed at helping the consumer in many ways. Services that provide information (e.g., restaurants, shops, bus stops, railway stations, and time tables) can all use location information to provide the consumer precise information wherever they may be located at any given time.

The service can request location information by using special request protocols or the location is requested simply by asking the consumer to provide it directly. Also the consumer or the browsing environment itself can semi-automatically provide it back to the service. Naturally, standard location information presentation formats and exchange protocols are needed to ensure interoperability.

Mobile Commerce

E-commerce is one of the hot topics of the legacy Internet nowadays and payment mechanisms are an elementary part of mobile commerce.

Mobile devices provide a natural place to implement electronic money management systems. Being small, always with consumer and always connected, makes it natural to incorporate, for example, mobile wallet type of functionality into the mobile device.

The browsing environment can provide a nice interface for many mobile commerce related services and as such it too has to interface with the payment mechanisms. Depending on the technology used, the integration can take place either in the mobile device or in the server running a mobile commerce service.

Billing

Billing is another mobile commerce related function and works closely together with mobile payments. Mobile billing provides mechanisms for receiving, viewing and paying bills from the mobile device. The browsing environment is very suitable for showing and handling bill information since it is designed to show information in page format.

Digital Rights Management

Digital content (e.g., in the forms of video clips, sound bytes, and ringing tones) are all going to be available also for the consumers. Content is a valuable commodity that needs to be protected and mobile Digital Rights Management (DRM) systems are designed to do just that.

The mobile browser is a natural platform for searching for and selecting different content due to its ability to provide information not only visually, but also, through content handler plug-ins, in any way the content is designed to be represented. After the selection (and preview) has been made, the integrated payment solutions together with DRM based content download can be used to provide the content to the consumer with the purchased rights to use it.

Device Management

Mobile devices preferably never need any complicated consumer configuration or maintenance. However, there are cases where the consumers would like to configure certain aspects of their device or the services used by it. The mobile browser can be the interface for operator and device manufacturer provided device management services by which the consumers can configure the device and the used services to their liking by selecting options from easy to understand alternatives. The actual configuration of the device is either done through other mechanisms or the browser can have (as one of its plug-ins) content handlers for different content types.

III

Visions

Directions for the Future of Mobile Browsing

In addition to the previously mentioned extensions, there are also several new trends and requirements that need to be covered by developing suitable mobile browsing technologies for the future.

Service Discovery and Installation

Service discovery and service installation are two important future features that need to be improved to make browser based mobile service use really user friendly. In most cases, the consumers do not have the time or interest for constantly looking for new mobile services. They want the most suitable one and they want to access them quickly and without too much hassle. New service discovery and service installation mechanisms will provide an easy way to look for a service and install a reference to the service for fast future access.

New XML Content Types

Another area of future technologies is the introduction of XHTML and other XML-based technologies in the mobile environment. Future mobile devices will have to have a highly optimized XML engine to handle all the different XML based services that will be introduced in the near future. New XML technologies and content formats are being created every day, many of which are highly focused also on mobile services.

Java™

Browsing and the network dependent page-based service creation technologies work well with certain kinds of applications. However, there are a large number of services that require the use of either native or interpreted programming environments that provide more precise control of device capabilities. Java™ technology will be embedded in millions of both low-end and high-end mobile devices in the near future. This makes it very important that Java applications and browser-based services are designed to work together in the most optimal way.

Offline Browsing

One of the elementary features of a mobile device is that it may or may not be connected to the network. This may be because the person is out of the coverage area or the device is simply used offline. Browsing, by nature, is designed to access the content in the network. However, offline browsing in certain cases would provide the consumer more flexibility to use these services even when not connected or, when only the main parts of the service are stored locally, the service could be faster to use even in cases where the network is present. Packaging XTHML services as downloadable entities should be supported.

Voice Browsing

When browsing technology is incorporated into a device with voice capabilities, the obvious next step is to make these two parts work together. Browsing by using your own voice, being able to hear the content in addition to seeing it and the creation of voice based services by using markup technologies are all important future voice browsing technologies. Voice Extensible Markup Language (VoiceXML) is one markup-based technology developed to support the creation of voice-based services.

Semantic Web

Current browser based services are highly rendering oriented and unfortunately many of the current HTML-based services are designed with only one display size or even one browser in mind. This creates a strong dependency between the device and the service meaning that any variation in the rendering characteristics of the mobile device also has an effect on the service. The goal of Semantic Web is to move away from the rendering orientation towards true device independence. In addition, it introduces technologies that can be used to augment content with formal semantics, thereby producing content suitable for consumption of automated systems. The value of this approach is that it helps the user to get more done by doing less.

Browsing in MITA

When we look at the MITA and its subsystems, a mobile browser has its place next to the two other main areas: Messaging and Rich Call. The following figure locates browsing related subsystems in the MITA layered model.

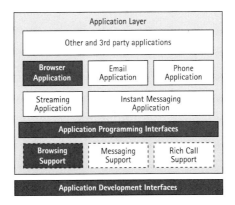

Browsing in MITA

However, the browser is not an isolated entity but it is designed to work together with the other applications and to provide basic content handling technologies (browsing support) to all applications needing them.

Messaging

Messaging is typically characterized by having intermediary end-points for store-and-forward or store-and-retrieve communication functionality. Store-and-forward messaging is based on the delivery of messages via intermediary servers to the recipient's device for consumption. Examples of store-and-forward messaging are Short Message Service (SMS) and Multimedia Messaging Service (MMS). Internet electronic mail (e-mail) is an example of store-and-retrieve messaging, where the messages are delivered to and stored on a server for later retrieval by the recipient.

Today, mobile messaging application services vary from SMS, MMS and e-mail to the emerging Instant Messaging (IM) form.

SMS emerged as a standard application service of the Global System for Mobile Communications (GSM) network for either one-way or two-way delivery of short text messages from a sender to another user. Currently, SMS is also being utilized to offer value-added services (e.g., chat, e-mail notification, weather information, banking transactions, sports news, and airline information services). Extensions have been made to SMS (e.g., Nokia Smart Messaging and Enhanced Messaging Service (EMS)) for the delivery of multimedia content over SMS. Smart Messaging supports, for example, ringing tones, operator logos, picture messages, business cards, and Internet access configuration data. These have opened up new service opportunities and introduced a whole new business using these as a channel for value-added services for the consumers.

MMS is an emerging mobile application service for one-way or two-way delivery of multimedia messages. MMS promises to provide the consumer with messaging services that allow not only the delivery of multimedia content but a broad spectrum of advanced mobile messaging-based services. Since MMS supports a wide variety of content formats, it can also be a seen as a technology that enables numerous services, not limited only to person-to-person messaging. Hence, the MMS technology can be further utilized as middleware for countless services that will function in the Mobile domain. Both push and pull MMS content will be available. These services can take the form of headline news or daily cartoon strips, for instance.

E-mail represents a messaging-based service that has been evolving for over thirty years. Today, e-mail means Internet electronic mail, as defined by the standards of the Internet Engineering Task Force (IETF). E-mail is a key application service for all segments of the Mobile and Web domains. Thanks to the enormous user base of e-mail, it will remain one of the most important and highly used forms of communication.

Instant messaging began in the early days of computers as a method to carry on short text conversations between logged-on users of a common time-sharing service. From a messaging perspective, IM has been described as a means of sending small, simple messages that are delivered immediately to online users. However, this definition has evolved over a period of time, and today's instant messaging services allow people to send more than simple text messages. They allow people to exchange rich text (e.g., picture files, to embed smileys, to use colored fonts). The advanced instant messaging services of today also come with many corporate features (e.g., white-boards, scratch pads and meeting features).

The messaging applications and services mentioned above are the starting point for the future messaging vision. The messaging services will evolve into even more versatile and flexible communication means, both between people and between a person and a machine. The new messaging paradigms, technologies and content types all call for interoperability between messaging systems, mobile devices, service providers, and Mobile and Web domains as well as with legacy terminals and services. The more people there are using these messaging services, the greater the value is added to the consumer.

Messaging Service Components

Traditionally, a messaging service has been composed of four component parts:

o   Contact information and addressing,

o   Message store,

o   Message transfer technology, and

o   Format of the message and related delivery information (e.g., timestamp and delivery log).

Each message transfer technology specifies a different addressing format. SMS uses an international phone number format; Internet e-mail uses an IETF Request for Comments formatted addresses [RFC822]; and IM can utilize still other address formats.

The second component of a messaging service is the message store. The message store is the location(s) where messages are stored. Support for different forms of multimedia messages can necessitate multiple message storage subsystems. However, one of the goals of the Messaging Interaction mode is to provide unified messaging to the consumer. An element of unified messaging is the ability to view different forms of content (e.g., e-mail, MMS, voice mail and facsimile) from a single messaging application. Another element of the unified messaging is to provide the experience of searching for all forms of contact and presence information independent of the messaging systems. Message stores provide a structure that allows a consumer to find incoming messages, and post out-going messages while the storage system maintains meta-information about the messages. For example, read and unread messages can be differentiated and calendar invitations can be differentiated from textual messages. As the number of messages grows, the management of the message store necessitates the introduction of time saving mechanisms including the organization of incoming messages into different folders based on specific categories; the search for a particular set of messages based on origin, subject, delivery or even content; archiving and restoring particular messages to/from alternate message stores; and the automatic filtering of incoming messages based on message parameters (e.g., subject, originator or content). In addition to time saving mechanisms, the message store needs to provide the ability to track communications, for example, by showing messages sent or received from a particular individual or with a particular subject. The Messaging Interaction mode can provide a wealth of features. However, this introduces a level of complexity that needs to be facilitated with individual usage profiles, for example, by including a sender's contact information with every new e-mail or including the original e-mail in a response e-mail. Usage profiles within message applications can also reduce the number of interactions that are required by a consumer, for example, by specifying the default message transfer type to be SMS.

The third component of a messaging system is the message transfer technology. Multiple forms of message transfer technologies are in use today. A mobile device needs to support many of these.

The fourth component of a messaging system is the format of the messages. Messages are the virtual container for delivery of content. The format defines the types of content that are possible within the specific message type, as well as the characteristics of the messages that can be used to organize and search for content. Today, the common format is based on Multi-purpose Internet Mail Extensions (MIME). MIME is widely accepted as the format for multimedia messaging. There are also numerous efforts to utilize Extensible Markup Language (XML) as a universal, common alternative representation for multimedia messages.

The complexity of messaging services needs to be managed. Consumers want to be certain that the intended recipient receives the message sent. Service providers want to be able to manage the components of a messaging system in order to provide the reliability expected by consumers. Mobile management facilitates providing a managed messaging service. For example, an operator can utilize mobile management services to identify failed message routing and minimize looping of messages between the originator and intended recipient faults in the distributed messaging service. The MITA messaging service will be a managed mobile service.

The core of MITA messaging is the consumer experience: the value and potential of extending basic messaging schemes to new services and for feature rich applications. MITA messaging creates new mobile communication possibilities and adds new feature rich flavors to the person-to-person communication and messaging-based value added services. The Messaging Interaction mode relates to communication needs, with a one-way messaging component as the core, enriched with rich content and other key enablers, such as presence.

Functional Architecture

Functional Service Elements

Messaging services typically include the following service element categories: message notification, service discovery, messaging service access, address lookup, message composition, message storage, message transfer and messaging system management.

The *Message Notification category* includes functions to allow a mobile device to initiate and terminate asynchronous notification of message or message report delivery.

The *Service Discovery category* includes functions to allow a mobile device to find the names or network address of a messaging service within the mobile network or Internet.

The *Message Service Access category* includes functions for initiating and terminating access to a messaging server and for keeping the access active.

The *Address Lookup category* includes functions for resolving a contact into its messaging address, addressing a message and for managing contact or address information in a directory service.

The *Message Composition category* includes functions to allow a mobile device to compose a message or format content. Normally, these functions are provided by the device messaging application, but they can also be provided by the network service for remote terminal access.

The *Message Storage category* includes functions to allow a mobile device to access, retrieve and manage a message store containing persistent messages. There can also be functions to allow for creating, deleting and maintaining hierarchical storage (e.g., folders) within the message store.

The *Message Transfer category* includes functions to allow a mobile device to submit or post messages for delivery to a recipient or list of recipients. There can also be functions for specifying notification context for the message within the messaging service.

The *Message System Management category* includes functions to allow the capture and reporting of both mobile device and service level events and exceptions related to the nominal messaging services.

Message Data Model

There are subtle differences between different messaging forms. However, without trivializing the diffcrences, these messaging forms can be described in terms of a common, generalized data model. The major entity in this data model is the message entity. The message entity is a representation of the delivery content and the delivery context information. The message entity is a container-type of object. It consists of two primary components, a header and a body.

The header component is a representation of a set of delivery context information (e.g., originator and recipient addresses, subject, body type, and transfer-encoding). This information is requisite for proper routing of the message from the originator to the recipient. The header entity is a container-type of object. It consists of a named set of attributes, commonly called fields. While the attributes in the header entity differ by messaging form, they can be generalized into the four basic categories: routing, description, categorization and disposition.

The routing category includes fields that describe attributes of the message in terms of its delivery and reply. Examples of routing fields include originator, recipient, copy and reply-to addresses. The description category includes fields that describe attributes of the message in terms of its body entity composition. Examples of description fields include the subject, content type, transfer-encoding and encryption scheme. The categorization category includes fields that describe attributes of the message in terms of how the recipient messaging user agent is to render it. Examples of categorization fields include priority level and confidentiality. The disposition category includes fields that describe attributes of the message in terms of how the recipient messaging service or messaging user agent is to handle it. Examples of disposition fields include restrictions on printing or copying and non-delivery or return-receipt replies.

The body component is the representation of the content in the message and can consist of either a single content or can consist of a more complex, multipart content (i.e., a body consisting of multiple content portions). The body entity is a container-type of object. It consists of header fields that describe the content portion, as well as of the content information, itself. The content-type model specifies the media type of a content portion; that is, an individual media type is identified by a two-tuple identifier that identifies both the primary content type and a secondary, sub-type identifier. For example, simple textual content is identified in MIME by the two-tuple of *text/plain*. The MIME multipart media type is the most common approach for encapsulation of multiple content portions in the body of a message.

Messaging Entities

The entities of the messaging service framework can be positioned into three service elements: terminal messaging service, network messaging service and server messaging service.

Terminal Messaging Service contains:

o   **Terminal Application** – a messaging-enabled application, generally with integration to the local phonebook application; and

o   **Terminal Messaging User Agent** – a client-side protocol engine, sometimes called a messaging user agent.

Network Messaging Service contains:

o   **Service Access Point** – a service enablement for common elements (e.g., authentication/ authorization/access rights, service provisioning, service discovery, billing/charging); and

o   **Messaging Server** – a server-side protocol engine.

Server Messaging Service contains:

o   **Service Access Point** – a service enablement for common elements (e.g., authentication/ authorization/access rights, service provisioning, service discovery, billing/charging); and

o   **Messaging Server** – a server-side protocol engine.

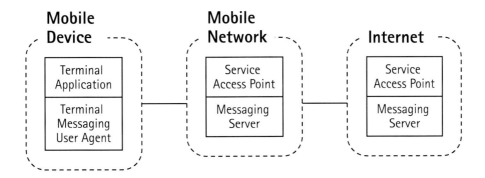

Messaging Entities

The terminal application entity is the actual messaging application on the mobile device for the particular message form. The terminal messaging user agent entity is the software component on the mobile device that implements the protocol engine for the particular message form. Also called the messaging transfer agent, the messaging server entities in the mobile network and the Internet are the messaging servers within the carrier's network and service provider network, respectively. The service access point is a functional aggregation of common service elements. This approach allows multiple application services to be packaged into an integrated server implementation. For example, separate messaging and presence application services could be provided as a single implementation with common authentication/authorization/access control, service provisioning, service discovery, billing/charging and other service elements.

Messaging in MITA

Messaging is one of the three Interaction modes in the context of the Mobile Internet Technical Architecture. In general, the Messaging Interaction mode deals with the characteristics and attributes related to end-to-end content transport and processing.

The positioning of messaging in the MITA layered element model is shown in the following figure.

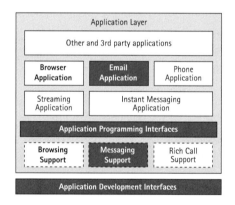

Messaging and MITA Layered Element Model

Rich Call

In the MITA, rich call is perceived to relate to consumers' immediate, personal, *right here, right now* person-to-person communication needs. Some of these needs can already be satisfied today with telephony services (e.g., basic voice call, voice mail and call divert) provided by carriers (e.g., using Global System for Mobile Communications (GSM) technologies). But, the key in rich call is the consumer experience: the value and potential of combining telephony with other elements and information to provide enriched services. Voice calls evolve into rich calls, during which audio, video, image or other data can be shared. For example, a rich call may start with plain voice, live video might be added during the call and the consumers can end the call playing an interactive game with their mobile devices.

Rich call creates new mobile communication possibilities and adds new feature-rich flavors to person-to-person communication, the most important communication service in the era of the Mobile Internet. As the Interaction mode, Rich Call relates to person-to-person(s) communication needs, which have a real-time two-way voice and/or video communication component as the core, enriched with presence information, text, graphics, images, animations, sounds, multimedia and physical effects before, during and after a call. In the different phases of a call, these dynamic elements are used to add value for the user, thus improving the user experience.

Typical examples of rich call services are:

o   Voice and video calls, both person-to-person and multiparty,

o   Voice and video conferences,

o   Application and display sharing during a call,

o   File transfer during a call, and

o   Networked interactive mobile games.

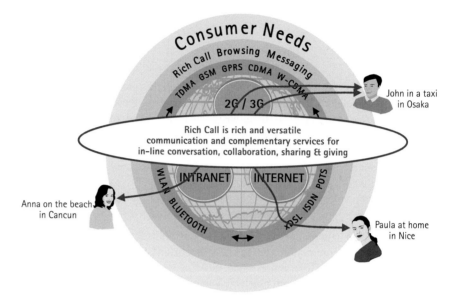

Rich Call – The Big Picture

Value to the Consumer

Connectivity – Being Together

Versatile reachability and connectivity schemes enable consumers to freely use services with whatever device best suits their communication needs at that moment and wherever they are, independent of access technologies and network environments.

Personality – Self-Expression and Continuous Mobile Awareness

Advanced service management features put the consumer in the position of mastering her personal communication. The consumer can create instructions which the service machinery uses, for example, when there is an incoming call with high priority from a supervisor and the person has indicated that her presence status is "in a business meeting."

Content Richness – Rich Communication Experience

The use of both audio and video, in addition to any visual content, enables many new services and applications, e.g., mobile interactive games, team collaboration and business-to-customer service center solutions. Emotional, personal content and presence information adds another dimension to person-to-person communication.

Rich Call Life-Cycle in Short
Making a Rich Call

Making a rich call is as simple as making a voice call today. For example, the user can make the call by selecting the parties he wants to call from a buddy list or a dynamic phone book, which includes presence and any other information users want to publish about themselves, or by clicking a name or number on a Web page. This kind of "click-to-talk" functionality facilitates easy response to push services which can be context- and location-related.

The call is routed to the called parties based on their preferences (e.g., route to voicemail at night or route to assistant during business hours when in a meeting) and the called parties are alerted personally according to their preferences (e.g., using distinctive ringing tones and showing the caller's contact card) and the caller's wishes (e.g., show call priority, call subject text, hello graphics or business card).

During a Rich Call

During a rich call the call participants can, as they wish, toggle between different media types. A participant can also share a visual moment with the other participants by adding live video to the voice conversation for a moment or by sending a snapshot picture instantly. It is also possible to share a display view of one's device for mutual browsing or showing a map, launch a game, or collaborate using common productivity tools.

The use of multiple media and user profiles also introduces new possibilities to add value in business-to-consumer communication. Imagine a scenario where a consumer calls a company's switchboard. While waiting on the line, the person can be directed to the company's Web site, or be pushed other related information or even some purely entertaining content. The idle time for the consumer becomes valuable, not just time wasted.

During the teardown of a rich call, personalized bye-bye messages, reminders or any other user-created information can be sent between call participants. Call context or location-related information can also be delivered.

Consumer Service Concepts
Seamless Interaction

Seamless interaction gives the consumer more versatility by easing the usage of different services simultaneously, or when the consumer has an incoming call, he may not want to take it *in his ears* but instead *in his eyes*, replying with a chat request or a homepage to the caller's terminal display.

Smart Service Routing

During a rich call, the consumer has more control over her communication, giving more possibilities for the consumer to personalize her service. For example, the consumer is able to determine how to handle incoming calls – to decide which calls are let through, which are redirected or even barred. Incoming call handling may vary between callers having different attributes (e.g., subject and priority of the call, media type and characteristics, user's location, calendar and presence information, and time) as parameters of the service.

For example, on the way home from work, a consumer might receive a rich call using the hands-free mobile device of his car. When he arrives home, he transfers the call to his personal device and later to the family's full-featured multimedia device.

Presence information combined with rich call services also enables smarter call routing. The user's presence information may, for example, direct all calls to an assistant, voice mailbox or Web depending on the presence information and caller type. A co-worker might get directed to an assistant, while a husband gets through.

End-to-End Communication

Rich call takes person-to-person communication to a whole new level of content and visual richness. Communication will move from ears or eyes to both ears and eyes. *Hear what I say* will be supplemented with *see what I mean*.

Content sharing opens up new usage scenarios. Depending on the situation, the consumer may want to share part of the display with another party and thus enrich non-verbal communication. Furthermore, a consumer may even allow other parties to access and edit shared content and thus enable true collaboration. A rich call itself may be initiated between two parties or involve a whole group of people – for example a work group or community – and it would still enable all the same rich functionality.

Rich Call Context View

The context diagram below represents an abstract and simplified context view of a rich call.

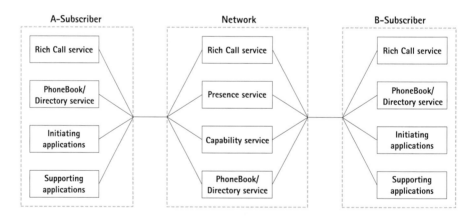

Rich Call Context Diagram

The rich call service is responsible for call and connection creation, modification and termination. On the network side, the rich call service is responsible for smart connection routing, for example. Initiating applications are capable of launching other applications to achieve a seamless rich call experience. Supporting applications are any applications (e.g., calendar or photo album) which can be used during a rich call to enrich the rich call communication experience. A phone book service provides a terminal or network based contact directory. A capability service maintains and delivers information about mobile device and network capabilities, while presence service maintains and delivers the consumer's presence information.

System Services

The high-level rich call system service architecture is based on the categorization of service expressions, as shown below.

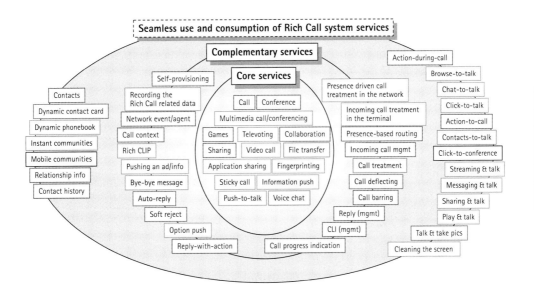

Rich Call Service Framework

The service architecture consists of two system service categories: core services and complementary services. These are presented in the following figure. The core services are the foundation of the rich call, as they provide consumers with the ability to communicate in-line with each other in real-time. The complementary services are the enriching element of rich call. They provide consumers with value-added features (e.g., the possibility to inform the called participant of the call subject and to automatically reject the call or route the call to the preferred device). An additional category, seamless use and consumption of rich call system services, contains issues which as such are not services but are more like enablers, which further improve the usability of services.

In-line conversation

In-line collaboration

In-line sharing & giving

Call off-line communication

Call instructions

Rich Call System Services

Core Services

The core rich call system services are content delivery services, which a consumer uses whenever having an in-line conversation, using in-line collaboration tools, sharing or giving content in-line directly to the other participant(s) of a rich call.

Conversation

The in-line conversation service is used for bi-directional person-to-person communication. The service requires transducers (e.g., microphone, or video camera), audio and video processing and secure transmission channels capable of delivering live and continuous audio and video content of a known format between participants engaged in a rich call. In the case of a multi-party conference, the service also requires live content processing (e.g., basic audio mixing and more advanced delivery of multiple video contents).

Collaboration

The in-line collaboration service is used for bi-directional communication by applications (e.g., real-time networked games and advanced conferencing applications). The service requires secure transmission channels capable of delivering live application data content (e.g., controls, or data) between participants engaged in a rich call and serves compatible applications. It is up to the applications to provide support for multi-party conferences either by centralized or distributed control and content processing using any connection topology between applications.

Sharing and Giving

In-line sharing and giving services are used for unidirectional person-to-person(s) communication. The service requires secure transmission channels capable of delivering possibly live application data content between participants of a rich call and in the case of sharing also a means to control the shared content.

Complementary Services

Complementary services are further divided into call instructions and call off-line communication.

Call Instructions

Call instructions are used to manage the delivery of rich calls and related in-line communication services. Call divert based on personal information (e.g., presence and calendar data) and publicly available attributes (e.g., time, weather) is a simple example of complementary services created and managed by call instructions.

Call Off-Line Communication Services

Call off-line communication services are used for unattended unidirectional person-to-person communication. The service requires secure transmission channels capable of delivering application data content between the intended participants of a rich call. For example, delivering a call subject text and hello animation, shown during alerting, is based on call off-line communication.

System Core

The rich call system covers communication between applications in remote devices. The core of the system can be described as an application support functionality which provides a set of services for client applications and hides the complexity and variety of underlying platforms, protocols, networks and other technologies from the applications. The rich call system core consists of call processing, call delivery content delivery, and service logic functions. The functions and the environment of the system core are depicted in the following figure.

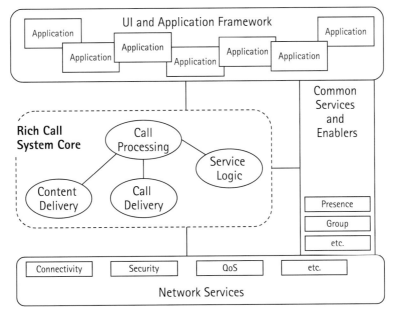

Rich Call System Core Functions and Environment

The call processing function is the core of the rich call system. It provides and maintains basic call processing functionality, which authenticates calls, processes authorized calls, and keeps the states of calls and communication sessions. It supports roaming and offers both local and home-based services together with service logic.

The call delivery function provides and maintains call routing functionality. It authenticates calls and routes authorized calls. It supports roaming and offers both local and home-based services.

The service logic function is the soul of the rich call system. It provides and maintains personalized service execution logic for the consumer, and also authenticates service requests from call processing and executes authorized requests based on the rules and instructions.

The content delivery function provides and maintains service-aware content delivery functionality for in-line communication. It performs content authentication, routes authorized content and processes the content according to the service (e.g., content format conversions and mixing of audio in multiparty calls).

Rich Call in MITA

Rich Call is one of the three Interaction modes in the context of the Mobile Internet Technical Architecture. In general, the Rich Call Interaction mode deals with the characteristics and attributes related to communication sessions and end-to-end content transport and processing.

The Rich Call Interaction mode defines communication capabilities to be provided for applications. It is characterized by having demanding real-time end-to-end requirements (e.g., latency, skew, integrity, and behavior) for the underlying transport and bearer services over various accesses in different network environments. On the other hand, network accesses and transport networks may impose constraints on the communication capabilities, which applications must take into account. Following the common MITA principles Rich Call supports seamless communication inside and between different network environments.

The positioning of Rich Call in the MITA layered element model is shown in the following figure.

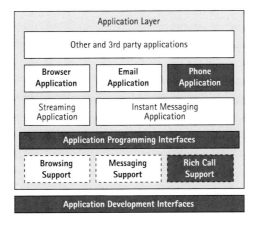

Rich Call and the MITA Layered Element Model

Rich Call applications and other applications, such as phonebook, contacts and chat, deliver services to the consumer. Rich Call support uses the services of the Mobile Internet layer for communication and local processing, and provides a common set of rich call service capabilities (e.g., call routing) for the applications above.

III

Visions

PART 3.2

Mobile Internet Layer

o Internet Protocols

o Application Framework

o Multimedia Content Adaptation
for the Mobile Internet

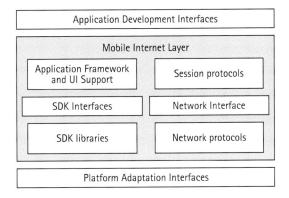

Internet Protocols

Internet Protocols provide basic communication services for applications over IP networks. Internet Protocols are largely independent of physical network media, providing a common abstraction of connectionless packet-switched communications that can be handled uniformly by application designers. This enables most applications to work over different physical channels without modifications.

The value of Internet Protocols is in the universal connectivity created through the Internet: as more and more devices become connected to the Internet, the value of the whole network increases. The worldwide population of consumers represents a potentially huge added value for the Internet when these mobile devices start using Internet Protocols as the basis for packet-based communication.

A critical element in IP connectivity is reachability. To be reachable, an IP device must be both connected and addressable. Clearly, the remaining IPv4 address space is not sufficient to provide efficient addressing for all potential IP devices in the future. Hence, the transition to IPv6 is a necessity, enabling the IP layer reachability of all devices using the Internet Protocols.

Universal reachability does not come free, however. To protect minors and the individual's privacy, the IP network must be able to filter indecent content and unwanted traffic from disturbing the consumer's service experience.

Internet Protocols are mostly invisible to the consumer of an IP connected device, but the provision of universal connectivity and reachability is a fundamental building block for end-to-end services of the future [Salzer84]. It has been said that if IP had come with Network Address Translation (NAT) by design, we would not have the Web we have today. We should not shut off the Web of the future, just because we do not yet know what they will be.

Wireless connectivity introduces challenges not faced in the fixed networks. The link quality changes constantly, and it is possible for the device to be moved to a location where radio coverage is not available. Recognition of the state of connectivity should be made available to affected applications, so the applications can inform the consumer when a break in service is due to a gap in wireless connectivity rather than faulty service.

Internet Protocols Architecture

The TCP/IP suite is usually thought to be simpler in architecture than the familiar Open Systems Interconnection (OSI) reference model. However, the development of application independent session control protocols and content presentation formats has largely changed that. Application design does not necessarily happen directly on top of a TCP socket any longer. Application designers can choose between different session management models for different application domains (e.g., HyperText Transfer Protocol (HTTP) for Web-based applications, or Session Initiation Protocol (SIP) for multimedia session management). Applications can also readily reuse existing, largely protocol-independent presentation formats for the data and content used over the application sessions (e.g., using Multi-purpose Internet Mail Extensions (MIME) types and Real-time Transport Protocol (RTP) payload formats for real time media and streaming).

The reference model for the MITA Internet Protocols architecture is shown in the figure below. Each layer in the model contains multiple protocols with different features. As the figure illustrates, MITA platforms provide Application Programming Interfaces (APIs), enabling applications to access the services of the Presentation, Session, Transport, and Internet layers. Application designers choose which interfaces to use depending on the needs of the application.

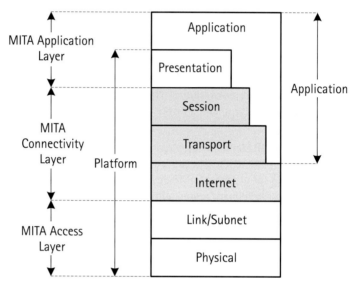

Reference Model for the MITA Internet Protocols architecture with the scope of MITA Internet Protocols shaded.

The figure also shows the relation to the simplified MITA 3-layer model presented in the previous chapter. In the 3-layer model, the network, transport, and session layers are bundled as the Connectivity Layer, providing network connectivity services to MITA applications.

The main functions of the layers in the reference model are:

Physical Layer

Provides transmission of bits over the physical media. Includes:

o   Channel coding

o   Channel access control

o   Signal quality measurements to help mobility management

Link/Subnet Layer

Provides highly reliable transport of frames over the physical link. Can include:

o   Frame start and end synchronization

o   Ciphering

o   Error detection and optional recovery

o   Segmentation and reassembly

o   Disconnect notification to help mobility management

Multiple-access links or subnets also include:

o   Link layer addressing

o   Broadcast and multicast delivery, if supported

If packet switching is performed at the Link/Subnet layer, consideration should be given to whether doing so supports or interferes with IP Quality of Service (QoS) and IP multicast.

Mobility management is made at the link layer, when the link layer mobility management improves overall cost efficiency and network performance. General Packet Radio Service (GPRS) in second and third generation cellular networks is an established example of a mobility management mechanism at this layer.

The Internet Engineering Task Force (IETF) is working on an informational document providing more insight on how to design IP friendly link layers.

Internet Layer

Provides connectionless, unreliable, possibly out of sequence, unicast, anycast and multicast delivery of IP packets to any node in an IP network. Essential features include:

o   IP addressing

o   Routing

o   Packet forwarding, queuing or dropping

o   Packet classification, metering, shaping (edge routers)

o   Group membership management

o   Congestion control

o   Access control

o   Security

o   Mobility support

Connection-oriented sub-IP methods can be utilized for Internet layer optimization. These include:

o   Header compression

o   Traffic engineering

III Visions

Transport Layer

Provides delivery of application data (either message or stream oriented) between any nodes in the IP network. Different transport protocols include features like:

o   Multiplexing to different application instances on the IP host

o   End-to-end flow control (congestion control and avoidance)

o   Segmentation to the path Maximum Transmission Unit (MTU), reassembly

o   Data sequencing

o   Error detection and recovery

o   Transport layer security

Session Layer

Provides the control structure for end-to-end communication. Different classes of applications utilize different control structures through different session control protocols. The features of session control protocols include:

o   Addressing and identification of application entities and/or consumers

o   Authentication, authorization and accounting

o   Routing of session control messages between application layer entities

o   Controlling the use of one or more transport layer connections for application data transport

o   Application/Device capability exchange

Presentation Layer

Provides support for different media formats, including:

o   Audio and video codecs for real-time and streaming delivery

o   Graphics file formats

o   Character encoding

o   Hypertext markup languages

o   User device adaptation

o   Location information formats

Application Layer

Applications can define their own presentation formats and session control protocols although the ones provided by the platform should be preferred to maximize interoperability and to minimize the code size in the IP devices.

As shown in the previous figure, the scope of the Internet Protocols spans from the Internet layer up to the session layer. The Internet Protocols are further divided to the user plane protocols and the control plane protocols. The user plane protocols are concerned with user packet delivery, including the whole stack of protocols from the physical to the application layer. Control plane protocols control the functions of the user plane protocols. The transport and Internet layer services for the control plane protocols are shared with the user plane protocols.

Internet Protocols in MITA

The following figure shows a view of the architecture for the Internet Protocols with most of the protocols considered in MITA. The presentation and application layers are shown for the sake of completeness, but are not further considered.

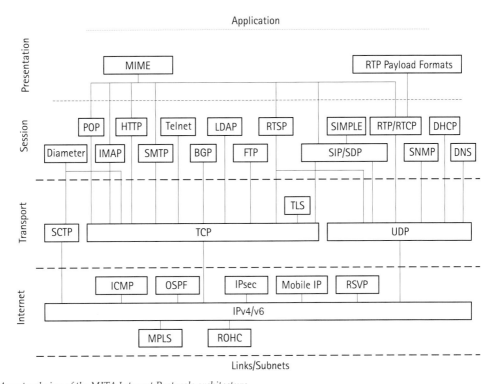

A protocol view of the MITA Internet Protocols architecture

Internet Layer Functions and Protocols

Addressing

IP addresses are unique within each addressing realm and identify IP network interfaces in IP nodes. Unicast addresses identify a single IP interface, while anycast and multicast addresses identify multiple IP interfaces. A packet sent to an anycast address is delivered to one of the interfaces, while a packet sent to a multicast address is delivered to all IP interfaces identified by the address.

An IP address consists of two logical parts: the network prefix and the interface identifier. The network prefix identifies the link or the subnet that the interface is connected to and is used by the routing infrastructure to route the packet to the right link. The interface identifier part identifies the interface within a link.

The Internet Control Message Protocol (ICMP) is used for discovering the IP addresses of the on-link IP nodes (Neighbor Discovery) as well as for IPv6 multicast group membership management with Multicast Listener Discovery (MLD) messages.

To support IP device reachability in the global Internet addressing realm, the longer addresses of IPv6 are needed.

IP Packet Forwarding

IP packets are forwarded towards the IP destination addressed in the packet. The forwarding decisions are made based on matching the packet's destination address against route entries in routing tables. The routing tables are configured with routing protocols, e.g., Open Shortest Path First (OSPF) for intra-domain routing, and Border Gateway Protocol (BGP) for inter-domain routing. Specialized multicast routing protocols, e.g., Protocol Independent Multicast (PIM), manage multicast routing.

Queuing Policy

Queuing decisions inside routers define what kind of service individual packets, and consequently entire traffic flows, get. There are two main methods controlling how packets are queued:

1. Signaled flows

    A flow is a stream of packets classified by a flow classifier. All packets in a flow are subject to the same queuing policy. The treatment of individual packets may vary, however, since flows typically have a notion of maximum bandwidth. Packets exceeding the limit may be dropped or otherwise treated differently from the packets deemed to be within the limit.

    The standard signaling protocol for flow state establishment is the Resource Reservation Protocol (RSVP). IETF is also working on new solutions for flow set-up.

2. Behavior aggregate classification

    Packets can be classified at the boundaries of a network into specific behavior aggregates. The behavior aggregate is marked on the Differentiated Services Code Point (DSCP) in the IP packet header, enabling routers within the network to determine the queuing policy for each packet based on the DSCP value alone.

    The DiffServ policies can be controlled with the Common Open Policy Service (COPS) protocol.

Routers should also use active queue management, e.g., Differentiated Services Urgency/ Importance (DSUI) or Random Early Deletion (RED), and should implement Explicit Congestion Notification (ECN).

Network Access Control

A consumer's access to Internet layer services is controlled based on the consumer's relation to the carrier providing the access services. On point-to-point links, the consumer's credentials are typically transferred over link layer specific protocols (e.g., Point-to-Point Protocol (PPP) and GPRS signaling protocols). IETF is also working on IP based solutions for device authentication. A typical network access router receiving the credentials will transmit them to the consumer's home domain over network specific protocols or AAA protocols (e.g., Diameter).

Mobility Management

Mobility management at the network layer is possible with Mobile IP. Mobile IP hides the changes in the network point-of-attachment from the layers above. Mobile IP enables mobile devices to receive IP packets via their home networks regardless of which network they happen to be roaming in at the moment.

IP Security

IP Security (IPSec) can be used to provide security services over IP, either end-to-end, or to/ from a security gateway. It should be noted, however, that if end-to-end applications utilize any intermediary protocol entities above the IP layer, IPSec cannot provide security services over the multiple application hops without explicit support from the protocols involved.

Each IP node using IPSec manages a Security Policy Database (SPD), based on which Security Associations (SAs) are created with a key exchange protocol (e.g., the Internet Key Exchange (IKE) protocol). Transport layer data is then encapsulated in the Encapsulating Security Payload (ESP) for encryption or in the Authentication Protocol for integrity protection only.

IPv6 Transition Support

Network layer support is required to assist in the transition from the current IPv4 Internet to the new IPv6 Internet. Tunneling is used to connect IPv6 islands or individual IPv6 nodes to the rest of the IPv6 network over IPv4 infrastructure. Dual stack nodes, running both IPv4 and IPv6, can connect to either IPv4 or IPv6 networks. Protocol translation can be used to provide limited connectivity between the IPv4 and IPv6 networks.

IP Layer Configuration

Protocols enabling zero-configuration for user devices are required. Stateless Address Autoconfiguration and Router Discovery are the basic configuration tools provided by the ICMPv6 protocol. Additional configuration information for IP hosts can be delivered via the Dynamic Host Configuration Protocol (DHCP).

III Visions

Transport Layer Functions and Protocols

Currently, there are two end-to-end transport protocols to choose from: the Transmission Control Protocol (TCP) and User Datagram Protocol (UDP). TCP provides connection-oriented byte stream service with sophisticated flow control and retransmission for error recovery. Due to the retransmission, TCP is not optimal for real-time data transport. UDP provides connectionless packet transport service, where individual datagrams may get lost, duplicated, or arrive out of order. Also, as TCP is connection-oriented (and between two end-points only), UDP must be used for multicast or anycast services. UDP is also used for services where connection setup is not needed or would cause too much overhead (e.g., DNS is run over UDP).

The Stream Control Transmission Protocol (SCTP) is a new contender, allowing multiple IP paths to be used to support the transport connection. Like UDP, SCTP maintains the message boundaries, but it also offers flow control and retransmission services like TCP. SCTP supports multiple application streams, avoiding ahead-of-line-blocking problems. Additionally, SCTP has built-in resistance to flooding and masquerade attacks. These features make SCTP especially suited for signaling applications.

Transport Layer Security

The Transport Layer Security (TLS) protocol provides communications privacy over connection-oriented transport protocols. TLS allows one or both of the end-points to be authenticated with certificates and provides keys enabling encryption of all the data in the transport connection. A common use for TLS, and its predecessor, Secure Sockets Layer (SSL), - is to secure Web transactions.

Session Layer Functions and Protocols

In MITA, a part of the Session layer space is controlled through the definition of the MITA Interaction modes. Each Interaction mode maps a set of supporting session control protocols.

Further session control protocols are defined for session categories not covered by the MITA Interaction modes. These include many generic services (e.g., network access session control, file transfer, terminal access, directory access, the Internet Domain Name System (DNS), and network management).

MITA Interaction Modes

Browsing

The session control protocol for browsing is the HyperText Transfer Protocol (HTTP). The HTTP enables management of transport layer connections for content transfer. The connections are addressed either to a proxy HTTP server or directly to the server identified by the host part of the Uniform Resource Locator (URL).

Buffered media access (streaming) sessions are managed with the Real Time Streaming Protocol (RTSP). The media streams themselves are typically transferred out-of-band with the Real-time Transport Protocol (RTP), although in-band transfer with RTSP is also possible.

Messaging

E-mail type store and retrieve messaging sessions are managed with the Simple Mail Transfer Protocol (SMTP) and the Internet Message Access Protocol (IMAP) or the Post Office Protocol (POP). SMTP is used both for sending e-mails from clients and for inter-server message transfer. Clients can use the POP to retrieve their e-mail to a device, or use the IMAP to access and manipulate messages in their e-mail servers.

The familiar e-mail addressing format (e.g., user@domain) is used to address e-mail recipients. Mapping human names to their e-mail addresses can take place either through directories local to the device or through network resident directories.

For instant messaging, the SIMPLE and Session Initiation Protocol (SIP) are used. Instant messages to non-reachable users can be sent to them later or be diverted to the consumer's e-mail.

Rich Call

The Rich Call session control is based on SIP. The Session Description Protocol (SDP) facilitates end-to-end capability negotiation for real-time multimedia communication sessions. The real-time media is transported over RTP with the aid of the Real-time Transport Control Protocol (RTCP).

Addressing for SIP sessions is based on the SIP URLs. SIP user agents are reachable through their registration to the Rich Call session control element in the home network, which is identified by the domain portion of the consumer's SIP URL.

Real-time transport resources are managed independently by each session participant for his or her own access network.

Other Session Layer Protocols

Name to Address Translation

Layers above the transport layer can utilize the Internet Domain Name System (DNS) to translate mnemonic names to numeric addresses required by the transport and network layers.

Service Discovery

Many protocols provide their own discovery methods, usually based on manual configuration, multicast-based discovery or specially formatted DNS lookups. For example, Simple Mail Transfer Protocol (SMTP) uses the DNS Mail eXchange (MX) records to locate the destination SMTP server for a given e-mail address.

In corporate intranets the Dynamic Host Configuration Protocol (DHCP) is used to provision IP hosts with configuration information, such as addresses of DNS servers.

To stop reinventing the same solution too many times, generic service discovery protocols are defined. The Service Location Protocol (SLP) allows locating services based on specific service attributes. SLP Service Agents advertise services on an IP node on behalf of service processes. Directory Agents provide scalability by collecting service advertisements and providing answers to service queries.

III

Visions

Directory Access

The Lightweight Directory Access Protocol (LDAP) provides access to directories supporting the X.500 model, while not incurring the cost of the X.500 Directory Access Protocol.

File Transfer

File transfer over the Internet can happen either over HTTP or over the File Transfer Protocol (FTP).

Network Management

Network management of the MITA entities can be provided via the Simple Network Management Protocol (SNMP), HTTP or a command line interface.

Authentication, Authorization and Accounting

Network elements utilize the Diameter protocol to exchange authentication, authorization, and accounting messages.

User-to-Network network access sessions are enabled either through link layer specific methods, such as PPP, 802.1x, General Packet Radio Service (GPRS), or over IP (standardization work is in progress in IETF). The specific authentication methods are encapsulated in the Extensible Authentication Protocol (EAP), enabling network access routers to remain independent of the utilized authentication method between the IP device and its home Authentication, Authorization and Accounting (AAA) domain.

References

[Saltzer84] J. H. Saltzer, D. P. Reed, and D. D. Clark. End-to-end arguments in system design. ACM Transactions on Computer Systems, pages 277-288, 1984.

Application Framework

The application framework is a part of the mobile device architecture, which provides various mobile applications with basic application domain independent services: User Interface, Application Interworking and Service Access Security.

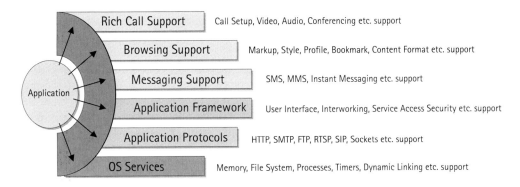

Application Framework and other MITA elements

The primary goal for the application framework is to provide applications and services with all the tools they need to efficiently provide user-friendly services. The application framework does not and cannot define how these applications and services use the tools given to them, so much of an application's usability still depends on the skills of its creators. However, the application framework can provide higher-level toolboxes to provide readymade solutions to certain common interaction needs (e.g., data exchange between applications and storing of content) to help the application and service providers and to help the consumer use the devices in a more consistent manner.

For the consumer, the application framework standardizes three important features: the look-and-feel (how the applications look and how the consumer can interact with them), interoperability between applications (how the services of and content generated by one application can be seamlessly used by other applications), and service access security (what kinds of applications the consumer can and cannot use in their mobile device and what they can access securely). The following sections look into these areas in more detail.

User Interface

The user interface is probably the first thing that the consumer must become familiar with when starting to use a mobile device. Long gone are the times when the mobile phone user interface was just a simple line of text showing the caller's phone number or the number being dialed. Nowadays, even a simple mobile device contains a lot of applications and services (e.g., a phonebook, messaging support, some form of calendar, phone and call setup systems, call logs, games, and a calculator). The list of applications and services provided is already long and gets longer every day. This increasing complexity emphasizes the application support provided by the application framework, especially the features provided by the core user interface system, which enables all different applications and services optimally to use the small display space available to them.

As is obvious from the number of different devices with their differing user interfaces all currently available on the market, there is no one approach to user interfaces today. The reasons for this are many (e.g., the devices are used for different purposes, they are used in different environments by people with different technical skill levels, they are made with different technologies, and a device's targeted price creates limitations on how advanced the device can be). However, although there are good reasons behind them, multiple designs are not always a good thing from the consumer's or even the service provider's point of view. Too much variation is hard to handle, especially if it happens inside a specific device category. One industry approach to this problem has been to come up with a few reference designs created to support the most common requirements coming from the manufacturers, carriers, consumers and service providers. This limits the number of user interfaces to a manageable number and lets service providers easily provide services for any of these categories, especially when supported by technologies that make it easy to tailor services to work with any device. Examples of such technologies are: Composite Capability/Preferences Profiles (CC/PP), Extensible Stylesheet Language Transformations (XSLT) and Cascading Style Sheets (CSS).

Two different approaches to the User Interface

The user interface is naturally more than just what a consumer sees on the display: it is about interaction with a device, of which the display is just one part. The display is probably the most important visual output mechanism for the applications and services, but voice, sounds, music, lights and vibration, for example, also can be used to convey messages to the consumer. Similarly, the keypad is not the only way to provide input to those same applications: microphones (for speech recognition and voice commands), rollers, joysticks, position sensing devices (e.g., location, tilting, or rotation) and touch sensitive displays also can be used to provide input. Moreover, since in many cases, these devices are used largely for rich call services, the good old voice-based user interaction is extremely important.

The graphical part of the user interface of an application is written by using some form of a windowing system that allows the application writer to define the user interface in more abstract terms than just low-level graphics primitives.

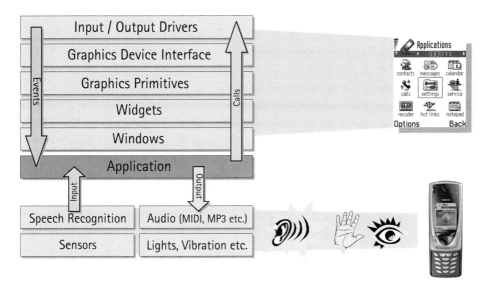

The different layers of User Interface technologies and their interaction mechanisms

Input and output mechanisms that are tied to the windowing system are typically abstracted behind the input and output device drivers. Such interaction mechanisms include, for example, joysticks, mice, touch sensitive displays, rollers and scroll keys. They are all just alternative methods for controlling the graphical display. Output and input mechanisms that are separate from the windowing system are supported by their corresponding interfaces.

For the consumer, the common windowing system approach to application interface creation helps keep the applications consistent. However, this does not mean that the visual representation of the graphical elements on the display always has to be the same as long as the consumer can recognize the elements and the interaction with them does not change. In the future, this will be done by providing the application and service developers with mechanisms by which the visualization of the user interface elements can be defined.

Application Interworking

In most cases, applications do not run in isolation; rather, they need to communicate and interact with other existing applications. Common interaction mechanisms include different data exchange mechanisms (e.g., file system, clipboard, application-to-application messaging, and shared memory) and application life cycle management mechanisms. One of the main functions for the application framework is to provide a common platform for all applications to interact with each other.

Application interworking benefits consumers by enabling them to use the right application for the right task nearly automatically and with minimal work. If a rich call application needs information about the numbers of all participants in a phone conference, the consumer can seamlessly use the phonebook application to provide those numbers. Better yet, if the conference was scheduled by using a calendar, and it already has the names of the participants, then the calendar application can initiate the conference call simply by invoking it and by providing it with the numbers from the phonebook.

Application interworking benefits the application developer by keeping the tools for creating these interactions available and ready for use. This way, the development of the applications can concentrate on the actual logic of the application and how to use these interworking mechanisms to create the best functionality and user experience.

The simplest form of application interworking is a global content storage that can be accessed by any application. This can be a file system where each application stores documents for other applications to access, or it can be a clipboard that provides storage for smaller pieces of content to be stored and accessed by other applications through cut-and-paste type of operations. In both cases, the consumer controls the whole process of information sharing,. and the applications support only the basic technologies by which they can be integrated with these storage mechanisms.

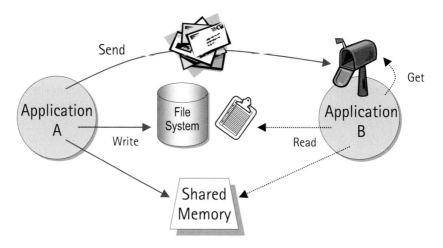

Different ways for two applications to communicate

Another set of interworking mechanisms are the direct data exchange mechanisms between applications that are not visible to the consumer at all. Such mechanisms include application-to-application messaging (where an application can send a message to another through a messaging channel) and shared memory areas (where one application can allocate memory and share it with other applications to exchange data). Because the exchange of information is totally automatic and controlled by the applications, no customer interaction is needed in these cases.

The third way for applications to interwork is a mechanism where an application publishes a request and all the applications that can fulfill the requirements of the request offer their services. The consumer can select the final operation to be performed from a menu that lists all the available alternatives, for example. After the selection, the application providing the service will either take care of the rest automatically or will open up its own user interface and interact with the user to finish the requested operation.

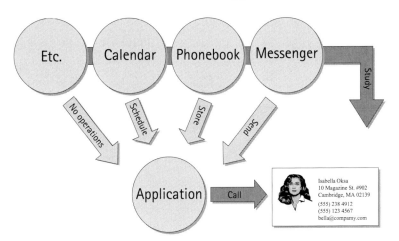

"Call for Offers" type of application interworking

The meta level of the application interworking is the level that allows applications to know about other applications and control their life cycle. An application, for example, can find out what other applications are available and what they can do, invoke them, change the focus from one application to another, communicate with them and finally suspend or end their execution.

All of these mechanisms require a common interworking framework for the applications. At the root of this framework, some form of an application registry is needed to keep track of the different applications and their capabilities. As part of this, the registry must provide standard Application Programming Interfaces (API) for searches and application life cycle management. In addition, there must be standard data representation mechanisms for data exchange to make the applications interoperate on the content level. All the previously mentioned higher level interworking services can then be implemented on top of this basic framework.

Mobile Device Service Access Security

It does not matter if a consumer installs a Java™ application, a native application or uses a browser to use Web based services, they all may need access to critical resources of the mobile device and, therefore, must comply with the security model specified by the application framework. Mobile devices have become highly personal devices that are used not only to contact people at any time or place but also to store valuable personal information. Consumers trust their mobile devices to store personal information (e.g., names, phone numbers, addresses, passwords, messages and banking information). The technology enhancement of these devices will increasingly be used for mobile commerce, meaning mobile devices will handle and store even more valuable data. The application framework must insure that only trusted applications have access to the mobile device services so trust is not broken.

III

Visions

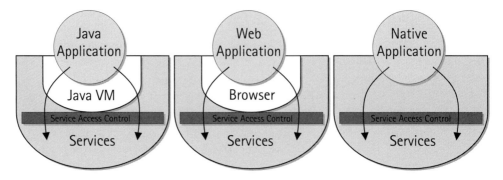

Service Access Control and different Applications/Services

There are two main ways to provide secure access to a service. These methods are not exclusionary and can be used simultaneously if needed. One is a form of a *fixed sandbox model*, where applications are divided into a set of security classes and each of them has access to a set of mobile device services suitable for the class. For example, an application that is downloaded from the Web and that does not have any credentials would fall into the lowest security class, providing it only with access to services that cannot harm the consumer or other applications running in the device. This could mean that that application only has access to the leftover idle time (to prevent denial of service attacks) and access to the basic User Interface (UI) and basic input functionality. On the other hand, an application with credentials provided by the carrier and written by one of the subcontractors of the carrier could access a wider set of services (e.g., call handling or a phonebook service), providing a better service to the consumer.

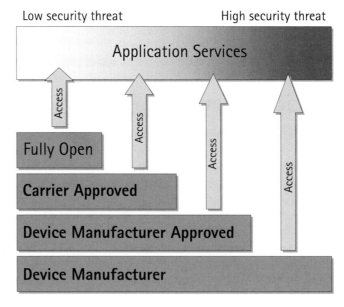

One example of different levels of access rights to application services

The benefits of this approach are simplicity, ease of implementation and intelligibility even by the consumers, who can directly see the link between the application and the level of trust in its credentials. Additionally, this approach allows the size of the applications to be kept small because each application needs to carry with it only one credential. The downside of this approach is that it does not provide much flexibility unless there are a huge number of security classes. But because too many security classes blur the concept for consumers, the best approach is to limit the number of security classes to only a few that are easily identifiable.

The second approach to service access security is based on applications having the access rights to each mobile device service individually. This means that for a particular application to access a specific service, it needs to have the credentials to do so. The benefit of this approach is its flexibility, but since each credential takes space, this approach puts a heavy burden on the size of the applications and the architecture that has to support access control every time services are accesses. It is also much harder to collect and manage all the required access rights, especially when a lot of companies are participating in the provisioning of the credentials.

By combining the *sandbox* model and the individual access rights model, we can come up with a hybrid system that, with just one credential, can give access to the basic set of services available, and, with the addition of other services' access credentials, can gain access to a larger set of services if needed. This approach has the benefit of providing flexibility only when needed, but also has all the drawbacks of the individual access rights model.

Application Framework in MITA

The application framework is part of the Mobile Internet Layer providing services to the Application Layer. Application developers can use Application framework services through the Application Development Interfaces. The next figure shows the top layers of the MITA Architecture and the location of the Application Framework.

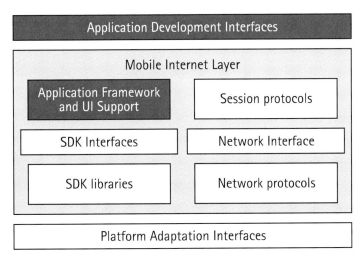

Scope of Application Framework in MITA

III

Visions

Multimedia Content Adaptation for the Mobile Internet

In defining the technical architecture for the Mobile World, the ultimate objective of Nokia is to provide a user-friendly Mobile Internet experience. Accordingly, various applications must interact seamlessly in any Network environment and with any type of access, yet the underlying technological complexities must be masked from the consumer.

Due to the diversity of mobile device capabilities and access methods, instances will arise where content generated by one device (the content source) cannot be delivered to a destination device (the content sink), at least not in a usable form. For example, a consumer may wish to view an image stored on a server, but the size of the image exceeds the memory capacity of their mobile device.

To provide an excellent user experience, in many situations the content should not be discarded, but rather changed to make it useful to the destination device (sink) or consumer. Specifically, this means that content must be made to conform to the constraints of both the delivery network and the sink, while remaining recognizable as the same content that emanated from the content source. An example is shown in the figure below.

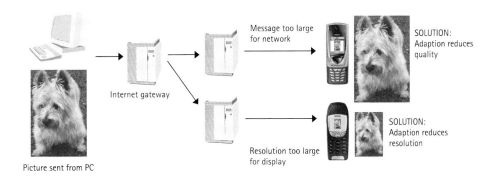

The basis for adaptation

The process of changing or modifying the content to ensure its conformance to both network and sink constraints is called *content adaptation*. To illustrate what content adaptation means in practice, we consider three sample scenarios:

o A Multimedia Messaging Service (MMS) [mms1999] may contain an image that exceeds the memory limits of the destination device. The image may be shrunk until the message falls under the size limit. The image is adapted, by decreasing its size, but it is still recognizable as the same image that was originally sent.

o A browser may request a Uniform Resource Locator (URL) referencing Synchronized Multimedia Integration Language (SMIL) [smil2001] content, but the device does not support SMIL. In this case, the SMIL layout may be converted to an alternative, although not necessarily equivalent, scheme (e.g., eXtensible HyperText Markup Language (XHTML) [xhtml2000]).

o A consumer may wish to receive instant messages sent using the Session Initiation Protocol (SIP) [sipf2001][sipm2001][sipm1999] as MMS messages on their phone. In this case, the instant message would need to be re-packaged using the MMS format.

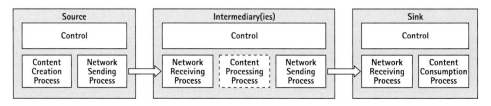

Adaptation using an intermediary

Adaptation is depicted in the above figure. Here, the network sending process in the content source end-point transmits the content to an intermediary, which receives the content, performs any necessary content adaptation, and forwards it to the content sink.

In some situations where content integrity is vital, where the sender does not wish content to be altered, or where Digital Rights Management (DRM) is involved, the task of providing content to the sink in a consumable form may be more complex or even impossible. This chapter recognizes that such cases exist, but focuses on situations where subtle degradations are permissible if they result in usable content.

Having understood the general concept and necessity of adaptation, the remainder of this chapter revolves around two issues: what must be done in order to adapt content, and which components of a system could be responsible for carrying out those tasks.

Although the section largely focus on messaging applications and cite existing protocols as examples, many of the concepts are equally applicable to other applications. Furthermore, when discussing the options for adaptation, we will not restrict ourselves to current offerings, but will look forward to applications and services that have not yet been developed.

Multimedia Adaptation

Having considered the rationale behind adaptation, and how it fits into the content creation-consumption process, it is considered what it actually means to adapt multimedia content. The receiving device (content sink) and the transport protocols that deliver the content support certain capabilities (e.g., maximum size or resolution) and the process of adaptation modifies content to ensure that it conforms to sink and transport capabilities. Additionally, several adaptation types may be distinguished, each motivated by the need to match content to one or more capabilities.

Types of Adaptation

The ensuing section discusses adaptation performed on a Multimedia Unit (MMU). MMU means a unit of data transmitted over the network that contains one or more multimedia objects (e.g., such as images, audio, video, text, formatted text or layout information).

Encapsulation Adaptation

Encapsulation refers to how one or more multimedia objects are packaged into one data unit ready for transmission. It encompasses both low-level binary encoding (e.g., Base64) and application-level protocols (e.g., HyperText Transfer Protocol (HTTP) [http1999] or MMS). Typically, a standardized binary encoding scheme can be expected, so the role of encapsulation adaptation at this time is largely to convert content from one application-level protocol to another. For example, instant messages using SIP may be converted to the MMS format and vice versa, or e-mail messages may be converted to/from MMS messages.

As new technologies lead to modification of the encapsulation standards, or even to parallel messaging/browsing applications, it may become necessary for an encapsulation scheme to be altered before content is transmitted over the receiving network. For example, in the future, a new generation of multimedia messaging may mean that a multimedia message has to be adapted, so it can be transmitted to receiving networks and devices that have not been upgraded to meet the new standard.

Encapsulation will generally involve repackaging an MMU without altering any of the content. Depending upon the exact encapsulation schemes used, this may mean that a single MMU is split into a sequence of several MMUs. An example of this can be seen in e-mail to Short Message Service (SMS) gateways, where a long e-mail may be split into several SMS messages. Conversely, some technologies may require several MMUs to be combined; for example, packaging the text and images on a Web page into a single MMU.

Size Adaptation

Size refers to the number of bytes in an MMU. Size constraints may be imposed by the underlying network environment, by agreement, or by device capabilities. Network constraints encompass not only restrictions on the size of the MMU, but also restrictions on bandwidth and transmission time (latency). Although a fixed bandwidth limit always exists (e.g., General Packet Radio Service (GPRS) CS-4 limits bandwidth to 21.4 kbps), often the actual limit is lower and varied

III
Visions

with time due to network congestion. For example, video originally streamed at 128 kbps must be reduced in size in order to be transmitted real-time over a 56 kbps connection. If part of the 56 kbps connection is suddenly reserved for another purpose then the video size limit will drop from 56 kbps to something less.

Agreements may further limit the size of an MMU. For example, standardization artificially curbs MMU size even though technology permits larger MMUs to be sent.

Restrictions imposed by the receiving device may be classified as static or dynamic:

o   Static limitations do not change over time. For example, a device may only have a limited receiving buffer, or a limited address space. In practice, the static device limitations and standardization limits are often synchronized so that devices are to some degree compliant with a standard.

o   Dynamic limitations (e.g., the amount of available memory) are not a characteristic of the device and change depending on how the device is used.

For whatever reason size constraints are imposed, when an MMU exceeds a constraint, its size must be reduced in order for transmission to be successful. Size reduction can be achieved in several ways.

First, size reduction can be achieved by eliminating parts of the MMU. For example, if an MMU contains two images and some text, eliminating one image may allow the MMU to meet its size constraint. Determining whether removing a part of the MMU should be allowed, and if so, which part should be removed in order to cause the least disruption, is beyond the scope of this chapter. Eliminating part of the MMU leads to a loss of content, meaning the receiver will not see the same content that was emitted by the content source. Certain technologies may mitigate this to some extent (e.g., by explicitly designating within the MMU which part of it is least important). Although this could be termed a *destructive adaptation*, it is nonetheless one means of reducing size.

Secondly, under certain circumstances, changing the encapsulation may allow size constraints to be met. For example, if the size limit is due to the transport layer or service protocol, splitting the MMU into several smaller MMUs may be acceptable. This would not be helpful for cases where the size limitation is due to the receiving device capabilities. Note that in this case, encapsulation adaptation is used to achieve size reduction, so the content of the message does not change.

Thirdly, format conversion can sometimes achieve size reduction. Different formats tend to be suited to media with different characteristics. For example, the Joint Photographic Experts Group (JPEG) [jpeg1999] format tends to be suited to natural scenes (e.g., photographs) and the Graphics Interchange Format (GIF) [gif1990] format tends to be suited to computer graphics. In cases where the current format is not ideally suited to the media, converting it to the optimal format may achieve size reduction. This involves minimal change to the appearance; in fact, format conversion is often imperceptible to the customer. Also, newer formats with more modern technology may store the same type of content more efficiently. For example, although JPEG2000 and JPEG are both intended for natural images, JPEG2000 is much more efficient. Converting content from JPEG to JPEG2000 may consequently lead to a size saving.

Fourthly, size reduction may be achieved through appearance adaptation. For instance, reducing the resolution of an image will also reduce the size. Such changes to the content may or may not be noticeable to the consumer and will be discussed shortly in the "Appearance Adaptation" section.

Fifthly and finally, size reduction may be achieved through altering internal media characteristics. In the case of an image, this may mean reducing the quality of the image or the number of colors it contains. In the case of audio, it may mean altering the bit rate. Generally, subtle size reductions are unlikely to be noticeable to the receiving user. More drastic reductions will become noticeable, and part of the size reduction challenge is to determine which method or combination of methods will present the receiving consumer with the best experience of the content.

There is no foreseeable case where size adaptation is pursued for the sole purpose of expanding the size of an MMU. Although an MMU may become larger as a consequence of other adaptation measures (e.g., format conversion), deliberately increasing the size of an MMU is not a logical operation.

Format Adaptation

A format is an agreed upon means of representing content (e.g., audio, video, and images) in a digital form. In this sense, a format is agreed upon either through standardization, or in a de facto way through widespread usage; however, this does not mean that all devices are capable of interpreting any given format. Put simply, lots of formats exist and no device will understand them all.

This fact alone reveals an obvious need for format adaptation: if the source encodes content using one format and the sink cannot decode that format, the content is useless. It must be changed from the original format into a format that can be understood by the receiving device. For example, if the content source encodes an image in the Portable Network Graphics (PNG) format and the receiver only understands JPEG images, the PNG would somehow need to be converted to JPEG in order for the receiving user to view it.

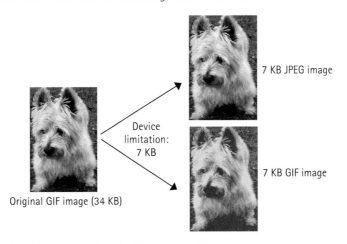

Good choice of a target format can make a big difference in quality

III Visions

Whether the format conversion process causes deterioration in quality depends very much on the specific formats - and possibly upon the characteristics - of the content. If the new or target format suits the content being modified, any decrease in quality should be negligible as, for example, when converting JPEG to JPEG2000 or a GIF photograph to JPEG. However, if the new format is unsuited to the content, the decrease in quality may be very noticeable (e.g., low-resolution computer graphics stored in GIF are converted to JPEG).

Appearance Adaptation

Appearance adaptation entails modifying the content of an MMU for the express purpose of changing how it looks (visually) or sounds (audibly). This is unlike size adaptation, where changes in appearance occur as an indirect result of requiring a reduction in size. Exactly how the appearance needs to be changed depends upon the content type: audio may require a change in the sampling rate; images may require a change in resolution; video may require a change in resolution or frame rate.

Appearance adaptation is generally motivated by the need to ensure compliance with the capabilities of the receiving device. The content parameters that are altered during the appearance adaptation process tend to be buried within the encoded content, and so are "masked" from the underlying network. Thus, appearance adaptation is rarely required for reasons relating to the underlying network.

Beyond ensuring that the media is compatible with the capabilities of the receiving device, adaptation may also need to dynamically adjust a layout (e.g., SMIL, Extensible HyperText Markup Language (XHTML)) to account for individual device settings. For example, a layout may need to utilize a specific font size or style, adjust the placement of an image to account for display size, or even adjust the layout to account for the removal or alteration of other multimedia objects due to adaptation.

In keeping with the MITA goal of usability, the sending consumer or application cannot be expected to know the capabilities or even the brand/model of the receiving consumer's equipment, yet it is compulsory that the receiving consumer is able to consume the content delivered to them.

Where to Adapt

There are three ways of attempting to conform an MMU to the capabilities of the receiver: modifying it before it is emitted from the content source; modifying it at the receiver; or modifying it at some intermediary end-point. Combinations of the three are also possible.

In some cases, a solution may be mandated. For instance, when the sender and receiver support a disjointed set of formats (e.g., for images, the sender only supports JPEG2000 and the receiver only supports PNG) an intermediary solution is the only viable option. This section explores the three possible locations for adaptation, and outlines circumstances where each may or may not be realistic.

Note that the process of adapting multimedia content is essentially the same no matter where it occurs. To illustrate, we can take the block diagram for intermediary adaptation, and move the intermediary block inside the content sink to end up with receiver-based adaptation (see the following figure).

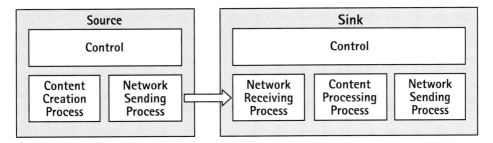

Moving the functions of the intermediary into receiver

Adaptation at Content Sink

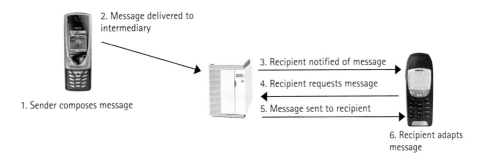

Adaptation at the content sink for a MMS messaging application

Certain types of adaptation can sensibly be performed at the content sink, notably, appearance adaptation. It could be argued that the receiving device is best suited to knowing how it should display content. Many content players already possess the capability of altering content appearance. For example, today's Web browsers render (i.e., adapt the layout) of each HTML page based upon the screen or window size and scale images to meet specified resolutions. Advantages of performing adaptation at the content sink include:

o   The receiving user potentially has access to the original, unmodified MMU. If the MMU is subsequently forwarded or transferred to a device with better capabilities, the third party experiences no degradation of content.

o   The intermediary that handles administrative and routing aspects of MMU delivery is not burdened with adaptation functionality as well. Such simplifications may mean cost savings to carriers.

But, for types of adaptation other than appearance adaptation, the story is very different.

o   The transport layer of a network may depend on the encapsulation being correct. Therefore, any necessary encapsulation adaptation must be done as the MMU transits from one network or application space to another.

o   The size may need to be reduced prior to the content sink receiving the MMU. For example, if size must be reduced to comply with memory limitations of a receiving device, the size reduction must be accomplished before the MMU arrives at the receiver.

o   Format adaptation fails when the receiver does not support the current content format.

For many applications, these major limitations will mean that adapting solely at the sink is not an option. At the very least, there must be some adaptation either at the sender or at an intermediary.

o   Adaptation that is performed automatically, i.e., without human guidance, is never completely foolproof and may lead to an unexpectedly severe or unacceptable degradation in quality.

o   If the MMU is being sent over a licensed spectrum, MMU size effects the cost of transmission and is, therefore, important: reducing the size of an MMU after transmission achieves zero bandwidth savings.

o   Performing adaptation can be a complex task and doing so on a mobile receiving device may shorten battery life.

o   The intermediary's more powerful equipment may perform the task faster than the receiving device. Electing to use the slower method could leave the consumer waiting while certain tasks are done, ultimately leading to a poor user experience for the recipient.

o   It is difficult to add new formats, since each receiving device must be upgraded. Using intermediaries would limit the upgrades to a small number of servers and often be achievable with a simple software update.

Adaptation at Content Source

Under this scenario, the content source must learn the capabilities of the content sink, ideally before composing the MMU, but at least before transmitting it. These capabilities could be discovered from the recipient device directly or via an intermediary, either through cache/database lookup, or by relay from the recipient. As an example, we consider browsing, where the content source generally receives information about the browser with each content request. The content source then performs any foreseeable adaptation and sends the MMU. Except for encapsulation adaptation, no modification to the content is required after transmission.

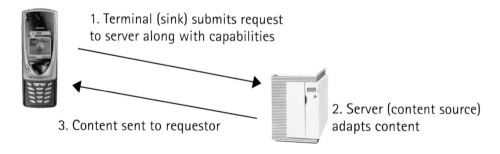

1. Terminal (sink) submits request to server along with capabilities

2. Server (content source) adapts content

3. Content sent to requestor

Adaptation at content source

Although we argued above that a receiving device is in the best position to know its own capabilities and thus is best suited to making decisions regarding content presentation, a strong argument can also be mounted to the contrary, contending that the sender knows best what they wish to convey and that certain intricacies may be lost if adaptation is left to the recipient.

Adaptation at the sending end affords the sender control over content appearance, informing them of exactly what will be done to their content before it is sent and letting them interact with the sending process. For example, if a part of the MMU must be removed, the sender may be given the option to re-edit the message and provide an alternative. Also, if the content source is an application, precise control over the results may be highly desirable.

On the other hand, it has been stated that it is not acceptable for a sending user to manually validate compliance prior to transmitting content. In such cases, the content source must somehow learn the recipient's capabilities automatically (i.e., without user intervention). This could be problematic if the recipient is unreachable and cached information about it either does not exist or is incorrect. Whatever the reason, if the recipient's capabilities cannot be accurately determined, the process completely breaks down. Plus, there are other problems with adaptation at the content source:

o   For mobile-originated messages, the process of adapting an MMU is slower and may adversely affect the sender's battery life.

o   The sender cannot perform format adaptation if there is no format common to both sender and receiver, for example if the sender supports only JPEG2000 and the recipient supports only PNG, the sender cannot convert an image to any appropriate format.

o   It is harder to add new formats since all sending devices need upgrading.

Reliance Upon an Intermediary

Reliance upon an intermediary means that the MMU is composed at the content source and submitted to the network for delivery. The MMU conforms to the encapsulation requirements of the sender's network (e.g., it is a valid MMS), but otherwise no regard is paid to the capabilities of the receiver.

Once the MMU reaches the delivery network corresponding to the content sink, an intermediary identifies the characteristics of the content sink. This could be done following message notification, or the capabilities could already be in the intermediary's database if the content sink had previously registered with the intermediary. This would allow the intermediary to perform all necessary adaptation before delivering the MMU, so at the time of delivery, the content fully conforms to the recipient's requirements.

The method used by the intermediary for performing adaptation could either be pre-configured or could utilize instructions from the sender, which have been embedded in the content.

III Visions

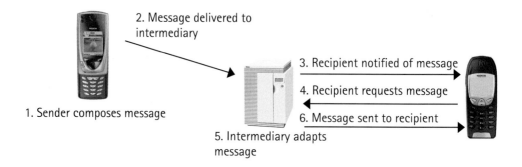

Reliance upon an intermediary

This approach avoids most of the disadvantages associated with the previous two methods, making it easier to introduce new content formats and relieving both the sender and receiver from adaptation duties. But it is not without drawbacks:

o   The recipient does not have access to the original unadapted content.

o   The sender does not know exactly what content the recipient will receive, although adaptation should ensure that the content is displayed at the maximum quality possible given the recipient's capabilities.

o   It does not suit ad hoc or personal networks, which generally involve peer-to-peer connectivity and shun the need for dedicated servers or intermediaries.

o   For size reduction, it would be more efficient in terms of bandwidth to perform the adaptation at the content source.

Whether to Adapt

Thus far, it has been assumed that the content source or sink is primarily interested in content being delivered in some recognizable form, even if it experiences mild degradation. In cases of casual interpersonal communication, this is a safe assumption - consumers value interoperability more than marginal changes to the multimedia. However, in some situations, the content owner may not want adaptation to occur.

In some cases, content may be protected using some form of DRM. When the content is modified via adaptation, depending on the type of DRM, the process could either clean the content so that it is no longer protected or make it appear illegitimate. Some types of DRM could prevent adaptation from working properly, for example, by corrupting the content. Accordingly, adaptation must either work with the DRM system or DRM-protected content should not be adapted.

Similarly, care must be taken when adaptation is performed without the control or consent of the involved parties because the integrity of content may be of high importance. For example, if a medical image is adapted, even a slight degradation in quality may be unacceptable.

Alternatives to Content Modification

The section "Where to Adapt" highlighted some of the dilemmas associated with adaptation (e.g., whether the content source or the content sink is best positioned to know how content should appear). While modification of content may be unavoidable for some applications, in others, content can be prepared in such a way that it can be consumed by a variety of device types without modification. Such preparation is notably useful in browsing applications, where similar operations could otherwise potentially occur each time some particular content is retrieved. This section briefly describes three steps that can be taken at the content source to aid consumption at the sink.

Content Selection

Rather than adapting content as needed, each conceivably necessary adaptation operation could be performed, producing several versions of the same content, each possibly subject to approval by the content owner. At the time content is requested or sent, the appropriate version of the content would be selected from the alternatives. For example, a video clip could be stored at several rates and resolutions (e.g., high-speed, high resolution and low-speed, low resolution), so when a consumer requests the clip, he or she could be provided with the version appropriate to network and display capabilities.

Naturally, this requires a method for selecting the appropriate version among from those available (e.g., by the SMIL "switch" statement) which makes a selection based upon given criteria.

Separating Content and its Representation

According to these separating methods, only one set of content is developed although the representation description (i.e., the appearance or layout) of the content is stored separately. By storing several different representation descriptions and delivering the most suitable one to the content sink upon request or by storing and adapting a single representation description rather than adapting the content, the best appearance of the content can be assured.

Cascading Style Sheets (CSS) and Extensible Stylesheet Language Transformations (XSLT) are technologies used to support adaptation of representation descriptions. CSS is one way of attaching styles (e.g., fonts and spacing) to content. This method is well suited to layouts involving structured documents or more than one multimedia object. It is less suitable for representing a single media object (e.g., images, video or audio).

Scalable Encoding Formats

Multimedia objects (e.g., audio, video, images and graphics) have traditionally been encoded with specific characteristics (e.g., quality, frame rate and resolution). Changing these characteristics has generally meant adapting the content using the techniques described earlier. Some newer encoding formats are scalable, meaning that an object only needs to be encoded once and then can be transmitted or decoded to suit a variety of characteristics. For example, JPEG2000 is a scalable image format. If the size of a JPEG2000 image is too large, elements of the bitstream can simply be removed to obtain a lower-quality version. Scalable Vector Graphics (SVG) is another example of a scalable format.

III

Visions

Case Studies

To close our chapter, we present case studies from two of the three Interaction modes identified by MITA - Messaging and Browsing. These not only illustrate how the adaptation concepts discussed above would operate in a practical system, but also show how various system components can work together to achieve the best overall adaptation result.

Store-and-Forward Messaging

With store-and-forward messaging, there are few restrictions on the timeliness of message delivery; a best effort approach is generally satisfactory. MMS is a good example of a store-and-forward application. As with MMS, the receiving user may neither expect nor be aware of the arrival of a message until it is fully stored within the receiving device. In this environment, the sending device is the content source and the receiving device is the content sink. Note that the sending device may be a mobile device or an application.

The store-and-forward term implies that the message is delivered via an intermediary, and given the benefits of utilizing an intermediary for adaptation, it would be logical to concentrate our adaptation efforts there. But, rather than leave all adaptation solely up to the intermediary, this case study demonstrates how interaction between the content sink and the intermediary could improve the process.

With two exceptions, such a joint effort would use the diagram from "Reliance Upon an Intermediary." At step three, rather than just giving a notification, the intermediary would include information about the message (e.g., the number and format of components and resolution). Then, in step four, the sink would not only request the message but also provide adaptation instructions to the intermediary.

This architecture provides the recipient with extensive control over the adaptation process, allowing the recipient to retrieve an unadapted message even if it is not immediately usable.

On the other hand, determining layouts is a complex operation, and asking the receiving device to provide complete adaptation instructions could adversely affect performance and battery life. Also, the result of one adaptation operation may effect decisions for future adaptations. It might be nearly impossible for the content sink to provide a meaningful and complete set of instructions in one message, but a highly interactive process would be an inefficient alternative.

Basic Browsing

With messaging, each device is potentially both a content source and sink, whereas browsing mostly involves content moving in one direction. In basic browsing, content is located on a server and not on a peer device. Often the source has the luxury of assembling content in advance rather than at the time of message transmission.

For content that can be created in advance, a content source could store many different versions of the same content, delivering the one that is best suited to the capabilities of the content sink. This is an acceptable approach when the generation of alternate versions can be automated or if the quality of the content is highly important, but generating multiple versions of content manually places an administrative burden on the content creator. Additionally, because not all content can be created in advance (e.g., interactive maps), adaptation will sometimes be unavoidable.

Unlike messaging, where the recipient either has no expectation of message arrival or does not know exactly when a message has been sent, browsing imposes certain latency constraints. The recipient explicitly requests content to be delivered. If the content does not arrive within a certain time frame, the consumer will grow impatient and feel that the system is not responding.

The two options offering the most promise are adaptation on the server and adaptation at an intermediary.

Adaptation on the server means that the content owner has control over the information provided to consumers. This can help optimize the overall experience of the content by the consumer. Although the server must be able to encode in some format supported by the receiver, this is unlikely to pose a real problem, because servers tend to have sufficient power and are subject to higher maintenance standards than regular devices.

The main disadvantage of server-side adaptation is the expectation that all servers will be able to supply data in a format appropriate to the receiving device. If a sizeable minority of servers could not perform adaptation, the consumer would be deprived of access to the content thereon. The usage criteria associated with server-side adaptation are as much logistical and business-related as they are technical.

Adaptation using an intermediary is the converse of server-side adaptation. The content provider has less control over the appearance (e.g., the intermediary may be controlled by a carrier), but the content provider is also freed from the responsibility of keeping their server's adaptation capabilities updated to support the latest devices. This task is now the responsibility of the intermediary owner, who often also controls browsing access, putting them in a better position to know what types of devices are likely to be connecting. A current example of this configuration is using a Wireless Application Protocol (WAP) [wap2001] gateway to reformat HTML pages for delivery to mobile devices.

A compromise is to perform adaptation on both the server and on an intermediary, as depicted below. Content is requested from the server, and although the server performs some adaptation, it may not be able to complete the process; for example, it may not support a media format. When the content reaches the intermediary, the intermediary completes the adaptation and forwards the content to the requestor.

The server can also tag the content it provides to disallow adaptation. This enables the owner to enforce full control over their content when so desired, but otherwise leave the burden of adaptation to the intermediary.

III

Visions

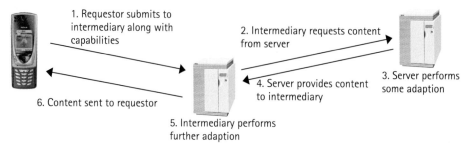

1. Requestor submits to intermediary along with capabilities

2. Intermediary requests content from server

3. Server performs some adaption

4. Server provides content to intermediary

5. Intermediary performs further adaption

6. Content sent to requestor

Adaptation using both server and intermediary

Such a scheme would not require the requestor to perform adaptation, would be relatively easy to upgrade, and would still provide the content owner with a degree of control over content appearance.

Conclusions

In this chapter, we have established the need for multimedia content adaptation, discussed the types of adaptation that may be needed, and also considered where that adaptation could best be performed. We have provided examples, some of which relate to current services (e.g., MMS), and others that described hypothetical services that could be offered in the future.

However, the success of adaptation, and hence the degree to which devices on the Mobile Internet can exchange multimedia content, requires certain steps to be taken. First, there must be an accepted method of representing the capabilities of the content sink, a method ideally shared among all applications requiring such information.

Secondly, the actual process of adaptation needs further development. It is worth observing that this chapter discussed in detail the what, why and where of adaptation, but not the how. We have also touched upon, but not resolved, the issue of who should control the appearance of content.

Finally, in keeping with MITA tenets, we must seek an adaptation framework flexible enough to work in all three Interaction modes. Development of such a framework will assist in meeting the overall objective of providing consumers with an excellent experience of the Mobile Internet.

References

[mms1999]   "Multimedia Messaging Service" (various subtitles), 3rd Generation Partnership Project TS 23.140 Release 1999. URL: ftp://www.3gpp.org/ftp/Specs.

[smil2001]   "SMIL 2.0: Synchronized Multimedia Integration Language," W3C Recommendation 7 August 2001. URL http://www.w3c.org/TR/smil20.

[xhtml2000]   "XHTML 1.0: The Extensible HyperText Markup Language," W3C Recommendation 26 January 2000. URL: http://www.w3c.org/TR/xhtml1.

[sipf2001]   "SIP Extensions for Instant Messaging," draft-rosenberg-impp-im-01," (work in progress), J. Rosenberg et al., February, 2001.

[sipm2001]   "SIP Extensions for Presence, draft-rosenberg-impp-presence-01.txt," (work in progress), J. Rosenberg et al., March, 2001.

[sipm1999]   "SIP: session initiation protocol," M. Handley, H. Schulzrinne, E. Schooler, and J. Rosenberg, RFC 2543, Internet Engineering Task Force, Mar. 1999.

[http1999]   "Hypertext Transfer Protocol HTTP/1.1," R. Fielding, J. Gettys, J. Mogul, H. Frystyk, L. Masinter, P. Leach, T. Berners-Lee, June 1999. URL: ftp://ftp.isi.edu/in-notes/rfc2616.txt.

[jpeg1990]   "Digital compression and coding of continuous-tone still images," ISO/IEC IS 10918-3, ITU-T Recommendation T.84, 1990 (JPEG specification).

[gif1990]   "Graphics Interchange Format, version 89a," Programming Reference, CompuServe, Inc., 1990. URL: http://256.com/gray/docs/gifspecs.

[wap2001]   "WAP Architecture," WAP Forum, WAP-210-WAPArch, at URL: http://www.wapforum.org/

III

Visions

PART 3.3

Platform Layer

o Multiple Access

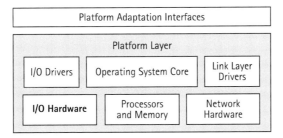

Multiple Access

Services should not be tied to specific access methods. If this were the case, all new access methods would render the Mobile Internet architecture useless. Therefore, the cornerstones for the MITA are a high degree of access independence and multiple access possibilities. Multiple access technology allows the use of services in different domains (i.e., in ad-hoc networks) where devices are connected using short range technologies, as well as in mobile networks, where the communication takes place over a longer distance. A transparent transport layer allows the seamless use of applications with different access technologies.

The MITA allows the use of a wide range of different access methods starting from wide area access with low or moderate data rates up to short-range hotspot technologies with high data rates.

Regulations of Technologies

In general, multiple access technologies can be classified into two main classes: licensed and unlicensed.

Licensed Access Technologies

For licensed access technologies, the radio frequencies are regulated by national regulation bodies and are licensed to carriers. Examples of regulated systems are the current second generation networks (e.g., Global System for Mobile Communications (GSM), Personal Digital Communication (PDC), Code Division Multiple Access (CDMA), the second generation CDMA standard elaborated by the Telecommunications Industry Association (IS-95)), as well as upcoming third generation networks (e.g., Wideband Code Division Multiple Access (WCDMA), Frequency Division Duplex (FDD), or Time Division Duplex (TDD) Enhanced Data Rates for Global Evolution (EDGE) and broadcasting media as Digital Video Broadcasting Terrestrial (DVB-T)). These frequencies are solely used by their licensee; thus, interference with other users is minimal and the Quality of Service (QoS) can be managed by the carrier, itself, through means of radio network planning and network (carrier) controlled usage of the radio resources.

In many cases, particularly in Europe, licensed frequency bands are utilized solely by a particular radio technology, which further reduces interference and improves QoS.

Consequently, with licensed access technologies, the business logic for network systems is biased towards the carriers deploying and owning the radio access network (e.g., base stations). The licensed access systems are typically scalable from wide-range to short-range with low latencies and turn-around times.

Unlicensed Access Technologies

For unlicensed radio frequency usage, national regulation bodies provide certain frequency bands for unlicensed usage. There are Industrial, Scientific and Medical (ISM) bands, which may be utilized by many different radio technologies, and there are bands dedicated for a single or a narrow group of specific radio technologies. Even though these frequencies can be used without any prior license, rules exist governing how these frequencies shall be utilized. These rules prevent systems from interfering with other systems to such a degree that they would make the operation of other systems in this band impossible. Also, special rules exist to protect the usage of older legacy technologies utilizing the same or neighboring bands. All radio transmitters and unlicensed systems have to undergo a type approval process by the national type approval authorities.

Nevertheless, within these frequencies, different systems are competing and interfering with each other, which makes it impossible to guarantee a certain level of QoS in all usage scenarios. However, since unlicensed bands are predominantly utilized by short-range radio technologies, a so-called premises owner, who is in control of well-defined physical space (e.g., company, home), can improve the QoS situation by controlling the deployment of radio devices, in particular through the choice of radio technologies and radio network planning for the radio access network.

Consequently, with unlicensed access technologies, the business logic for network systems is biased towards the premises owners deploying and owning the radio access network (e.g., access points).

Classification of Technologies

Besides the classification of access technologies regarding regulations, the technologies can be classified according to their potential use cases. MITA classifies the technologies into four categories:

o   Distribution
o   Mobile network
o   Local Access
o   Fixed Access

Distribution Technologies

Distribution technologies are used for point-to-multipoint distribution of data or TV content. The communication is unidirectional and can be used efficiently to multicast popular content. While in the past these technologies were based on analog content, currently they are shifting towards the distribution of digital content. The distribution technologies have a wide coverage of both population and geographical area. Because the communication is unidirectional, it makes sense to combine distribution technologies with bi-directional communication technologies to form a hybrid network.

Digital Video Broadcasting (Terrestrial)

DVB-T is complementing and replacing terrestrial analog television broadcasting in the near future. In addition to the traditional concept of video broadcasting, the concept allows multiplexing general data to the broadcast channels, which offers a good opportunity to broadcast digital content within a wide range. Especially when the DVB-T system is combined in the Mobile Internet with systems capable of bi-directional communication, new services can be established on top of this hybrid network. The DVB-T network allows wide area coverage as well as picocells with high capacity in hot spot areas. Since the available bandwidth is large, the cumulative capacity of the system exceeds 1 Gbps.

Mobile Network Technologies

Cellular technologies mainly offer a bi-directional point-to-point communication, and to some extent point-to-multipoint communication as well. Starting with analog voice communication, the mobile networks have transformed into digital networks with both voice and data capabilities. The most recent enhancement extends the networks with packet switched data functionality. The medium range allows a wide coverage of radio network access.

Second Generation

The GSM radio access network offers bi-directional data and voice services. It is one of the most deployed technologies of the second generation mobile network standards. The new standard GSM phase2+ improves communication capabilities through improved voice codecs and the introduction both of High Speed Circuit Switched Data (HSCSD) and the General Packet Radio Service (GPRS). Portions of the available frequencies are licensed to the carriers. The maximal radius of a GSM cell is about 35 km, but in urban areas the cells are much smaller to provide higher capacity through closer frequency reuse. The introduction of a packet-based service makes access to the IP type of data communication smoother.

Third Generation

The third generation mobile networks are a family of similar standards defined in the three major mobile network markets. The decision about the European Universal Mobile Telecommunication System (UMTS) network was made in 1998, and a combination of a FDD and a TDD system was selected for the available frequencies. The FDD approach (WCDMA) was selected for a paired frequency band, with one of the frequencies for the uplink, and the other for the downlink. For the remaining unpaired spectrum, a TDD system called WCDMA/TDD was defined. In 2000, an alternative radio access system GSM/EDGE, including Enhanced General Packet Radio Service (EGPRS), was added to UMTS standards. In Japan Association of Radio Industries and Businesses (ARIB), the Japanese regulation authority, selected WCDMA in 1997, which, with some modification, was later adopted in Europe. In the US, the government adopted a quite neutral approach, which resulted in a multitude of standards: WCDMA N/A (which is similar to the ARIB/European WCDMA system), UWC-136 (a narrow and wideband TDMA system), and CDMA2000 (the wideband version of IS-95).

III

Visions

Currently, higher data rate extensions to WCDMA are called High Speed Downlink Packet Access (HSDPA).

Cellular technologies are typically optimized for high spectrum efficiency since their dedicated frequency bands are narrow (compared to local access technologies) and are typically licensed.

Local Access Technologies and Ad-Hoc Connectivity

Often wireless data access is provided by local access technologies (e.g., Wireless Local Area Network (WLAN) or Bluetooth), which often need no license for operation. Due to the limited range of these technologies, the service access is local, but data rates can be quite high. Local access can be also provided on an ad hoc basis, where two or more devices form their own network.

Wireless Local Area Networks

The WLAN systems are typically working in the ISM bands, which have regulated usage conditions, but are generally license free. The systems have limited coverage with very high user bit rates. Best suited for office, home and hot spot networking, these systems are severely limited in wide-scale outdoor coverage. Typical use cases are computing-intensive applications and infotainment (e.g., high-quality streaming video) services. The WLAN networks are interesting to carriers since they provide high-speed access and bandwidth extension in limited areas and extend networks beyond the standard license coverage. The most deployed system today is IEEE 802.11b, which offers 11 Mbps data rate in the 2.4 GHz ISM band, whereas the new specification IEEE 802.11TGg will offer up to 22 Mbps. Future systems (e.g., IEEE 802.11a or HiperLAN/2) will offer rates up to 54 Mbps, with later versions offering up to 100 Mbps working in the 5 GHz unlicensed frequency band.

Bluetooth

Bluetooth has a very limited coverage with moderate to high user bit rate. It is best suited to link together various personal devices and to provide short-range access to wired backbone networks in offices, homes and hot spots. Typical usage cases are transactional types of applications where the bit rate requirements are lower than with WLAN applications. Some of the typical WLAN use cases can be covered with Bluetooth as well, though the smaller operating range and lower maximum throughput must be kept in mind. Due to its low cost, small size and low power consumption, Bluetooth is better suited for mobile devices as a secondary air interface, compared to WLAN. Like WLAN, Bluetooth has unlicensed radio access on the 2.4 GHz ISM band.

The Bluetooth specifications also include a profile called Personal Area Networking (PAN), describing the use of IP in the Bluetooth protocol stack.

Local access technologies are typically optimized for low cost and/or high data rate. Spectrum efficiency is somewhat lower than that of mobile networks, but integral spectrum capacity is typically higher because the frequency bands are much wider.

Fixed Access Technologies

In addition to these radio access technologies, there are also wired access technologies (e.g., Universal Serial Bus (USB), or USB On-the-Go). The technical architecture over the actual transport for fixed access technologies should be identical to the wireless accesses; however, here and there will also be differences in terms of communication characteristics (e.g., QoS, latencies or bit rates).

Legacy access technologies also include technologies (e.g., Digital Subscriber Lines (DSL)), which provide broadband Internet access. DSL finds a wide acceptance already today, and fixed broadband access will assume an even more important role in the future. Integrated Services Digital Network (ISDN) and Public Switched Telephony Network (PSTN) modems are other legacy access technologies.

III
Visions

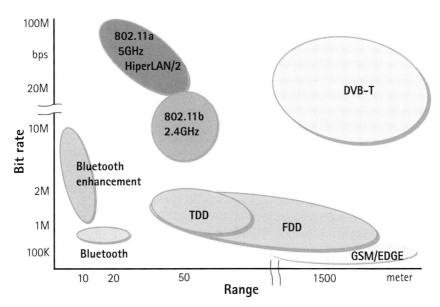

Wireless Access Technologies

The Role of IP as Common Transport

For all different access technologies, Transmission Control Protocol (TCP)/User Datagram Protocol (UDP) Internet Protocol (IP) has a special role as a uniform transport mechanism, separating the actual access technology from the middleware protocols. The services, which use common middleware protocols as service enablers, become independent from the underlying access technology by using IP technology. However, it is obvious that the physical behavior of the access technology will differ depending on the selected access technology. The differences will result from the ability to control attributes (e.g., QoS, latencies, or data rates). Moreover, the cost structure of services depends on the underlying transport costs.

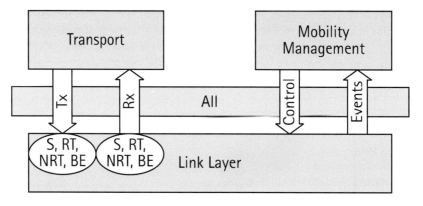

Access Independent Interface

The transport layer and functions to control multiple access technologies can be defined by an Access Independent Interface (AII). Other tasks which are needed to exploit different access technologies (e.g., the use of selected authentication and service discovery technologies) are included in this interface description. For licensed access technologies, the licensor has to select solutions. For unlicensed technologies, technologies from the Mobile domain can be reused, i.e., Subscriber Identity Module (SIM) based authentication based on the 802.1x/EAP authentication framework or solutions deployed on the Internet today (e.g., one-time-passwords) will be implemented.

PART 3.4

Key End-to-End Systems

- o Service Discovery

- o Mobile Web Services

- o Privacy

- o Location Services

- o Naming, Numbering and Addressing

- o Presence

- o Reachability

- o Access Independent Connectivity

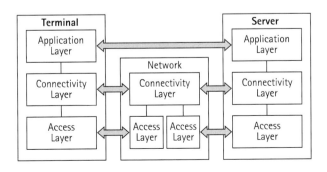

Service Discovery

Current search or service discovery in the Web domain is an Internet mechanism mostly directed towards consumers who have access to the Legacy Internet and use a PC or laptop for services. In this context it is tolerable to get irrelevant search results. In the Mobile domain, the consumer does not want to search hundreds of irrelevant links on a small mobile device screen and so needs fast and precise results with a simple search logic. The most important aspects in this scenario are:

o   An efficient search infrastructure concentrating on the content relevant to a consumer.

o   A simple user interface with ready made search templates for a keyword search

o   A context-based search infrastructure taking into account

-   User profile and preferences (previous search attempts and favor services)

-   Mobility and the customer's location

-   The Device and the profile the consumer is presumably using

-   Time of searching

The process where an entity searches/discovers/finds the required service dynamically is called service discovery. This is not as simple as it appears: a service is a function of many attributes (e.g., type of content, value of content, time, location, consumer and categorization). These attributes along with the context of the device make the search criteria a complex issue to handle. Moreover, the mobility aspect of the requesting entity and the requested service makes service discovery even more challenging.

There are three players in the process of service discovery:

o   Client: An entity which is trying to find or discover what it needs. The entity can be a consumer, a device or specific software on a device.

o   Service: An entity which is being discovered by the client or the source able to provide what the client entity needs.

o   Registry/Directory: A registry maintains a list of available services. The registry is not mandatory, however in practice, the registry might logically be a hierarchy of registries.

Service Discovery Concept

Service discovery spans different parts/domains in the end-to-end scenario depending on who is searching/discovering and what is being discovered. Different service discovery scenarios are described in the next figure.

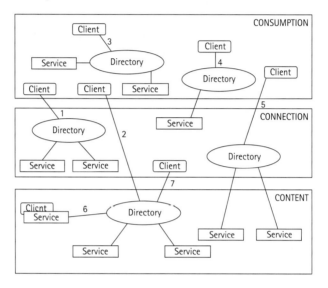

Different service discovery scenarios in MITA

Below is a brief description of the different scenarios presented in the above figure.

1. The network maintains a list of services which the client can search. Examples are discovery of basic network resources (e.g., name servers or Voice over IP gateways).

2. A client contacts the service directory residing on the application server (content end). Examples of discovered services include Mobile Information Device Profile (MIDP) applications hosted by a content provider, mobile commerce services hosted by a service portal, and customer services hosted by a department store.

3. A client in the mobile device can directly search applications in the same mobile device or another device. Especially in Bluetooth, the Bluetooth Service Discovery Protocol (SDP) can be used to search services and their attributes in a neighboring device.

4. A mobile device can host a directory of networking services. For example, it may contain communication access points for Global System for Mobile Communications (GSM) Data, General Packet Radio Service (GPRS), Wireless Local Area Network (WLAN) and Bluetooth.

5. In contrast to case 2, the network may host the directory of the services.

6. A client can be an application running in the application server and use the discovery system to find components it needs to implement its function. A yellow-page service could be one example.

7. The network could also use the directory of services in the application servers.

MITA has three main service discovery use cases:

o   Service discovery in ad-hoc networks

o   Customer service discovery for finding services on the Internet

o   A special type of service discovery is presence and virtual community navigation

This chapter describes a technical architecture providing an enhanced search/discovery service so the consumer can discover Internet services. This architecture consists of an additional component (Service Discovery Engine (SDE)) in the network. SDE enhances the search functionality with additional features (e.g., using the user profile and context information).

End-to-End Architecture

The end-to-end model of service discovery on the Mobile Internet is shown in the following figure.

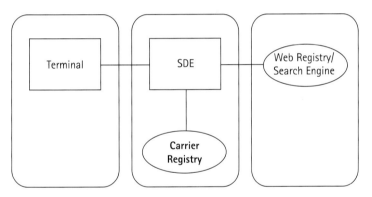

End-to-end model of consumer service discovery on the Mobile Internet

End-to-End Functionality

Functionality of the Mobile Device

The mobile device plays an important role with respect to the consumer in finding services on the Mobile Internet, for it has the basic functionality of connecting to the Service Discovery Engine (SDE). This basic functionality is required to send queries and receive results from the SDE. The mobile device needs to be able to send information on its capabilities to the SDE if necessary. In addition to these mobile device profiles, the user profiles are also of use in this end-to-end service discovery scenario, and the mobile device needs the functionality to send the personal preferences to the SDE if necessary. User profiles might be partially residing on the mobile device and partially on the network.

Functionality of the Network

Network functionality is divided between the mobile network and the Internet Service Provider (ISP) network. The carrier can provide and support connections from SDE to other services (e.g., location information, personal content storage and billing system). ISP network functionality can include the services required to conduct interaction between the SDE and other services (e.g., registries).

Functionality of the SDE

SDE is the crucial element of service discovery, for it enhances the search functionality with added features. The SDE can have the following functionality:

o   The SDE provides the interface for the consumer to interact with it. This interface acts as a single interface point for the consumer to interact with the carrier registry and with Web domain registries.

o   The SDE does not contain authentication and authorization functionality but uses the provider's authentication and authorization subsystems.

o   The SDE might be a free service or a paid service depending on the business model of the provider. The SDE does not have any billing system of its own, but does have an interface to the provider's Billing System.

o   The SDE maintains the session information of the consumer's interaction with it, as well as transaction and interaction histories.

o   Personalization is one key functionality of the SDE. The personalization process includes the personalization of queries, query results, and the delivery of results. SDE interacts with the user profile and preference servers.

o   A query sent by the consumer is processed and adapted depending on the registry the SDE contacts to obtain results.

o   In order to improve performance, the query and the corresponding results are cached by the SDE.

o   The SDE does not contain any information about any services by itself. Instead it collects such information from multiple registries in the Mobile and Web domains.

o   Context information, including location and time, is used in query attribute for improving the query and its results.

o   The SDE can support an asynchronous reply to the query.

o   The SDE needs to support push functionality in order to support the asynchronous reply functionality. This functionality can also be achieved if the SDE uses an external subsystem which has push functionality.

Functionality of the Registries

As mentioned above, the SDE does not maintain any descriptions or information about the services which the consumer is trying to discover. Rather, the registry contains descriptions of value-added services. These registries also contain a considerable amount of information the consumer needs to interact with the service.

Interacting with the SDE by Browsing

The most commonly used combination of request/response uses the browser. Hence, the HyperText Transfer Protocol (HTTP) is protocol between the mobile device and the SDE. In this combination of the request/response mode, the mobile device contacts the SDE by a Uniform Resource Locator (URL). The SDE can provide an Extensible HyperText Markup Language (XHTML) interface for the mobile device. In this alternative, control completely lies on the network side, so there is little processing on the mobile device side. Because of this dependence on the network, only few demands are made on the mobile device. The only additional requirement is a browser, which exists in many mobile devices even today. The interactions in the sequence diagram below show that the SDE gets context information (e.g., user location info, user profile and mobile device capability information) from the consumer.

III

Visions

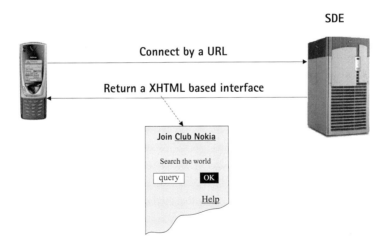

XHTML browser scenario for mobile device and SDE interaction

Interactions between the mobile device and the SDE in this alternative are shown below:

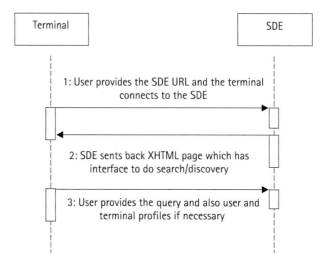

Interaction between an XHTML browser and the SDE

Interaction with SDE by a Query Tool

Interaction with SDE by browsing uses a general-purpose client to interact with the SDE. Hence, it is restricted by its general-purpose functionality and may not measure up to all the requirements of the service discovery scenario on the Mobile Internet. A Query Tool scenario is very specific to service discovery and requires additional mobile device capabilities, though its mode of request/ response can give added advantage to the mobile device. The query tool can have these basic capabilities:

o   When initiated, the tool can automatically connect to the default SDE. Once connected, the tool can get some information (e.g., search categories and useful links).

o   The query tool can have a user interface for the consumer to interact with the SDE.

o   The query tool can have the capability to automatically provide the context information to the SDE during the search.

o   The query tool can support different Interaction modes in interaction with SDE.

o   The consumer can configure the query tool, if necessary

The query tool can have these advanced features:

o   The query tool can store queries and contact the SDE during non-peak hours. This feature can also be used when the consumer is changing from one profile to another.

o   Depending on the capabilities of the mobile device, the query tool can have advanced user interface options (e.g., a voice interface or a visual interface).

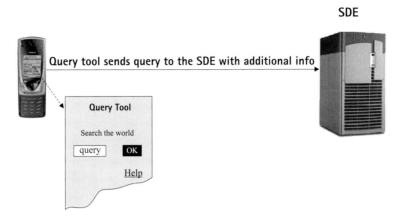

Query tool scenario for mobile device and SDE interaction

Interaction between the mobile device and the SDE is shown below:

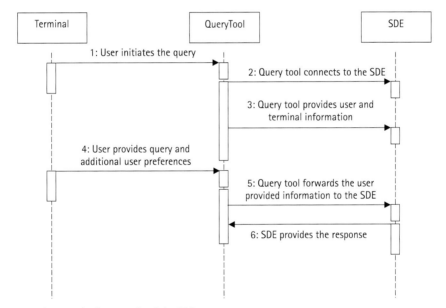

Interaction between the Query tool and the SDE

Service Discovery in MITA

The scope of service discovery on the Internet can best be represented in the layered network model as shown in the next figure.

In the MITA model, the Service Discovery covers the Connectivity and Application layer service discovery technologies, as illustrated in the next figure. Access layer related service discovery technologies are covered in Multiple Access Technologies specification.

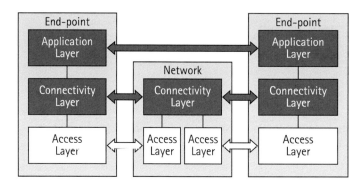

The scope of the Service Discovery in the MITA Network model

Service Discovery Specification addresses requirements for Access Independent Connectivity. When the AIC Subsystem identifies a need to change into a new access network domain, after proper authentication, a discovery service should be activated. In a similar way, the service discovery service provides control and event triggering interfaces for the Application layer Subsystems and applications.

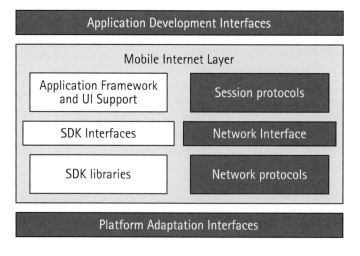

Location of the Service Discovery related Subsystems in the MITA Element

Mobile Web Services

Web services are well-defined and published protocol interfaces through which businesses offer electronic services. The Information Technology (IT) industry has already succeeded in automating most of the operative processes taking place inside corporations, so the next logical step for Web services will be to provide the tools to automate business-to-business relationships over the Internet. Indeed, we have already seen the emergence of Web services protocols for service-oriented electronic business.

Web services provide a common and interoperable way to define, publish and use well-defined messaging-based services. They build on existing and emerging technologies (e.g., Extensible Markup Language (XML), Simple Object Access Protocol (SOAP), Web Services Description Language (WSDL), Universal Description, Discovery and Integration (UDDI) and HyperText Transfer Protocol (HTTP)).

Web Services in the Mobile Domain

The Mobile domain has grown as the voice has gone wireless. One booster for the next wave of business growth is expected to come from mobile consumers accessing Internet content, as addressed in *content goes wireless* paradigm.

The emerging Mobile Internet demands an easy method to connect mobile networks to Internet Service Provider (ISP) systems. Such a connection can be implemented according to the Web Services paradigm. This paradigm makes it possible to automate services between carriers and their business partners, creating new business opportunities for all players throughout the value system.

Mobile Web Services Interfaces provide an opportunity for carriers to increase their revenues by offering their mobile assets (e.g., billing capabilities, location or presence information) to any service provider who would benefit from such services. For consumers this enables convenient and innovative mobile-enriched services.

Framework for Mobile Web Services Interfaces

To apply Web services technologies to the Mobile domain, each industry sector needs to define a set of business-specific Web service extensions and interfaces. This means that there is a need for Mobile Web Services Interfaces between the Web and Mobile domain.

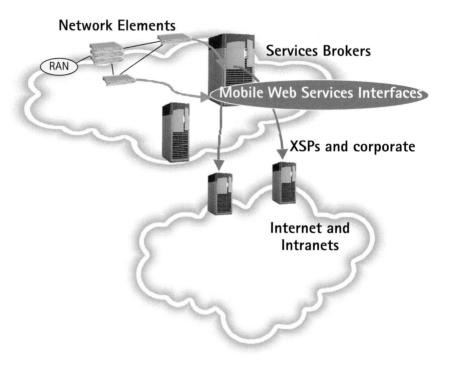

Mobile Web Services Interfaces

Mobile Web Services Interfaces are located in between the Mobile and Web domains, as described in the previous figure. Interfaces enable carriers to offer services to other parties related to user identity, privacy and billing. They also enable other service providers to access the value-added elements in the Mobile domain (e.g., billing and location information). And further, they enable consumers to get enriched mobile services in a way which creates new business for carriers and other service providers.

Mobile Web services effectively form an *intelligent edge* front end between carrier connectivity services and the public Internet. This intelligent edge refines carrier assets into a set of sellable Web services.

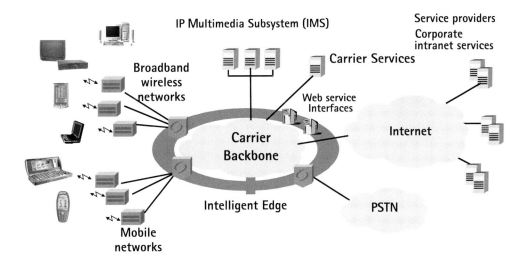

Web services in the carrier architecture

All Mobile Web services respect individual privacy. The consumer has the right to control his own personal information and who is able to view and use it. While this information may physically reside in the carrier domain, the consumer has the final say over it. Carriers take the role of protecting the consumer's information and thus provide value.

Indeed, Mobile Web services are a set of technologies enabling the carrier to become the trusted party protecting the identity of the consumer. One role for the carrier in the context of Mobile Web services is to maintain consumer anonymity in browsing sessions, for example, when purchasing content or requesting personally adapted content.

The success of Global System for Mobile Communications (GSM) mobile services has largely been based on the thriving market created by open standards. Mobile Web Services Interfaces are in the same position as over-the-air interfaces in GSM. Therefore, Mobile Web Services Interfaces based on open global standards are important to build up the size of the market and provide economies of scale for all players. This in turn attracts innovative content and application development and results in more appealing services for consumers.

Legacy Terminal Support

Mobile Web services will also work in legacy terminals, i.e., all terminals will benefit from Web service interfaces. However, the user interface might not be the best possible and not all services will provide the best possible user experience when used in legacy terminals. The Mobile Web service architecture includes user agents as a way to provide legacy support for these services.

Legacy terminals may also use Mobile Web services.

Mobile Web Services Interfaces

In addition to increasing revenues from Mobile services, standardized Web services interfaces may also cut costs. Standardization means that carriers do not need to integrate their technology platforms for each of their content and service providers separately. These interfaces also provide business process automation and easy system integration, which can lower the cost to carriers, corporate bodies and service providers.

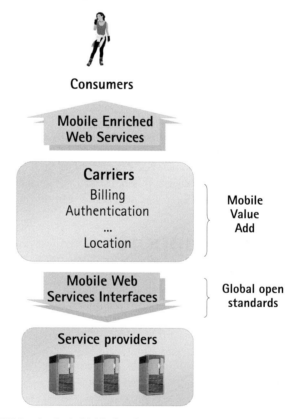

Value chain for Web Services in the Mobile domain

For carriers, their importance in the value chain increases as they become the trusted party though which consumers provide their valuable information for service creation (e.g., presence, location and user profiles). Carriers maintain consumer anonymity in commercial transactions and take care of consumer billing on behalf of the service provider. In practice this means 1) more traffic for the carrier and 2) new revenue sources for both, service providers and carriers).

For content providers, Mobile Web services provide lucrative, personally adapted, context-aware content for consumers. Mobile Web Service Interfaces provide access to a customer base in the Mobile domain for content and service providers in the Web domain.

For IT vendors, Mobile Web services make it possible to build up application development tools and provide support for Mobile Web Service Interfaces. Mobile Web services mean more features for IT platforms.

For consumers, Mobile Web services will bring a broader selection of content and service providers to choose from. It means attractive and useful content well-adapted to the consumer's mobile device and personal preferences. Thanks to the trusted party role of the carrier, it is also possible to use and pay for services anonymously.

Some of the most lucrative candidates for Mobile Web services are:

o   Delivery with payment

o   Notification

o   Device profile

o   Authentication

o   Presence

o   Location

o   User profile

o   Data synchronization

Delivery with Payment

The Delivery with payment is a Web service which can be used to download content or other information to a mobile device. It provides guaranteed delivery for applications requiring confirmation of a successful delivery. This Mobile Web Service Interface provides the necessary checks enabling a carrier legally to charge the consumer for the downloaded content (e.g., games or music).

With guaranteed delivery the consumer can be sure that she is not charged for unsuccessful downloads. When used in combination with other services (e.g., notification and terminal profile), this is an efficient service for secure and reliable download.

In Delivery with payment, the consumer first requests a piece of content. The carrier receives the request and forwards it to the content provider. The content provider delivers the content and the carrier charges the consumer. Here the originator is the consumer, who pays for the content in her mobile phone bill. The role of the carrier is to check and store the transfer operation and to forward the agreed compensation to the content provider.

For the content provider, mobile micro payment means cost savings since it can use the carrier's existing payment infrastructure and consumer billing relationship. On the other hand, for carriers it means new revenue through the revenue sharing business model.

Delivery with payment allows the consumer to pay anonymously and provides a convenient payment method, through her mobile bill. The main benefit of the payment interface is that it enables simple and secure micro payments.

Notification

The Notification Web service uses Mobile domain service practices, where the sender pays for the message delivery, thus helping to reduce the amount of spam to a level that consumers will tolerate.

The main benefit of the Notification Web service is that it enables bi-directional messaging between Mobile and Web domains. The Notification Web service selects the most appropriate delivery method for a particular consumer. For the content or service provider this means device independent service as this device information resides in the Mobile domain.

Device Profile

One of the key characteristics of the Mobile domain is the heterogeneity of the mobile devices in terms of both user interfaces and their capabilities. Some mobile devices have color displays, while others have only small two-color versions. In addition, different manufacturers have implemented different voice and keypad capabilities.

The Device Profile Web service enables the content provider to fetch mobile device capabilities before a transaction takes place. Based on this information the content provider is able to pre-adapt the content to the mobile device capabilities before content delivery.

Authentication

The Authentication Web service allows applications and other Web services to check the identity of consumers. It allows consumers to authenticate themselves to services automatically with the existing mobile identity. Mobile devices have a limited capability for inputting text, so the automation and reduction of such services is important to make services appealing and easy to use.

At present, authentication/Single Sign-on can be done in two ways:

o   Verinymous authentication

o   Pseudonymous authentication

In Verinymous authentication, the customer mobile identity (e.g., Mobile Station International ISDN Number (MSISDN)) is revealed to the service or content provider.

In Pseudonymous authentication, the authentication is performed in a way that maintains the privacy of the consumer. The service or content provider is able to track the successive sessions of a certain consumer but cannot track consumer movements between different service portals, nor is it easy to find the real identity of the consumer without his/her explicit permission.

The consumer benefits from this service by having a single sign-on process. The system is easy to use and understand. For the service or content provider this service enables it to offer trusted services without investing in their own authentication infrastructure.

Presence

Presence Web service is a dynamic profile of the consumer containing customer information (e.g., availability, mood, intentions, and contact preferences). The Presence Web service allows applications to obtain information such as how to contact the user.

Some of the customer contact information can be relatively static, for example:

- o   Telephone number (home and/or business)
- o   E-mail address
- o   Street address

Other customer contact information may be more dynamic or transitory:

- o   Current sessions (e.g., phone call, browsing, retrieving streaming content)
- o   Customer context (e.g., in a meeting, on holiday)
- o   Customer willingness to participate in a certain type of communication (e.g., instant messaging, pager, phone calls)

The relatively static information can be used for services (e.g., directory) that can be accessed from home or corporate Personal Computers. The more dynamic presence services can be used for buddy list-type of services, where a buddy or friend can see in her address book the availability and context of her friend.

A presence service interface enables service and content providers to purchase the information they need to make their services more personal and to add the value of mobility.

Location

The Location Web service can be used to request the location of the consumer. At a minimum, the location information consists of the consumer's coordinates in some coordinate system (e.g., latitude and longitude). It might also include optional, easily understood geographical location information (e.g., city, state/province, or ZIP/postal code).

III

Visions

Location information could be provided by a client in a mobile device (e.g., a mobile phone or Personal Digital Assistant (PDA) with Global Positioning System (GPS) capability) or it could be provided by a carrier.

The location information enables service and content providers to align their services with customer location content. It provides a single Web services interface to positioning technologies regardless of the actual positioning technology the carrier has implemented. There is no need to integrate systems to fit every possible location technology.

User Profile

User Profile Web services provide information about the consumer over and above what the presence service and the location service provide, such as:

o   Nickname

o   Occupation

o   Gender

o   Language preference

o   Interests (e.g., sports, gardening, cars)

The user profile service is targeted towards content providers personalizing content with a nickname greeting and language-adapted content.

Data Synchronization

The Data synchronization Web service enables two versions of a data set to be synchronized. The synchronization service is content-agnostic and can be used by practically any application that needs to synchronize certain pieces of information.

Some example applications for the synchronization service are:

o   Synchronization of calendar information

o   Synchronization of device file information with corresponding centralized backup and storage in the corporate/carrier network

o   Synchronization of personal contact book information between devices (e.g., laptops and mobile devices)

o   Synchronization of favorite bookmarks between devices

The consumer could benefit from this service by the ability to back up critical data or share it between devices. For carriers, data synchronization works as an attractive service to reduce customer churn when user data is stored in the carrier's domain.

The carrier may host the personal information about a mobile device. This virtual mobile device information can be used as the central point for synchronization of the personal information with, for example, corporate calendar or address information databases.

Conclusions

The next wave of growth is expected to come from the *content goes wireless* paradigm, and Mobile Web Services interfaces are a tool for making this possible. Mobile Web services will bring new business to carriers and help them to extend their mobile assets to the Web domain.

III

Visions

Privacy

Privacy on the Mobile Internet

The growth of the Internet and mobile communications has rapidly increased the amount of personal information, which is collected about individuals. As consumers surf the Internet, use mobile services and engage in electronic transactions, they leave a vast amount of information behind. Much of the personal information that is requested from a consumer by a service has potential uses for many purposes and by many companies beyond those originally indicated or reasonably expected by the consumer. Such use may indeed occur without her consent or knowledge. This information has an increasing commercial value and can also be used in a way that is harmful to a consumer's privacy.

On the Mobile Internet, privacy concerns become greater, because even more personal information is involved than ever before. Since a mobile device is used and carried by a consumer all the time, it is possible to collect more accurate information about the consumer's habits, usage patterns and personal preferences. Once location and presence services become available, it will be possible to determine, in connection with other data, increasingly accurate profiles of the consumer's activities.

A consumer's privacy in relation to the outside world is often considered to cover her visibility, i.e., what she reveals to other parties. Another aspect is awareness, analogous to what the consumer wants to see and know about other parties. It is likely that as the amount of available information and services increases, a consumer will not be interested in all that information. Thus, the prevention of unwanted information overflow can also be seen as part of privacy. Visibility and awareness are interconnected in the sense that if you choose to be very visible (e.g. you give out your e-mail address), you may also affect your awareness mode (i.e., you get a lot of offers and spam).

Privacy is a human right related to such fundamental values as dignity, freedom of association and freedom of speech. This definition of privacy is broad, but in the MITA the focus is on what personal information is revealed about the consumer and to whom.

Privacy and Trust

Privacy is strongly related to both trust and security, but privacy should not, however, be confused with security. From a technological viewpoint, security is an important privacy enabler. Security methods can provide the means to verify the identity of another consumer and security solutions can prevent unauthorized parties from obtaining or misusing private or proprietary information. However, good security does not guarantee privacy. In practice, even though the communication link between the consumer and the service may be secure, this does not mean that the consumer trusts his/her communication party or their handling of the sensitive information which may have been transferred during the communication. Trust is an end-to-end relation.

Trust is a key element in privacy. Consumers must be able to trust both the devices and the services they are using. This means that acceptable methods of handling the collection, use and release of information are provided. A good way to achieve trust is by giving consumers control of their own information and letting them decide what, when and to whom their information can be released. Both security and privacy play a role in creating trust. Utilizing these methods will leverage existing businesses as well as enable new businesses which guarantee proper identity sharing.

Person-to-Person Communication

On the Mobile Internet, the phone number is not the only information available in person-to-person communication. Personal information (e.g., location and presence) may be available and many, more personally identifiable names and addresses (e.g., e-mail address), can be used. Therefore, it must be possible to choose what personal information is visible to others and in what circumstances.

In general, consumers want to be reachable through their mobile devices. The problem is that, in principle, everybody can contact you. So, from the privacy point of view, there is a need to control who can reach you. This can be done through restricting your visibility in public, meaning that your name is not listed in directory services, it is only visible to limited groups, or you can only be contacted with a nickname. In addition to restricting visibility, it is also possible to limit the methods of contact.

If visibility allows a connection to be made, the next privacy problem becomes what the opposing party can learn about you and what you can learn about him/her. A classic privacy problem of telephone connections, for both mobile and fixed, relates to presenting the phone number of the calling party. Phone numbers can be used to link consumers with other information (e.g., such as matching the number with a name through directory services). Numbers can also be used for telemarketing purposes. Delivery of the calling party number can usually be prevented, but this may cause a privacy problem for the called party: he does not know who is calling unless he answers the call, thus compromising his privacy. The phone number is also present in other mobile services like short messaging, and is used as an identifier when accessing Mobile Internet services.

Other Services

Consumer Perspective

Privacy is a major concern among consumers. Consumers feel that they have lost control of how their information is collected and used, and they would like to regain control of their own data. Consumers dislike automatic tracking of their activities and are opposed to the release of their data to third parties without their consent. Consumers are reluctant to provide personally identifiable information online. For example, the majority of Internet users have at some point of time refused to release information about themselves because of privacy fears. However, many consumers would be willing to provide information about themselves in exchange for some benefits, as long as they would be in control of how information about them is collected and used. Consumers usually prefer opt-in type of information collection to an opt-out process. Additionally, they are in favor of privacy policies which are easy to understand and which companies are committed to implement. Many consumers are also in favor of stricter legislation to protect their privacy.

What makes privacy difficult is that personal information is present in many Mobile Internet services. In order to get some personalized service a consumer must reveal something to the service provider. For example, location-based services are not possible without information regarding a consumer's location. Personalization by using mobile device capability profiles is also advantageous in the Mobile Internet, since services are used frequently, and devices have small displays and limited bandwidth connections. However, the device capability profile can be considered to be personal information if it can be linked to a consumer's identity.

Two key issues are often overlooked. Only a small part of the consumer's personal information is usually needed, and the actual identity is often not required. Thus by providing only the necessary information and applying anonymity towards the service provider, privacy can be achieved.

Business Perspective

The problem for the service provider is either that consumers will not use a service because of a privacy threat, or will give false information when asked for personal information. A service provider can improve the situation by clearly stating in their privacy policy how they handle personal information, by collecting only the necessary information and offering the possibility to use the service anonymously. After all, having a small amount of correct information to provide better service for customers is better than having huge amounts of false information.

An especially privacy-sensitive area is mobile advertising. Consumers do not want to receive information they are not interested in, nor do advertisers want to waste money on targeted advertising if the target is not interested. Proper handling of privacy is the answer to both these problems. Consumers should be able to select what kinds of advertising they want and when. Advertisers should know which consumers are willing to receive information, and also what kind of information they are interested in. Consumers can also be rewarded for revealing part of their personal information and for accepting advertisements, making them more likely to have a positive attitude towards advertising.

The advantage of anonymity for a consumer is that it reduces the risk of how the information is used because it cannot be connected to his identity. On the other hand, this creates a problem for service providers who would like to know as much as they can about their customers to enhance their services based on customer attributes (e.g., age or sex), to provide some benefits for regular customers, or even to provide targeted offerings or event advertising. A solution is to use a nickname or pseudonym provided by a trusted partner instead of full anonymity. The trusted partner between the consumer and the service provider maps the real identity to the pseudonym of the consumer, and provides assurance to the service provider that there is a real identity behind the pseudonym. If the consumer decides not to use the service any longer, the pseudonym can simply be deleted, removing all connections between the service provider and the consumer's real identity.

Privacy from the Consumer's Point of View

Personalization and Privacy

Privacy is strongly related to personalization. They are indeed two sides of the same coin. Personalization is a good thing: the service remembers me, its service fits my preferences and I have the overall feeling that the service is designed or tailored for me. But when it is too personal it becomes a privacy issue (e.g., the service reaches one when she does not want it to, it knows too much about her or it sells information about her without her knowledge).

As services become more and more personalized, privacy becomes more and more important. If a consumer can choose between two possibilities – be they services or any other products – with roughly the same richness of features but one providing better privacy than the other, the consumer will choose the first one. And because of the consumer's behavior, service providers will choose the more privacy-enabled infrastructure in order to serve customers better.

Privacy Threats

Uncontrolled use and distribution of personally identifiable information can easily lead to abuses. Unsolicited direct marketing, in the form of mealtime phone calls and spam e-mails, are common examples of the abuse of address information. Personally identifiable information can be abused even if the information is unreliable or inaccurate; the direct marketer has a low level of risk related to use of unproven address information. Common reasons for privacy becoming compromised are presented below:

o   **Traceability** – Consumer actions (online or physical) can be traced based on a unique piece of information (e.g., that is disclosed during the actions, e-mail address, name and home address or the Internet Protocol (IP) address of the consumer's device). Some companies are placing online advertisements on many Web sites, allowing them to trace consumers when moving across sites. Buying habits can be tracked when consumers present their loyalty program identifications, often linked to payment solutions used for each purchase.

o   **Linkability (Profile Cumulation)** – An identity includes a unique identifier. Observing the actions engaged in using that identifier, even if the actions are independent, a comprehensive profile of the consumer can be accumulated. An address (e.g., an IP address) may be utilized in lieu of an identifier for profile accumulation. For example, personal data entered to participate in a competition may be linked to the information collected on the browsing habits of the same consumer.

o   **Errors** – There is little guarantee that the data in all the various databases is accurate. Inaccurate data can lead to a variety of negative consequences, from loss of important rights or benefits to annoying mistakes and inability to achieve intended goals.

o   **Loss of Control** – Consumers most often have no control over what happens to the data that is personally identifiable to them.

o   **Identity Theft** – If authentication information (e.g., password or signature) gets out of the consumer's hands, other parties are able to act under the consumer's identity. This is an extremely serious threat against privacy.

In the digital networked environment, secure authenticated transactions often involve a certificate authority. It is a paradox that sophisticated privacy and security procedures introduce additional steps where personally identifiable information is stored and exchanged and thus represent further security risks. In addition to these threats, there are others:

o   **Non-Repudiable Evidence** – The digital signature of a transaction (by means of cryptographic techniques) will serve as evidence which cannot be denied later. Any such data can be added to the consumer's dossier; the data collected from self-signed statements which cannot be repudiated thus potentially adds to a cumulative profile of a consumer.

o   **Certificate Revocation Issues** – It is a regular task of certificate verifiers to check the revocation status of certificates. Either they must regularly download a digitally signed update of a Certificate Revocation List (CRL), or they must resort to an online certificate validation service. Since CRLs are distributed to all verifiers, and potentially to anyone who requests them, entities can collect data about key holders they have never communicated or transacted with.

o   **Openness of Key Servers** – Key servers are usually open to anyone, making it possible to match public keys with identity information, and these requests are usually not logged.

A particular set of issues is associated with systems based on a centralized database. The centralized database server, after checking the validity of the identity certificate, may use the identification of the consumer for indexing into different databases (e.g., to retrieve the date of birth of the person, or the marital status). There are many problems with this approach:

o   The server can use the identification of the consumer for purposes beyond what the consumer is aware or has authorized (e.g., it can look up information from other databases than what the service would require, or it can link the consumer's actions);

o   The databases can also monitor and accumulate the usage history of the consumer's data;

o   The data in the different databases are not guaranteed to be correct and up-to-date.

If privacy has been compromised, it can lead to unwanted consequences. A couple of examples are described below:

o   **Unsolicited Marketing (Spamming)** – The ability to reach consumers makes it possible to engage in unsolicited marketing at unwelcome locations, unwelcome times or concerning items and consumers do not need, do not want and do not like.

III

Visions

o **Discrimination** – Personally identifiable data can be used to discriminate between consumers. A typical example is direct marketing based on the income or net worth of the consumer group, for instance, based on membership data or consumption habits. Political, ethnic or religious affiliation is a piece of sensitive information which, when illegally abused, can lead to significant harmful consequences.

Eliminating Privacy Threats

It is in the consumer's interest that privacy threats are eliminated. There are many possible ways to do it, but we can distinguish between two main approaches:

o **Privacy technologies (hard methods)** – There are technical solutions that securely eliminate privacy threats, usually in a specific application domain. For example, non-transferable signatures eliminate the threat of non-repudiable evidence of digital signatures, or anonymous e-cash eliminates traceability and linkability in e-commerce. Consumers usually do not want to understand how the technology works; they are satisfied if it gives enough protection.

o **Privacy rules (soft methods)** – Not all privacy threats can be eliminated in a secure way by pure technologies. In many cases, consumer's attitudes towards privacy threats and violations are much more critical than the technologies themselves. For example, if the consumer gives his home address to a service for the sake of delivery, there is no secure way of preventing the service from giving out the information to a third party.

Information Handling Practices

Personal information is collected from many different sources using a variety of techniques. How this information is used is often stated in the privacy policies of the organization in question. Although commonly used by big organizations, privacy policies are not, however, generally mandatory. Additionally, privacy policies do not usually inform consumers about the information handling practices of information which the consumer has not explicitly provided.

Fair Information Practices are a widely accepted set of guidelines on how privacy should be handled, and can be summarized through eight key principles as follows:

(1) **Notice** – An organization must inform consumers about the purposes for which it collects and uses information about them, how to contact the organization with any inquiries or complaints, the types of third parties to which it discloses the information, and the choices and means the organization offers consumers for limiting its use and disclosure.

(2) **Choice (Opt-out / Opt-in)** – An organization must offer consumers the opportunity to choose whether their personal information is (a) to be disclosed to a third party, or (b) to be used for a purpose that is incompatible with the purpose(s) for which it was originally collected or subsequently authorized by the consumer. Consumers must be provided with clear and conspicuous, readily available and affordable mechanisms to exercise choice.

(3) **Opt out** basically means that a consumer must inform a company not to disclose information, and without doing so the information may be used freely. Opt-in means that a consumer must specifically choose to disclose information, and if this is not done, the information cannot be used.

(4) **Onward Transfer** – To disclose information to a third party, organizations must apply the Notice and Choice Principles.

(5) **Security** – Organizations creating, maintaining, using or disseminating personal information must take reasonable precautions to protect it from loss, misuse and unauthorized access, disclosure, alteration and destruction.

(6) **Data Integrity** – Consistent with the Principles, personal information must be relevant for the purposes for which it is to be used. An organization may not process personal information in a way that is incompatible with the purposes for which it has been collected or subsequently authorized by the consumer. To the extent necessary for these purposes, an organization should take reasonable steps to ensure that data is reliable for its intended use, accurate, complete and current.

(7) **Access** – Individuals must have access to their personal information held by an organization and be able to correct, amend or delete that information where it is inaccurate, except where the burden or expense of providing access would be disproportionate to the risks to the consumer's privacy in the case in question, or where the rights of persons other than the consumer would be violated.

(8) **Enforcement** – Effective privacy protection must include mechanisms for assuring compliance with the Principles, recourse for consumers who are affected by non-compliance with the Principles, and consequences for the organization when the Principles are not followed. Sanctions must be sufficiently rigorous to ensure compliance by organizations.

Laws and Self-Regulation

Comprehensive laws govern the collection, use and sharing of personal information by both the public and private sectors. An oversight body ensures compliance with the law.

Sectoral laws are laws that govern privacy in specific sectors (e.g., the financial, medical and telecommunication sectors). Sectoral laws can be used alone or to complement comprehensive legislation by providing more detailed protection for certain categories of information.

Self-regulation means that companies and industry bodies establish a set of recommended practices and carry out self-policing to make sure that the practices are followed. In the United States, privacy is mainly protected by the use of sectoral laws and self-regulation.

Note that consumer awareness also plays an important part in privacy protection. The consumer can do much to protect her privacy by carefully choosing the service provider and being cautious about what information is given out.

III
Visions

Context

In general, any action related to privacy is surrounded by circumstances or facts which have or should have an effect on how the action is performed. For example, a consumer may prefer not to be contacted by advertisements when sitting in a meeting, though might nevertheless let messages related to the project come through. The set of such circumstances is called context. Possible contextual information includes, e.g., location, work/private and meeting/indoor/outdoor/car.

Privacy from the System Designer's Point of View

Identity and Linking

Identity is a central notion of privacy. The primary meaning of the word is abstract: "the condition of being a specified person" [Oxford dictionary] or "the condition of being oneself ... and not another" [Macquarie dictionary]. In information technology, the word is also used to refer to a set of information about an entity which differentiates it from all other, similar entities [Clarke 1999]. The set of information may be as small as a single code, specifically designed as an identifier, or may be a compound of such data as given and family name, date-of-birth and postcode of residence.

Linking means establishing connection between data. In the context of privacy, it becomes important when the information about an entity gets linked to its identity (e.g., buying habits to name and address).

Definitions of Privacy

Based on the notions of identity and linking, an ideal definition of privacy can be given:

A system is privacy-enabled if no party is able to link data about a consumer to its identity or its other data, unless the consumer has explicitly allowed it.

The definition involves the following characteristics of such a system:

o   Enforcement by pure technology.

o   Opt-in always. *Gravity* attracts towards total anonymity: if consumers do not do anything special, they remain anonymous. This is in line with the natural attitude that consumers prefer not to reveal their identity unless there is a purpose for it

o   Consumers are in full control over the linkability of their data.

The above definition refers to an ideal point that might never be reached. First of all, it might prove technically unfeasible to provide enforcement of privacy in such a system. Nevertheless, it can serve as a *reference idea* to which real solutions can always be compared. A more practical definition can be given if pure privacy technology is accompanied by a privacy policy:

A system is privacy-enabled if no party is able to or has the right to link data about a consumer to its identity or its other data, unless the consumer has explicitly allowed it.

It is desirable to incorporate privacy technology wherever possible, and policies/rules are to be used to eliminate all remaining privacy threats which technology cannot address.

Nymity

Nymity is the extent to which identity information disclosed during a session or transaction is linked to the true identity of an entity. There are three nymity levels: verinymity, pseudonymity and anonymity. The word nymity most probably originates from Lance Detweiler [Detweiler 1995] and has been widely used in the privacy context. The words verinymity and verinym came into widespread use after Ian Goldberg used them in his Ph.D. thesis [Goldberg 2000].

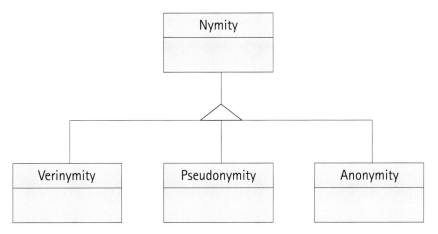

Structure of nymities

In the case of verinymity, a verinym is used. "By verinym or True Name we [...] mean any piece of identifying information that can single you out of a crowd of potential candidates. For example, a credit card number is a verinym. So can be a telephone number, or a street address. In the online world, an e-mail address or an IP address can also be considered a verinym" [Goldberg 2000]. A related notion is Personally Identifiable Information (PII). Of PII, we mean a collection of data that identify the person (e.g., name, home address, social security number and credit card number). In other words, PII is a collection of verinyms.

In the case of pseudonymity, a pseudonym is used. A pseudonym is a persistent fictitious name. It is unique enough so that the communicating party can be distinguished from other parties but does not contain enough information to get to the real person. A person can have several pseudonyms, establishing a different virtual person for different services. Persistency means that one pseudonym is typically used multiple times. On this basis, one party can remember the other party. Login names at free Internet storage providers are pseudonyms.

Finally in case of anonymity, no persistent name is used. An anonymous communicating party cannot be remembered. It is also known as unlinkable anonymity. Although some identifier has to be used to distinguish from other communicating parties, this identifier becomes meaningless after the communication session. In other words, a transient fictitious name is used. On application level, the distinguishing identifier is usually the session itself, whereas on lower levels a transient identifier is used, e.g., an ad hoc (anonymized) IP address.

Personalization and Profile

In order for a service to be personalized, it needs information about the consumer. This information is called the consumer profile. Profiles typically contain the following types of information:

o   Identification information (e.g., identifying numbers, names),

o   Contact Information (e.g., postal address, telephone number, e-mail address, Web site),

o   Demographics (e.g., gender, birth date, number of dependents, income level),

o   Activities (e.g., hobbies, occupations),

o   Interaction history (e.g., traces of sessions),

o   Payment information (e.g., accounts with financial institutions and credit cards), and

o   Preference information (either explicitly provided, or inferred from past behavior).

Separation of Identity and Profile

Because of the sensitivity of PII, it should be handled separately from the rest of the consumer information. Without disclosing her real identity, a consumer can disclose a relatively rich set of personal information so that service personalization becomes possible. For example, in order to get good restaurant suggestions, it is enough to give an anonymous profile of eating habits. From now on, profile means data without identity information.

Profile Disclosure

Disclosing a consumer's profile, or part of it, is an extremely critical operation. Special care must be taken with what part of the profile (e.g., to whom, for what purpose, for how long, with what usage rights) is given out. Techniques such as the authentication of the requestor, determination of the purpose and signing of legally binding (digital) contracts support profile disclosure.

An important thing to mention here is triangulation. It means that two or more harmless and independent profile disclosures can represent a privacy risk if they can be linked. Imagine, for example, that a consumer's postal zip code is disclosed in one session and birth date in another session. Neither of the two data elements, in itself, tells too much. But if one knows that they belong to the same consumer, the consumer's identity can be found out if there is a demography database at hand.

Another important thing to know is that a complicated enough profile, even if it does not contain direct identity data, is a pseudonym. That is, if a profile is individual enough, then it may serve as basis for linking. Because of this, special care has to be taken with what part of the profile is disclosed in a given situation.

Relation of Basic Notions

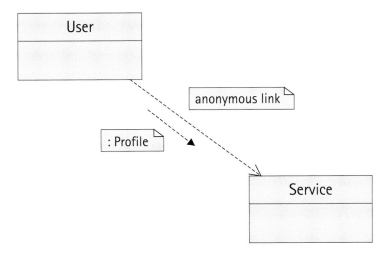

Relation of Basic Notions – Anonymous Connection

In the case of anonymity, there is only an anonymous link between the consumer and the service. The service is able to use a profile of the consumer only if the consumer sends it explicitly, as shown above.

In the case of verinymity and pseudonymity, the service is able to maintain and use a profile of the consumer, for the sake of tailoring itself for the personal needs of the consumer, based on the disclosed nym. The service establishes confidence towards the nym by means of authentication. Thinking in even more general terms, the service can rely on an external authenticator party when establishing confidence towards the nym. The map of basic notions then looks as shown in the following figure.

III

Visions

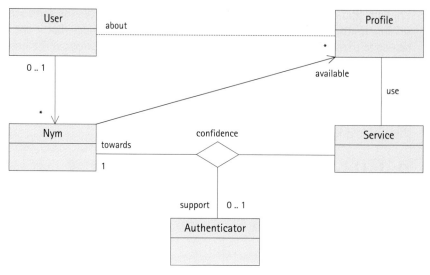

Relation of Basic Notions – General Picture

Practical Approaches to Privacy

Principle of Minimum Disclosure

Personalizing services requires personal information. But it should not require all the information about a consumer. Special care has to be taken when PII is disclosed for a service. In general, if no more information is disclosed about the consumer than what is absolutely necessary, maximum privacy can be maintained. This intuitive approach is called the principle of minimum disclosure.

Intuitive Privacy Model

Consumers should be provided an intuitive privacy model. They want to get privacy in a seamless way, and do not want to study complicated theories and principles. They need a couple of easily understandable options on their mobile devices or customization Web pages through which they can quickly set their privacy preferences. Opt-in and opt-out should both be possible, with opt-in being the default.

Consumers should also be able to define the terms related to the disclosure of personal information through the use of contracts. These digitally signed and legally binding contracts should define how the disclosed information might be used.

Building Blocks of a Privacy Enhancing Architecture

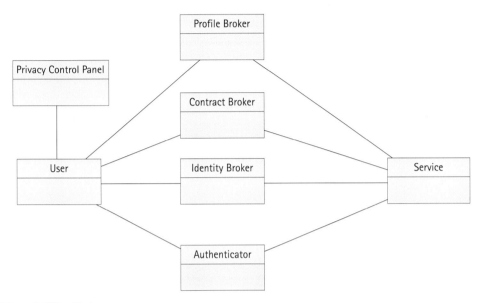

Privacy Building Blocks

Between the consumer and the service provider, the following functional elements can be separated from each other regarding privacy.

o **Identity Broker** – Consumers may or may not want to reveal their real identity to the service provider. In the case of anonymous or pseudonymous relations, an intermediate entity, the identity broker, hides the consumer's real identity so that it is not revealed. In the simplest case, the identity broker exists only conceptually and identity translation is done by the consumer himself. But real identity brokers can appear either in the terminal or on the network side. In the case of verinymity, the identity broker is not needed.

Note that identity translation (what the identity broker actually does) is related to various layers of the architecture. If identity translation is taking place on the Application layer, then at least the same or stronger translation should be done on lower layers, otherwise the lower level identifier may inadvertently reveal the identity of the consumer. On the Connectivity layer, it means IP address anonymization or call redirect.

o **Profile Broker** – Service providers get access to user profiles via profile brokers. The responsibility of the profile broker is to give access to consumer profiles in a controlled way.

o   **Disclosure Contract Broker** – This broker is strongly related to the profile broker. The contract broker is responsible, for example, for letting the consumer choose the privacy contract describing the terms related to the disclosure of a user profile and negotiating the contract terms with the receiving party.

o   **Authenticator** – The responsibility of the authenticator is to authenticate identity, i.e., to ensure a party that another party is really the one it claims to be.

o   **Privacy Control Panel** – Consumers should have full control over their privacy via setting privacy preferences by means of the privacy control panel. These preferences may/should include nymity related preferences, profile related preferences (e.g., what part of the profile the consumer intends to disclose to which service and for what purpose) and service related preferences (e.g., black/white lists of services).

More details on this topic and on possible architecture solutions can be found in the paper by Alamäki, et al. [Alamäki et al., 2002].

Privacy in MITA

Privacy is not an add-on feature. The whole technical architecture has to be designed with privacy in mind. Especially all parts where identity related information is involved are potential sources of privacy-problems. And the issue is not at all black-and-white, since more or less all information is, or may be, related to someone's identity. Also, privacy protection must be convenient to use. If any difficult configuration operations are required, consumers will not like it nor use it. Therefore, privacy functionality should be something that a consumer can rely on, meaning that she knows her privacy is being protected, and she is warned, informed and asked for further preferences when necessary.

Privacy in MITA covers all relevant principles, solutions and technologies related to consumers' privacy on the Mobile Internet. Privacy is not simply an Application layer feature: it has to be taken into consideration at all levels from the Platform layer to the Application layer. For this reason, privacy is strongly related to many of the other areas of MITA:

o   **Security**: privacy concerns are closely related to security concerns and are addressed by similar technologies and processes, including reliable access control and cryptographic techniques;

o   **Naming, Numbering and Addressing**: threats against privacy depend on the level of knowledge about the identities;

o   **Presence, Reachability and Location**: since the status, availability and location information is private;

o   **Access Independent Connectivity**: since Connectivity Identity handling, due to their strong links to real identity, pose significant risks from the privacy point of view;

o   **Rich Call, Browsing and Messaging**: consumer agent and preference profiles should be handled in a way that does not threaten consumer privacy;

o   **UI and Application Framework**: setting privacy preferences should be as simple and intuitive as possible for the consumer;

o **Internet Protocols**: Internet protocol information should be used in a privacy-aware way (e.g., taking care of what exact information is put into protocol headers and transmission packets).

Conclusions

The increased focus on consumer information collection, and the emergence of information aggregation businesses, have led to a situation where massive amounts of personal profile data are collected and stored in numerous databases. The individual, whose personal data is in these databases, has very little control over how the information is used or traded.

Privacy legislation is developing, but is still not sufficient in most parts of the world. Self-regulation efforts have proved to be ineffective due to lack of enforcement.

Technology development helps to automate information collection in a way that is often unnoticeable and intrusive to consumers' privacy. New wireless technologies and ubiquitous connectivity pose additional privacy threats. Mobile devices are highly personal: they contain unique identifiers (e.g., phone number, Bluetooth or IP address) and track location information. This information enables even more detailed consumer profiling in a manner that is invisible to consumers. These environments will commonly involve communication with a party who is unknown or not trusted.

As technology brings new threats to privacy, it can also be used to protect privacy. Several standardization and industry forums are defining better technological solutions for proper privacy handling. The challenge here is that the field of privacy protection technologies becomes too fragmented, or too difficult to use for a non-expert consumer. Therefore, the goal must be that a minimum number of technologies are used on the Mobile Internet, and the consumer interface for controlling them is simple and intuitive.

Company investment in privacy protection has been low, as companies have undervalued privacy issues. Internet services and vendors are, however, starting to experience the negative effects of consumers' concerns about privacy issues. More and more consumers are questioning companies' information collection practices, and are refusing to purchase online because they fear how their information is being used. Mobile Internet needs to trust providers, as most of the Internet services cannot be considered trusted. One natural choice for this is carriers.

As awareness of privacy issues increases among consumers, the pressure to maintain or build general trust rises for companies. Companies need to take consumers' privacy concerns seriously. Whoever is able to provide working solutions which give control of the collection and use of information to the consumer is likely to gain the trust of consumers in the Mobile Internet.

III

Visions

References

[Clarke 1999]

Roger Clarke: Identified, Anonymous and Pseudonymous Transactions: The Spectrum of Choice. http://www.anu.edu.au/people/Roger.Clarke/DV/UIPP99.html

[Detweiler 1995]

Lance Detweiler & The Theory of Nymity. http://www.geektimes.com/michael/culture/humor/items/Geekish/theoryOfNymity.html

[Goldberg 2000]

Ian Avrum Goldberg: A Pseudonymous Communications Infrastructure for the Internet. Ph.D. Thesis. http://www.isaac.cs.berkeley.edu/~iang/thesis-final.pdf

[Alamäki et al, 2002]

Tero Alamäki, Margareta Björksten, Péter Dornbach, Casper Gripenberg, Norbert Gyorbíró, Gábor Márton, Zoltán Németh, Timo Skyttä, Mikko Tarkiainen: Privacy Enhancing Service Architectures. Workshop on Privacy Enhancing Technologies (PET), San Francisco, USA, 14–15 April 2002. http://www.pet2002.org

Location Services

Location Services are an integral part of the Mobile Internet. Adding real time location information to traditional Internet applications gives a new dimension to mobile applications and adds value for consumer by improving their safety and productivity as well as the quality of the offered information.

After the positioning of a mobile device has become possible with the needed accuracy, the location information must be made available for applications through appropriate software or protocol interfaces. When these interfaces are public, the development of applications becomes more attractive, their number rises rapidly, and location services can achieve the critical mass they need to be highly popular. Also, if location information is easily available, many existing and new applications can become location aware. This means that location can be used to enhance most applications without the application being a strictly location-based application built around the location feature.

The consumer may access location services through applications residing in the mobile device or the server. Applications can be roughly divided into three different categories based on their relation to the mobile device, network services and the origin of the content presented through the application.

o   **Standalone mobile device applications** (e.g., a buddy list application capable of presenting the location of a selected buddy).

o   **Mobile device based applications utilizing content from the network** (e.g., a map or driving instruction service).

o   **Browser based location services** (e.g., weather forecast services that consumers can access with any browser).

Location Architecture

The Location architecture consists of software and protocol interfaces and the location service layer below the interfaces. Location interfaces are used by applications to access the location information. The location service layer is for delivering and/or enhancing location information and also for delivering assistance data.

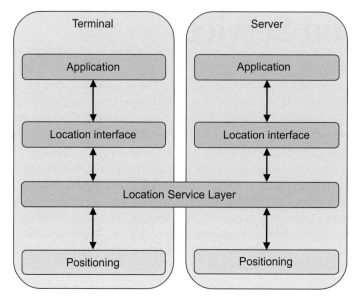

Location architecture

Location Service Layer

There are several technologies for determining mobile device position, and the important divider is whether they are network or mobile device centric. Saying that a method is *mobile device based* or *network based* refers to where the actual location calculation and determination takes place. In addition to pure network or mobile device based positioning methods, positioning can also be either mobile device or network assisted, meaning that the other party is providing the calculating party extra data to improve positioning accuracy.

Cell identity based positioning is a network centric solution. It is important because not all mobile devices can support sophisticated positioning technology. Device centric technologies (e.g., Global Positioning System (GPS)) enable more accurate positioning. Local positioning methods are methods based on location information from a network access point or even a beacon-like device telling its position to a mobile device. These are usually also mobile device centric. An important thing to notice is that different positioning technologies are complementary.

The location service layer hides the complexity and differences of any location system or positioning method from the applications, provides necessary connections between entities if positioning is a distributed functionality, and takes care of privacy. The location service layer also selects positioning methods according to availability, needed accuracy and price, and makes decisions based on user-defined preferences. The location service layer is presented in following figure.

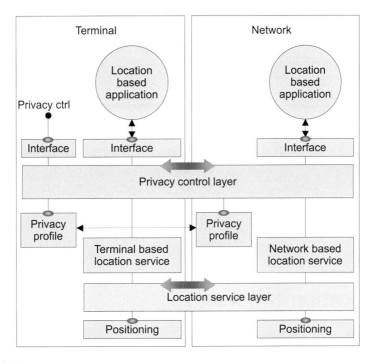

Location service layer

Providing Assistance Data for Positioning

If the selected positioning method requires assistance data, which is not already available through the positioning method, the data is provided through location service layer. As a practical example, in Enhanced Observed Time Difference (E-OTD) the assistance data is provided through GSM signaling.

Interfacing to a Privacy Controlling Entity

A consumer's privacy profile controls the availability of her location information and must be respected at all times. The only exceptions are emergency calls and special situations defined by the laws of different countries. An interface between a privacy controlling entity and location service layer is needed. This interface provides permission to give location information to an application and communicates restrictions (e.g., the accuracy of location, to the location service).

Transformation of Coordinate Data

If an application needs location information in a more advanced form than just coordinates, the location service layer takes care of transformation. A typical example of a more advanced form of location information is a street address, but it could also identify something meaningful only to the consumer and his/her friends, through a word like home, for instance.

Location Information Relaying

In addition to carrying assistance data or location information to be transformed, the location service layer can also perform a relay function just to make location information available in another environment than where it was originally available. Location information can be relayed when an application needs it, periodically, or when it changes.

The benefits of relaying are:

o   An application can always get location from one interface.

o   Location can be made available through software interfaces in program execution environments just like any other local resource. Therefore, it is easy to develop location based applications for any environment with no need for location service agreements.

o   If the application is not able to pay for location information or there is no agreement for payment between the application and the location service provider, the consumer may pay for it.

Location Interfaces

Location interfaces must be available in both the mobile device and network. The location interface supports at least two basic operations: location request and the delivery of location reply. These are further divided into different variations. In addition, there might be a possibility to query about the capabilities of the interface.

Location in MITA

In the MITA layered model in the next figure, location functionality is existent in location interfaces and the location services layer. A target for mobile location services architecture and interfaces is to be able to deliver location no matter what positioning technology is used and regardless of the division of functionality between terminal, network and servers.

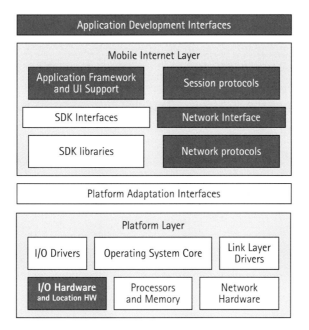

Location related subsystems in the MITA element

Naming, Numbering and Addressing

In MITA, the consumer can select which address format to use in peer-to-peer communication. Naming, Numbering and Addressing (NNA) translations serve applications, enabling application level communication between mobile devices and between a mobile device and a network application.

The consumer can use any naming formats independently of the communication mode. It is possible to send e-mails, instant messages and even to make voice calls with an e-mail address type of name or with an E.164 telephone number. If the consumer wants to use her personal phonebook entries or nicknames, the mobile device and the network automatically translate them to the suitable address format, according to the applications requirements for the address type.

For the consumer, the main benefit is a seamless user interface. Such service can be local in the mobile device address book or can be a dynamic link to the phonebook entry in the network user profile (dynamic phonebook).

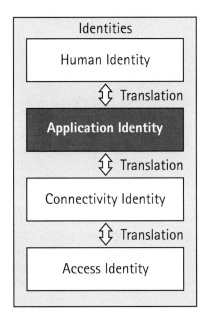

Scope of the NNA in the MITA Identities model

Name

A name is a mixture of characters used to identify someone or something (e.g., a person, a piece of equipment, an interface, a service, an application or a location). Characters used may include numbers, letters and signs. Functionally, a name is a different entity than an address, which identifies the specific termination points of a connection and is used for routing. Addresses are mandatory for communication, but names are not as essential. In some cases, names are increased to identify the end point more specifically or to provide external identification, which is out of the carrier networks. [UMTSforum]

There are two common naming schemes:

o   E.164 names (numerical strings) defined by ITU-T Recommendation. This scheme is a mixture of names and addresses. It started primarily as an addressing system but has become more of a naming system because location and carrier portability are functions of names rather than addresses. [E164]

o   Names of the form "user@domain" defined by RFC 1035 [RFC1035].

The customer usually has both the E.164 and e-mail format names of the called party in the address book of the mobile device. For this reason, the establishment of the connection usually starts automatically with the right address format. In some cases, however, full address information is not available and a translation in the network is needed.

The following identifiers can be regarded as names:

o   User@domain name idiom

o   www.nokia.com device address

o   John Doe in an electronic phone book (device or server)

Number

E.164 numbers are most commonly used in telecommunication networks to identify subscribers. In mobile networks the number is usually associated with the Subscriber Identity Module (SIM) card. In fixed telecommunication networks, the number identifies the fixed subscriber.

The E.164 number contains information about the consumer, network carrier/region and, optionally, the country. A number is not the user-friendliest way to identify a consumer because people find it hard to remember numbers. So instead, most devices are able to associate a more human readable name with the actual number. A number identifies the consumer more unambiguously than a name, however; there can be two people with the same name but their telephone numbers are most likely different.

Address

The address is the most fundamental piece of information, which must be known before any entity in any network can communicate and exchange data with another entity. Entity A must know the address (or "identifier" which in the end is resolved to the address) of entity B before establishing a connection between entities A and B.

The following identifiers can be regarded as addresses:

o   Internet Protocol address

o   User@domain

o   E.164 number

The address is usually associated with the device and in many cases it identifies the device to the network. Because a consumer may have more than one device, the address is not the best way to identify users unambiguously.

The Internet Protocol address is the address which identifies devices. In theory, every device has a unique Internet Protocol (IP) address. Based on these addresses the Internet Protocol stack then "knows" what address to use to route data packets to the receiver device.

In mobile networks, devices do not have a similar address compared to the Internet Protocol address used in data communication networks. Mobile devices have an International Mobile Station Equipment Identity (IMEI) identifier, which uniquely identifies the device, but this IMEI code is mainly used for security purposes.

The mobile network identifies consumers based on their SIM card and International Mobile Subscriber Identity (IMSI). IMSI is unique in the sense that every subscriber has a unique IMSI. A consumer may have more than one device but if the consumer wants to have only one IMSI identity a single SIM card must be used. IMSI also contains information about a consumer's country and carrier.

Naming, Numbering and Addressing concentrates on the names and addresses of individual people or devices and how names and addresses appear on the user interface of the mobile device. Nickname-type information, favored by customers, is translated into globally unique names and finally to routable addresses. Translations between globally unique names and the related directory infrastructure are thus part of the scope of Naming, Numbering and Addressing.

III

Visions

Naming, Numbering and Addressing in MITA

Naming, Numbering and Addressing protocols are Application protocols on the Application Layer as illustrated in the next figure.

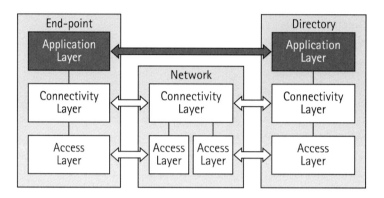

Naming, Numbering and Addressing protocols in the MITA Network model

Implementing NNA service addresses mainly sets requirements on the Internet protocol stack and its interfaces. In the terminal, the application framework should provide access to the local phonebook, as well.

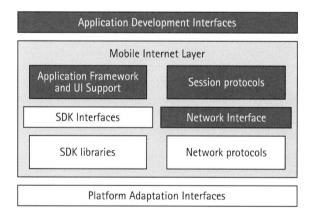

Positioning of Naming, Numbering and Addressing subsystems in the MITA Element

References

[RFC1035] P.V. Mockapetris; "Domain names - implementation and specification," RFC 1035; November 1987

[E164]   ITU-T Recommendation E.164 (International Public Telecommunication Numbering Plan).

[UMTSforum] Naming, Addressing & Identification issues for UMTS, UMTS forum report 2000, TG-NA 00(057)

Presence

It is believed that presence will be one of the key enablers in the future communication environment, and indeed may become so ubiquitous that the default way to start person-to-person communication will be to rely on presence information, especially in the Mobile domain. Moreover, it can also be used to enrich many other applications and services (e.g., gaming, mobile commerce and conferencing).

Presence - defined as "the consumer's willingness and ability to communicate" or "subscription to and notification of changes in the communications state of a consumer" - is already widely used in today's Internet. There are many variants of *buddy list* applications available on the market, mostly based on proprietary protocols. They are popular especially among certain user groups, such as college students or geographically distributed communities. In these applications, presence is usually used in conjunction with instant messaging.

This chapter covers presence from several angles. It first introduces the basic features and possibilities provided by presence from the consumer's perspective, focusing on the Mobile domain. Then, consumer privacy-related issues are discussed and some possible service scenarios are presented. Finally, we describe presence standardization for mobile networks, focusing on the Third Generation Partnership Project (3GPP) and Internet Engineering Task Force (IETF).

User Perspective

Mobile networks allow consumers to be reachable almost all over the globe at any time of day. However, a consumer's willingness and ability to communicate may vary. Willingness is mostly determined by the consumer's current situation (e.g., is she having lunch, at a meeting or on vacation). Ability is influenced by the same kinds of situations, for example, is the consumer driving a car. In addition, the capabilities of the devices and networks available for the consumer set limits on her ability to communicate.

In the current situation, a consumer has quite limited possibilities to describe his willingness and ability to communicate to the network or other consumers. This often leads to annoying situations and poor efficiency: consumers get phone calls or other communication requests at inappropriate times or places.

Presence protocols allow consumers to update their own willingness and ability to communicate to the network, along with other useful information. This does not have to be limited to a textual format, as visual content could also be included to make it more appealing. The presence update is done by the consumer's device(s), and possibly by collecting further information (e.g., geographical location information) from network elements. From the consumer's point of view the updates can be almost transparent, i.e., changing a profile from *general* to *in a meeting* in the device, or when the device notices that the consumer is for instance in a specific geographical location. One possible place to get presence-related information is the consumer's electronic calendar.

The published information is then available for various purposes. Presence protocols allow other consumers to fetch this information or even to subscribe to changes in it. This can be done through a contact list, where the consumer maintains a list of consumers whose presence s/he is constantly monitoring. Ad hoc fetches or subscriptions are obviously also possible (e.g., by selecting a consumer from the phonebook or some directory). Addressing should work with both telephone numbers and an e-mail type of addresses.

In the basic form, presence information might look like this:

```
<presentity> John Smith
<status> Not available
<note> Swimming, back at 10:30, send Short Message Service(SMS)
```

Whereas in an extended form, it could contain a huge amount of information:

```
<presentity> John Smith
<picture> Picture of John Smith (or Uniform Resource Locator (URL) of the
picture)
<personal info> URL to John Smith's Web pages
<general info>
  <status> Not available on-line
  <status logo> Personal logo describing the status
  <note> In a meeting
<geographical location>
  <position> Coordinates of the device John Smith is currently using
  <mapping> Helsinki, Finland
  <timezone> Greenwich Mean Time (GMT)+2
<voice>
  <status> not available
  <address1> sip:john.smith@company.com
  <address2> tel:123456
  <note> Will be diverted to voicemail
<voicemail>
  <status> available
  <address1> sip:john.smith-vm@company.com
  <address2> tel:1234567
<multimedia messaging>
  <status> available
  <address1> mms: john.smith@company.com
  <address2> tel:123456
<e-mail>
  <status> available
  <address> mailto:john.smith@company.com
  <note> Mail last read June 22, 2002, 16:38 GMT
```

In principle, the list of possible presence attributes is infinite, so the language used to describe them should be extensible. How the information is presented to the interested consumer (Watcher in presence terminology) is a consumer interface issue. In a mobile device with a small screen, some kind of compact form is needed, whereas in a laptop computer the presentation could be totally different. Typically, the consumer would be able to browse the presence of other consumers and see the overall status of all his friends or colleagues at a glance and be able to select a more informative view for individual persons. An example screen-shot of a prototype contact list application is shown in the following figure.

Screenshot of a contact list application prototype

The same information could also be parsed by applications with non-human interaction, for instance, having triggers for consumer location or availability.

Privacy Issues

There are obviously many privacy issues when publishing this kind of sensitive information on the network and for other consumers. For this purpose, a consumer who is publishing her presence information (*Presentity* in presence terminology) should be able to control the access rights to this information. In the simplest case, this would be maintaining a list of people who are allowed to it, though in a more advanced case there would be different levels of access for different groups, and even the same attributes might have different values for different Watchers.

The following figure shows a conceptual model of how to describe the rules for different levels of presence access. The presentity has defined a number of groups containing other consumers or other groups. He also has a number of *presence views*, each showing different levels of presence information. Then there is a policy document (or Access Control List), which defines the rights of the groups to the presence views. In this example, if a person belonging to Group 1 subscribes to presentity's presence information, the rules say that she is given the information in view 2. This type of authorization requires that Watchers are authenticated so their identities can be trusted.

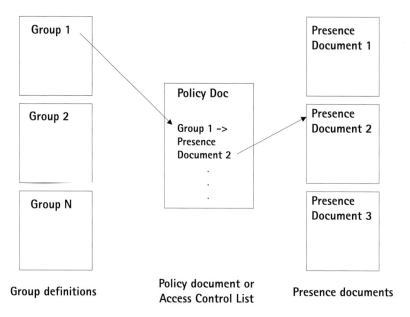

Conceptual model for presence authorization

It is clear that most consumers are not interested in managing complex authorization rules, so it is a major challenge for user interface designers and service providers to make the basic management simple and attractive enough so presence can break away from the niche application category to the mass market.

In theory, it is also possible to ask the presentity online to allow or deny subscriptions to her presence information. This obviously works only if the consumer is online and available to answer such requests, and may become too cumbersome in practice.

Service Scenarios

In addition to basic contact list presence applications, presence can be integrated into other services as well. Examples include:

o   **Presence-based session or request handling**: All the communication attempts to a consumer (e.g., phone calls or instant messages) can be intelligently handled based on presence information. For example, when a consumer is in a meeting, an incoming phone call could be diverted to an announcement server telling the caller that the consumer is in a meeting, and providing different options for the caller.

o **Presence-driven conferences:** Two- or multiparty conferences can be set up when it is suitable for all participants. The conference requestor can tell the conferencing server that s/he wants the conference to start when all the participants are available. The conferencing server can subscribe to the participants' presence and when all are indeed available, initiate the conference. It may even ask for a confirmation beforehand with an instant message.

o **Other presence triggers**: In addition to conferences, other actions might be also be triggered based on the consumer's presence status. Geographical location information is a good example. For instance, when a consumer enters a certain area, some announcements might be sent to him, or to some other consumer willing to follow the Presentity's location. Actually, it seems logical to make the access to geographical location information analogous to presence in general, providing major synergy benefits (e.g., solutions to privacy, authentication, charging and authorization issues). In addition, it is possible that the mobile device will learn from the radio access network some further attributes of its current location. This is extremely powerful with short-range radio technology, where the device location can be pinpointed even to a single room, whose properties can be then given to the device, and thus be part of the consumer's presence information. An example might be that Watchers can see that the Presentity is currently in a department store or a movie theatre.

o **Application- or community-specific presence**: A person might actually have several presence identities for different purposes. She might be a representative on various communities (e.g., her company or hobby club). Also, for example, network gaming servers might contain their own presence-like information telling who is available to play which games. The multi-identity issue can be solved in two ways: either all information is stored in a single server, or it is distributed to various domains. The latter option seems simpler and more scalable.

o **Local presence**: A specific instance of different presence identities is a scenario where for instance an airport provides its own presence service where all people at the airport can publish their presence and see who else is there. This way people can search for colleagues or friends at the same location.

Presence Standardization for Mobile Networks

Until now, presence systems have been mostly based on proprietary protocols, which has lead to market fragmentation. Also, the applicability domain of most current presence protocols is clearly in the legacy Internet. However, this should change in the future, when standardized solutions start appearing.

III Visions

There are two major standardization efforts relevant to mobile networks: the Wireless Village (WV) consortium and the Third Generation Partnership Project (3GPP). Both will have a major impact on the market, but their timing and scope are clearly different. WV has a shorter-term focus on bringing presence and other services (e.g., instant messaging) to mobile devices, making best use of currently available technologies. The 3GPP-based solution will be a longer-term goal unifying mobile presence with other applications (e.g., voice or video communication).

3GPP bases many of its specifications on the work done in the IETF. In IETF, the Session Initiation Protocol (SIP) appears to be the winning protocol unifying the different approaches into a single interoperable *Internet presence* framework. However, many solutions are needed beyond current IETF specifications, and the interworking among the different standards and proprietary protocols must be ensured as well. In mobile networks, the whole system is done on top of 3GPP IP Multimedia Subsystem (IMS), so other capabilities of IMS (e.g., session establishment and Subscriber Identity Module based authentication) can also be utilized.

Once the IMS-based presence service is in place, it will provide an excellent platform on which to develop further services. This would be to the advantage of consumers and carriers alike. Consumers could benefit from the ease of use, trustworthiness and reliability that the IMS carrier can provide, while also being able to use third party enhancements. Carriers would be able to combine presence with their other applications (e.g., voice, multimedia and location services) and in general would be able to offer their customers more value.

Presence in the 3GPP IP Multimedia Subsystem

A simplified architecture of a presence system, applicable to 3GPP IMS as well, is shown in the following figure. It includes a Presentity, a presence server keeping track of the Presentity's presence status, and a number of Watchers subscribing to the presence status. A protocol is needed for communication between these entities. The different sources in the figure could be different devices (the Presentity might have several) or network elements providing presence information. It is the responsibility of the presence server to integrate the information from several sources into actual presence documents.

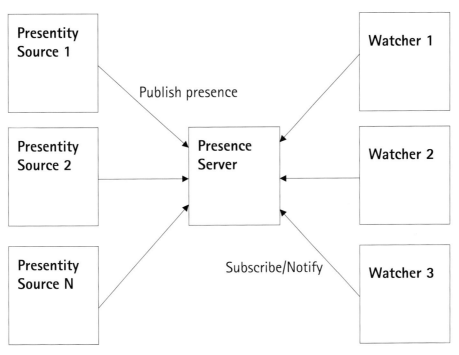

Simplified model of a presence system

The SIP for Instant Messaging and Presence Leveraging Extensions (SIMPLE) working group in the IETF has defined the basic set of mechanisms needed as building blocks for a complete presence service using the SIP protocol. The SIP has many features which make it suitable for presence subscriptions (e.g., a common addressing and routing model) as well as good extensibility and capability negotiation mechanisms. Since SIP is used for generic session setup anyway, there is also a clear synergy benefit to building things around a single protocol.

SIP provides the following presence-related functions:

o   Subscribing to presence information (one-time fetches also possible).

o   Getting notifications of changes in the Presentity's presence status.

o   Subscribing to and getting notifications about the Watchers making subscriptions to the Presentity's presence. This can be used for showing the consumer who is "watching" his presence, or even for online authorization purposes.

Many other functions, however, are needed in a presence system, which are beyond the scope of SIP applicability. These are mostly data update or manipulation, something for which the obvious solution is some form of a remote procedure call mechanism on top of HyperText Transfer Protocol (HTTP). The needed functions include:

o   Publishing of presence information.

o   Managing the authorization rules for presence. This includes managing the policy document and related groups. If online authorization is used, pushing decisions from the Presentity to the presence server is needed.

o   Other management functions.

A SIP- and HTTP-based presence service is a natural addition to IMS capabilities, requiring the addition of a presence server with SIP- and HTTP-interfaces, as well as presence extensions to the IMS device. The following figure shows a presence service as part of the IMS architecture from one carrier's point of view. In practice, each carrier has the network elements shown in the figure and they are interconnected to each other.

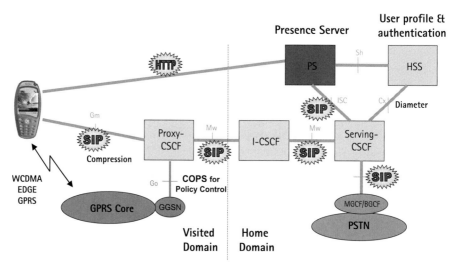

Presence service in the 3GPP IMS architecture

The Presence Server (PS) is connected to the consumer's Serving Call State Control Function (S-CSCF) elements, through which presence subscriptions from different Watchers are routed to PS. The PS sends notifications carrying the Presentity's presence status via S-CSCF to the Watchers as well. The Presentity uses the direct HTTP interface between his/her device and PS to publish his/her own presence information, and to do the previously mentioned management operations. The PS may in addition have interfaces for instance to the Location Information server, from where it learns the geographical location of the Presentity's device. A diagram of these various procedures is shown in the following figure.

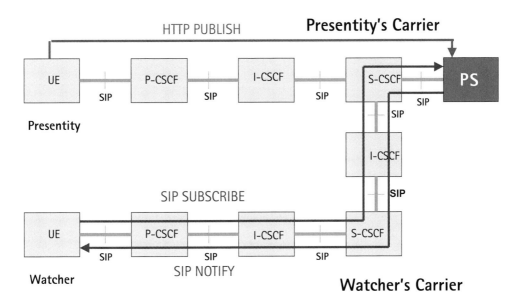

Presence subscription, notification and publishing in IMS

If the presence document to be carried in a notification message is very large, it can be passed to the Watcher's device as an HTTP Uniform Resource Locator (URL) reference, with which the Watcher can then fetch it with HTTP at a suitable time.

The benefits of using IMS include that most of the security and charging issues are already taken care of by the existing architecture. All authentication transactions in IMS utilize SIM cards, so consumers do not have to configure passwords or other security information themselves.

An IMS-based presence service should also include gateway functions between IMS presence, non-extended SIMPLE-based presence and Wireless Village-based presence. This allows consumers having different technologies to use presence services with each other, and ensures a smooth evolution path from the WV to an IMS-based solution.

Presence in MITA

Presence deals with the issues of providing dynamic information about the status and availability of consumers and mobile devices, as shown in the next figure. Presence is a Key system for a number of specifications.

III

Visions

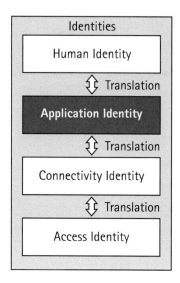

Scope of the Presence in MITA

The presence service utilizes application layer protocols (e.g., SIP). A terminal or other end point which would like to update the presence information interacts with the presence server as illustrated in the next figure:

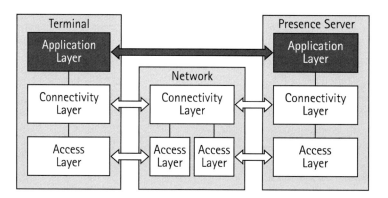

Presence service transaction between a terminal and a server

The Presence Specification identifies related protocols on the Session protocols layer and specifies subsystems and interfaces, which are needed for the presence service. The location of presence-related Subsystems in the MITA Elements is illustrated in the next figure:

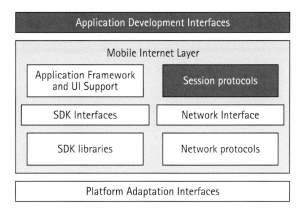

Location of the Presence Subsystems in the MITA Element

Conclusions

Presence is a powerful enabler for communication services. It can be offered as a standalone service in the form of a contact list application. It can also be used to enhance other services (e.g., conference setups). The biggest potential of presence will come when it is utilized in mobile devices which consumers carry with them constantly. Mobility and powerful mobile concepts will extend presence from simply being online with your Personal Computer (PC) to being a highly usable tool of self-expression and mobile awareness. The key for presence to succeed in the Mobile domain will be utility within mainstream mobile communication, excellent usability and support for rich and varied consumer needs, from managing your own availability to maintaining your relationships with others.

In order to get the most out of presence, a unified standard must be created. In the first phase, presence services in mobile networks will be based on Wireless Village specifications. In the longer term, the IETF SIP and 3GPP IP Multimedia Subsystem offer an excellent platform for designing a set of flexible and extensible presence enablers which can be utilized by applications. In addition to the SIP, other protocols (e.g., HTTP) are needed to achieve a complete and optimal presence solution.

III

Visions

Reachability

The reachability of mobile devices refers to issues related to how a mobile device or consumer will be reached through the network. In most cases, reachability can be addressed as device reachability because, after all, it cannot be known, if the consumer is available even if her mobile device is turned on and is online.

In the future, the Mobile Internet is a combination of networks (e.g., the IPv4 Internet, IPv4 Intranets, IPv6 Internet, carrier IPv6 network and gateways to Public Switched Telephone Network (PSTN)). Further diversity comes from the fact that these networks consist of multiple carrier and enterprise networks with strict rules on what traffic can pass the border routers and firewalls. Seamless mobile end-to-end connectivity over these fragmented networks is the target of MITA reachability.

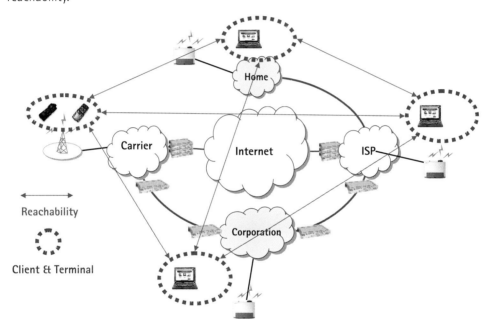

Landscape of reachability

When integrating telecommunication networks with the Internet or intranets, the main issue is to build gateways and routers, which convert the protocols used in telecommunication networks to be compatible with those used on the Internet and in intranets.

Functions

In terms of reachability, the main functions are in application functionality and protocols, but also in the infrastructure and gateways between different networks. Reachability mechanisms and technology must support the end-to-end architecture to be useful in practice. Another important issue in end-to-end functionality is simplicity and performance. Communicating over several networks and supporting different protocols is challenging enough without adding complicated functionality and processing. Application protocols must be robust enough to support various kinds of uses.

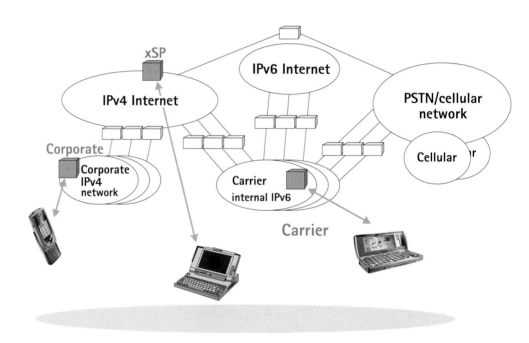

Identity ownership alternatives for reachability

It is necessary to know the identity of the calling party in order to link the reachability infrastructure to authentication and authorization services.

The Session Initiation Protocol (SIP) gateways between the Mobile and Web domains are the necessary building blocks for Reachability functionality.

Layered Model

Reachability and end-to-end connectivity belong in the MITA Mobile Internet layer. Applications need not be aware of the machinery when making a connection, for the only thing they need is the name or number of the endpoint in a format which is acceptable to the connecting endpoint and is converted in the network to a form which can be accepted by the connected endpoint.

The reachability infrastructure will offer applications the following services:

o   Finding the target for the caller

o   Forwarding the caller's name and basic personal information to the called party

o   Negotiating the type of connection between end-points

o   Reserving the necessary bandwidth between end-points

o   Establishing the connection

o   Maintaining the connection (status awareness, quality, flow synchronization)

o   Releasing the connection

The reachability layer also further negotiates some services with other Mobile Internet functions.

In MITA, Reachability provides address translation services for endpoints, from Application identity addresses to Connectivity identity addresses as illustrated in the figure below:

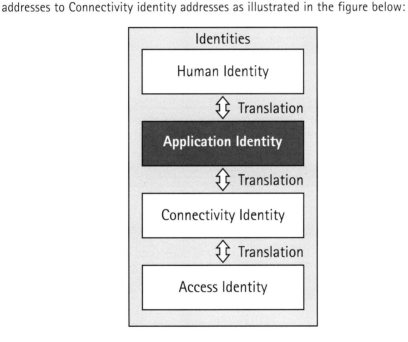

Scope of the Reachability Specification in MITA

Session establishment-related reachability services require interactions between end-points on both application and connectivity layers as shown in the next figure:

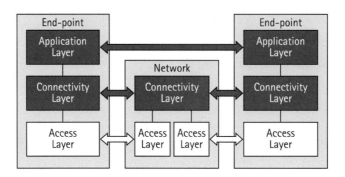

Scope of reachability in MITA network model

The reachability layer negotiates some services further on with other Mobile Internet functions (e.g., reserve bandwidth from Internet protocols). Reachability service provides comprehensive service interfaces towards applications, as illustrated in the following figure. All the complexity related to the Reachability service is hidden from applications.

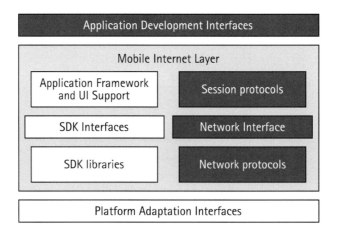

Location of reachability related Subsystems in the MITA Element

As described above, the Reachability Specification focuses on two primary functions: session establishment related address translations and session establishment support services between connecting end-points.

Access Independent Connectivity

Personal Subscriber Identity Module (SIM) and Wireless Identity Module (WIM) authenticated services are available from home, office and mobile networks. The personal smart card authenticated services are no longer available only through the mobile network, making roaming to several types of access networks possible.

Personal services are no longer simple narrow band services; broadband personal services have become possible and cost effective. The variety of access methods and the cost structure of the Internet as an access method make the personal services cost effective.

Access Independent Connectivity (AIC) deals with seamless access to personal services at the corporate premises, the carrier premises and in the Web domain.

Connectivity can be roughly divided into two categories:

o   Access Dependent Connectivity (connectivity and services are combined with access)

o   Access Independent Connectivity (connectivity is isolated from access)

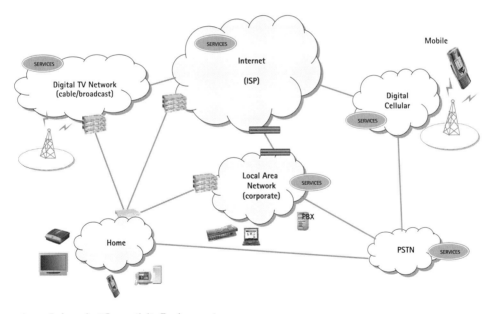

Access Independent Connectivity Environment

Connectivity

Access Independent Connectivity provides a subsystem for seamless service access, authenticating and authorizing personal services with the same identity as the mobility management or authentication, and separating authorization from mobility management. From the Mobile Internet point of view, this means that consumers must be able to establish connections from mobile devices to the servers in the Mobile and Web domains using the Internet Protocol (IP) as the main carrier protocol. The next figure illustrates Access Independent Connectivity from the service point of view.

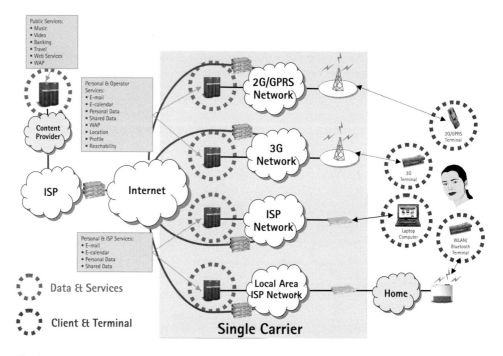

Service transparency

Function and Services

The main function of Access Independent Connectivity is to ensure fast and reliable Internet Protocol connections from the mobile device to the services and between mobile devices. In addition, AIC should execute mobility management, including:

o   Availability of personal services available independently of the type of access

o   Invisibility of mobility management to the application layer

o   Independence of the access network type

Because of the many services found in the Internet, no single device can support them all simultaneously. Therefore, the consumer must choose what services he/she wants to access, what functions she/he wants to use and what software she/he wants to install to the mobile device. If a device does not support the installation of external software, a basic set of functionality software must be provided by default.

If a consumer moves from one location to another or changes from one device to another, she/he must be able to seamlessly access same service.

Layered Model

The primary focus of AIC is to provide continuous connectivity for interconnected MITA end-points, as illustrated in the figure below.

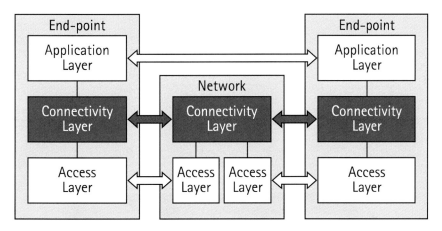

Scope of AIC in the MITA Network Model

The AIC Specification handles issues related to address translation from Connectivity identity addresses to Access identity addressing methods as illustrated in the following figure.

Identities

Human Identity

⇕ Translation

Application Identity

⇕ Translation

Connectivity Identity

⇕ Translation

Access Identity

Scope of the AIC in the MITA Identity Module

Access Independent Connectivity provides access independent mobility management for the connectivity layer. This means that the present definition influences all highlighted interfaces in the figure below.

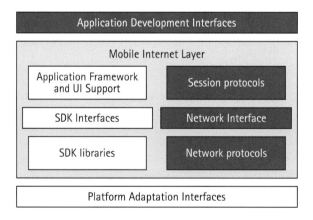

Scope of the Access Independent Connectivity in the MITA Element

PART 3.5

Frameworks

- o Security

- o Mobile Internet Interfaces

- o Quality of Service

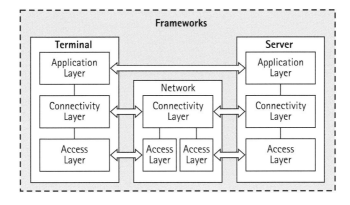

Security

Security is about safety and trust. Trust is an elemental part of communication and transactions, and without safety, it is hard to create trust between unseen entities. Therefore, it is important to understand that security creates requirements for all entities of the MITA. For example, security functionalities and features protect the consumer information from being revealed to someone or being altered when making an electronic monetary transaction, sending a message or during a call.

Objectives

The objectives of security in MITA are integrity, confidentiality, availability, authentication and authorization. In short these terms are defined in the table below

Integrity	Preventing erroneous and malicious modification of information.
Confidentiality	Preventing unauthorized disclosure of third party information.
Availability	Preventing unauthorized withholding of information or resources.
Authentication	Verifying that consumers are who they claim to be.
Authorization	Allowing only authorized consumers to access and use information, resources and services.

Framework

The MITA security framework has been divided into five categories: fundamentals, protocols, application enablers, applications and policies, as illustrated in the next figure.

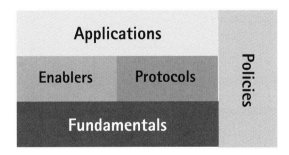

MITA Security Framework

Fundamentals are the basic components, and are essential for Mobile Internet security. System security has to be developed from the ground up and the fundamentals provide the basis for creating security functionality in the system.

Protocols relate to data transmission and moving content between end-points. Some of the security-related protocols protect the communication channel and fully transparent to applications, while others provide applications with visible security services.

Service enablers (e.g., authentication, payment and digital rights management) are the higher-level security framework services which are visible and provided to consumers by the applications. The service enablers utilize a set of fundamental security services and protocols to build up security critical functionality which is commonly needed by many applications. Thus, they typically hide the fundamentals and protocols from the application.

Applications use fundamentals, protocols and service enablers to create security functionality which a consumer can make use of. In most cases, applications make security visible to consumers by providing feedback on system security states.

Policies are a set of rules defining how the fundamentals, protocols, service enablers and applications must behave in order to maintain and enforce system security. If a party does not follow policies, it may be excluded from the system or some other punishment may be issued. Usually, the consequences of breaking a policy are stated in the policy itself.

The following figure illustrates the MITA security framework in more detail. The numbered elements are considered critical for the framework.

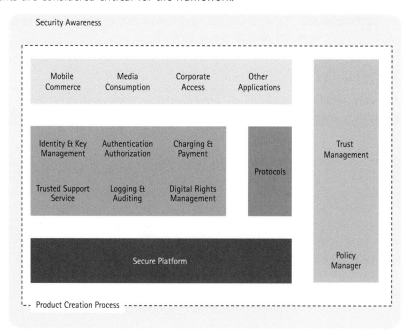

Elements of the MITA Security Framework

Framework Elements

Secure Platform

A secure platform offers the fundamental services and functionality necessary for secure end-to-end solutions. Many of these can be seen as mandatory or highly recommended features for both mobile devices and network elements (e.g., routers, radio network controllers, gateways and servers). A secure platform has been further divided into platform infrastructure and platform services.

Platform Infrastructure

Security services require a secure platform. Security services running on an insecure platform only direct attacks against the platform itself, bypassing any security that has been built into the security service. The secure platform infrastructure consists of components for intrusion detection, virus protection, device integrity, high availability and failure resistance.

The main building blocks of the secure platform infrastructure are hardware support, the system kernel and secure software installation. Some security services (e.g., confidential and secure storage) need to rely on hardware that is tamperproof. This may come in the form of a smart card or a bespoke application-specific integrated circuit. Securing user input and output may also require hardware assistance, as well as certain cryptographic operations (e.g., bulk encryption and random number generation). A system kernel can restrict access to specified resources, grant access to some resources only to certain processes and programs, and supply identifying information on processes and programs to the resources that they are using. These resources include the file system, interfaces offering security services, interprocess communication, network interfaces, memory, device drivers and consumers' data files. The secure software installation framework takes care of verifying installed software, assigning it a trust and capability level. The system kernel makes the access control decisions based on the information originally decided on during software installation.

Platform Services

Platform services are based on the secure platform infrastructure and provide both general and specialized security services for applications. A secure execution environment, trusted user interface and secure storage space are the fundamental components, and these in turn enable the security services of other components (e.g., crypto library and random source, trusted time and device identity).

A secure execution environment is the environment where the application software is run. Authentication results and authorization capabilities must be coupled in this execution environment, meaning that what software can do on the device should depend on what kind of origin authentication it has. Software for the device must be forced through one gate only, meaning that there must not be any way for software to run unless it has come through the proper software installation system. This is important in order to curb the distribution of viruses.

III Visions

The user interface is the first leg in the chain of communications between consumers. Therefore a device cannot claim end-to-end security without a trusted user interface. A trusted user interface can be split into two parts: trusted input (e.g. keyboard, pointing device, or any other user events from the consumer to the trusted target application) and trusted output (e.g., display for *what you see is what you should be seeing* from the trusted application to the consumer).

Secure storage is one of the main issues in secure platform services. Secure storage can be split into two different categories, each having a different set of requirements. First, there is integrity-protected and confidential storage for encrypted data that cannot be reproduced even by reverse engineering. The data is only given to the entity that originally stored the data. This storage type is used mostly for private and secret keys. Second, there is integrity-protected storage, where the data is not necessarily protected against reverse engineering, but its integrity can be guaranteed. Data could be given to the entity that stored the data, or possibly also to another entity which can produce a "receipt" given to the original storing entity. This kind of storage can be used for public keys, trusted certificates, trust parameters, integrity hash values of other integrity-protected components, policy databases, configuration information and logging.

A crypto library and random source offer cryptographic primitives to other programs. Cryptographic primitives can be roughly divided into the following categories: public key (asymmetric) cryptosystems, secret key (symmetric) cryptosystems, digital signature methods, key exchange algorithms, hash functions and keyed hashes, and random number generators. Cryptographic primitives are used by different applications and protocols to create security services. For example, a typical secure communications protocol utilizes a public key cryptosystem for peer authentication, a key exchange algorithm for negotiating the encryption key, a secret key cryptosystem for bulk data encryption, and hash functions and message authentication codes for integrity protection. A collection of a certain selection of key exchange, authentication, bulk encryption and hash algorithms is often called a cipher suite. Each communicating party has to support exactly the same cipher suite in order to interoperate. Therefore, the crypto library usually has to support multiple key exchange and bulk encryption algorithm choices.

Trusted time provides evidentiary data for parties relying on it when a certain transaction occurs, and the trust is always specific to the relying party. *Trusted* here means that (1) the time source, (2) the communications channel, and (3) the target device and its ability to make precision estimates are trusted.

Protocols

Security protocols are used to protect data transmission channels. MITA divides these Connectivity layer protocols into Session protocols, which provide visible services to applications and into Network protocols, which do their task without application intervention. Internet Protocol Security (IPSec) is a typical network protocol used today to protect the communication of all applications in the communication channel. On the other hand, a session protocol (e.g., transport layer security protocol), protects only the sessions and transactions of an application.

Another fundamental feature of the protocols is the data they are protecting. At least two different solutions are needed, one for store-and-forward type messaging communication and another for browsing communication. Transaction-based protocols protect separate messages. These are needed in store-and-forward-type messaging applications and also in applications where non-repudiation is needed. Store-and-forward type solutions do not allow negotiation of the parameters, so the whole solution must be based on pre-distributed information. Public key technology provides the most flexible solution (e.g., Pretty Good Privacy, (PGP) and Secure Multi-purpose Internet Mail Extensions (S/MIME)). The flexibility of the session-based security solution depends on:

1. the protocol layer where the security protocol is applied,

2. the possibility to separate authentication, authorization and key agreement,

3. the possibility to use different authentication methods to authenticate each end of the session, and

4. the possibility to provide single sign-on and integration to application authentication.

Identity and Key Management

Identity management is the registration and revocation of identities. Furthermore, it provides means to define roles for identities and compose groups to which multiple identities are attached. Identities can be defined for consumers, mobile devices, servers and services. One entity can have, and typically has, multiple identities whose level of official characteristics vary. For example, authorities can grant officially-approved identities (e.g., driver's licenses) while some virtual hobby clubs can leverage self-invented non-reality based identities.

Key management consists of the generation, storage, distribution, deletion, backing up, restoring and archiving of keys, along with key escrow and enrolment for certificates in accordance with a security policy. Key management defines tools to create, manage and use public, private and symmetric keys and other secrets needed by other security subsystems. Pre-distributed secrets create the initial trust between communicating entities. The main task of key management is to generate these secrets and deliver them to the entities.

Identity

Identity in the MITA security framework is defined as any set of parameters linking a human being, application, service, terminal or server device, network element or any virtual or physical object to those parameters. An identity is not usually permanent, but only valid for a certain time which is less than the lifetime of its holder. Also, the same identity may be linked to a different consumer or object over time. One of the parameters is always the identity's name, which uniquely separates it from others in its own name space.

When an identity is tightly linked to the certain consumer, verification of the consumer is needed before the identity can be granted and registered. In most countries, the police have the authority to grant and register official identities and certificates of the granted identity. By legislation, these official identities are respected by multiple institutions (e.g., banks, credit card companies, educational centers, the health care system, insurance companies and other institutions). Usually these institutions issue their own identities to their customers or employees, but trust in these identities is derived from official identities.

III

Visions

In many cases, it is not necessary to really know who the consumer is or what the system is, but only to separate different clients from each other. In these cases, pseudonyms (e.g., aliases or fictitious names) may be used. The key characteristic for a pseudonym is that normal users of the system cannot track the real life person behind the pseudonym, although persons with the required authority would be able to track the real person.

Real, bullet-proof anonymity is when there are no means to track the real identity of the consumer using the service. Of course, this would also make it impossible to provide that consumer with customized service. In practice, bullet-proof anonymity does not exist, but here *anonymous identity* is defined as a pseudonym which third parties can neither link to other identities of the consumer or to other sessions or transactions done by the identity. The purity of anonymity varies according to the degree of difficulty of linking the pseudonym to other identities of the principal by other principals.

The assurance level of an identity defines how the identity is initially registered. A legal identity is used for legal authorization (e.g., voting, entering a country, some forms of payment, imprisonment and taxation). Typically, the system authorized by government authorities is responsible for providing the link between a consumer and his/her legal identity. Trusted identity is a pseudonym or an identity which can reveal a legal identity if the person requesting the information has the appropriate authorization. A trusted party, responsible for providing the link between the trusted identity and a legal identity, issues it. Proclaimed identity is a pseudonym or an identity which does not easily reveal a legal identity. Providing the link between the proclaimed identity and the consumer or his legal identities is nobody's responsibility. Anonymous identity is a pseudonym, which third parties can neither link to the consumer's other identities or other sessions or transactions committed by the identity.

Roles and Groups

Typically rights are not granted to the identity directly, but instead to the role the identity holds for a particular time. A role is a virtual identity which can be attached to multiple identities of multiple entities. Roles have a set of parameters describing their characteristics (e.g., their rights). A group is a list of identities characterized by a certain role. The use of roles and groups essentially reduces the costs of rights management, as the characteristic can easily be granted to multiple identities.

Authentication and Authorization

Authentication

Authentication is the process of determining whether the identity of a principal, i.e., someone or something is, in fact, who or what it says it is. In some definitions, authentication is also considered to contain verification of the data's integrity. For example, in digitally-signed messages it is difficult to separate authenticity and integrity verification. In MITA, however, data integrity is handled separately.

Authentication is needed to build trust between the parties involved in communication or a transaction, for example when a contract is signed between parties represented by particular identities, a payment transaction is enforced, confidential information is disclosed or access to a limited resource is granted. In some cases, it is necessary to authenticate just one party to the transaction and in other cases it is necessary to ensure the authenticities of both parties. In other words, authentication can be defined as a method to build trust between identities.

Authentication is preceded by an action where the communicating party tells who it is. This action is called identification, which is more officially defined as a process of providing or acquiring a claim of one's identity.

Authentication mechanisms differ in the assurances they provide:

o   Some indicate that data was generated by the principal at some point in the past, a few indicate that the principal was present when the data was sent, and others indicate that the data received was freshly generated by the principal.

o   Mechanisms also differ in the number of verifiers: some support a single verifier while others support multiple verifiers.

o   A third difference is whether the mechanism supports non-repudiation, the ability of the verifier to prove that the recipient has actually received the message.

Authentication is needed in two contexts. Data source authentication assures that specific data originates from a specific endpoint, typically a consumer, host or application. End-point authentication provides assurance that the end-point is what or who it claims to be.

In end-point authentication, it is essential to separate consumer authentication and device authentication. In cases where no consumer input is required for an authentication credential to be used, the entity authenticated is primarily the device in which the secret is stored. If consumer input (e.g., typing a password) is needed before the secret can be accessed and sufficiently strong access controls exist for the system housing the credential, then there may be a strong binding between the authorized consumer and the credential. This same separation may be needed at the server end-point, too. The application and the physical server device are not logically one and the same entity. After successful authentication, integrity is needed to maintain the trust reached during the transaction or communication.

In data authentication, there has to be the means to prove who originally created the data packet, which can be a message, transaction record, payment or any valuable digital token or voucher. Typically, data authentication also has to function in an off-line situation when it is not possible or desirable for cost reasons to validate the authenticity of data from a trusted third party. A digital signature is the typical way of implementing data authentication.

Sign-On Levels

The sign-on enables a service to be personalized, improving the user experience. In a sign-on process, the consumer (or more accurately the identity) identifies and authenticates him/herself to the other party, which is typically a service, a computer system or some kind of access server, (e.g., a virtual private network gateway). The other party i.e. the destination system can reside either on the network or on the same physical device the consumer is using. Also, authorizing the consumer on the destination system is typically part of the process.

Single Sign-On (SSO) is a mechanism whereby a single action of user authentication and authorization can permit a consumer to access all computers and systems where he has access permission, without the need to authenticate explicitly to all systems. As a downside, the introduction of SSO increases the security risk: if the consumer loses his key to the SSO, anyone who gets hold of the key can access all of the consumer's systems. On the other hand, by increasing the usability of the security system, SSO reduces human error, a major component of systems failure. When designing the SSO, however, one has to carefully analyze how to keep the right balance between ease of use and security.

Since plain SSO does not take into account the requirements inherited from the need to respect privacy, MITA defines three levels of sign-on, which enable consumers to reach the appropriate privacy protection with the convenience of a single sign-on. When a consumer accesses the service for first time, she enters a procedure, which is called first-time-sign-on, also known as registration to the service. In the procedure the consumer selects an identity to be used with the service. The consumer can select a default pre-selected identity, select a previously created identity, create a new identity or use the service anonymously.

After the first time, the consumer can continue to use the first-time-sign-on method or pick either the conscious or seamless sign-on method for further service access. In a conscious sign-on, the consumer is aware that her identity and potentially some other consumer information is given to the service and she needs to explicitly confirm the operation (e.g., by pressing ok) when the identity to be disclosed is shown. Conscious sign-on requires successful registration (i.e., first-time-sign-on). Seamless sign-on is similar to conscious sign-on, but no confirmation is required, nor is the disclosure of the identity and consumer data indicated. A seamless sign-on is only possible from an identity provider with whom the consumer already has performed at least one conscious sign-on and at least one sign-on within the pre-defined time period. If the latest sign-on is older, then a new conscious sign-on must be performed.

Authorization

Authorization is the process of giving a particular identity permission to do or have something. In other words, the identity is granted credentials by the authorization process. These credentials describe what rights an entity holding the declared identity has in the system. Logically, authentication and authorization are separate processes, although they often seem to be combined: authorization is meaningless unless the identity to whom or to which a right is granted is authenticated. Authorization includes both setting up permissions and checking permissions when a consumer is trying to do or have something.

If somebody is authorized to do an action on someone's behalf, one must trust the other party. Authorization trust may be set between two end-points or between an end-point and a service. The trust relationship may be symmetric or asymmetric. Authorization trust is related to two or more parties and their interrelationships. Thus, trust cannot be created before knowing or contacting the other party. All parties can and must define beforehand a set of rules the other party must fulfill in order to allow the trust relationship to be formed. A trust relationship can be set up directly between the communicating entities or through a third party or a chain of third parties which the communicating entities trust. Note that the authorization trust relationship does not always need real identities, as pseudonyms are enough.

A trustworthy authorization system also requires that there are means to revoke the authorization if needed. One way to implement good enough revocation is to require the authorization to be refreshed regularly, or authorization can be granted for only a limited period of time.

Charging and Payment

Payment services enabler covers all payment-related systems and solutions, including local payment at point-of-sales, remote payment over the network, micro payments, electronic cash, support for debit and credit cards, and provides functionality to manage value transfers between consumers, service providers and merchants. Value transfers can be tied to a service or to goods which can be either tangible or intangible. In charging, there is always a pre-made charging agreement between the parties whereas in payment, each value transfer is treated as a separate contract. The payment service enabler provides many types of clearing methods, including pre-paid and post-paid accounts as well as debit cards and credit cards.

Payment

Payment describes the activity of funds intermediation between payers and payees, assisting in the purchase of goods and services without the direct exchange of cash. Payment services consist of financial networking between payers (e.g., consumers) and payees (e.g., merchants) using third-party accounts. Payment methods can be categorized as credit, debit, pre-paid and post-paid according to the third-party account used to settle the payment. Merchants and payment service providers offer a variety of payment methods, allowing service providers and consumers to conveniently choose their preferred method of payment. Using pre-paid and post-paid methods, payment service providers can extend the variety of methods beyond the traditional methods available at the point of sale.

Charging

Charging for next generation services requires the capability to analyze and measure a highly expanded range of parameters. In addition to duration, time and destination the ability to identify and evaluate the content element of a charging record is increasingly regarded as fundamental.

Security Issues in Charging

In the telecom-centric world, authentication has not traditionally been a significant issue for charging, as the source of charging data and charging/billing systems have invariably existed within the carrier's domain. However, scenarios to be supported in Mobile Internet charging may necessitate that charging record sources and charging systems be separated across the networks of different carriers and/or service providers. In real-time prepaid charging, it cannot always be assumed that the charging request is trusted as it may arise from a source outside the control of the carrier, who maintains the prepaid account/balance. Requirements will arise to authenticate both the supplier of the charging request and the consumer of the associated service.

III

Visions

Data Encryption

Encryption of usage records creates significant difficulties for charging systems wherever the encrypted data contains required parameters for price selection and rating. Security objectives (e.g., confidentiality, privacy) must be implemented without restricting the ability to create functional charging records.

Digital Rights Management

Content distribution has been traditionally based on the distribution of physical media such as Compact Discs (CDs). The physical form of the container and good penetration of copyright laws has made copying difficult enough so that profitable business has been possible. The Internet and digitalization of content, however, have enabled large-scale digital distribution, both legal and illegal. Rights owners and distributors need to respond to the new challenge by creating business models and technologies enabling digital media distribution through new distribution channels.

Digital Rights Management (DRM) can be described as concepts or technologies purposed to ensure the proper handling of media in digital media distribution. DRM is defined to be rule-based governance of content using well-known encryption algorithms and obfuscated tamper resistance. Digital rights management constitutes rules governing the usage of content as well as the usage of platform-provided content-encryption methods based on symmetric keys, key distribution using asymmetric keys and tamperproof storage.

In a typical DRM system, media or rights to a media are targeted so that only one or a specific list of devices can consume the media. Typically, this targeting operation is done on the server side after making sure that payment has been properly performed. Before such targeting, however, the system must make sure that the clients in question are going to handle the media as previously defined. Moreover, this need for a trust relationship between elements in the DRM system generates the need for system level trust management, typically implemented with cryptography technologies, key management and distribution technologies. Put simply, the DRM system should not give any information to a device that cannot be proven to be secure from the system point of view. Device authentication/authorization should be used to take care of this issue.

Trusted Support Service

The trusted support service is a collection of generic common security-oriented services and service enablers required by many applications and used in both devices and networks. Trusted network time, providing automatic time stamping of transactions, is a typical network service, needed for non-repudiation purposes (e.g., auctioning and billing claims). Personal trusted storage is an example of a trusted support service enabler in a mobile device, needed to store in a reliable and secure way any valuable consumer data (e.g., credit card information). Access to trusted storage is validated against required authorization. There is also a backup system to protect this valuable data against the physical failure or loss of the device. Remote access to the personal trusted storage is also validated against required authorization. These two enablers together form an end-to-end personal trusted environment with high mobility as well as high capacity.

Logging and Auditing

Logging and auditing are means to verify fulfillment of security on a regular basis. Logging services are used to prove non-repudiation of transactions by collecting information into logs for later examination. Logs, which are write-once type databases storing the most important actions committed in the system, can also be used to trace technical problems, find out the usage patterns of the system, clear up offences and as the basis for charging. Auditing examines the logged information for security enforcing purposes, and is the only means to detect security failures which do not include any functional changes in a system. Thus, any large-scale system must be audited in order to keep it secure over extended periods of time.

Applications

Mobile commerce, media consumption and corporate access are typical applications, which by nature are heavily related to security. Typical mobile commerce application areas are online and retail shopping, ticketing, auction, banking, stock trading and betting. Media consumption is an action where media is rendered (e.g., for display or play) by a consumer, most likely using a mobile device or some other personal device. Media consumption also covers functions like personal media storage management and media-related metadata handling and management, as well as the distribution of media to other consumers. Media consumption needs to take into account different kinds of protection and DRM technologies used in media distribution. Manageability is the key element in corporate access. Manageability includes a scalable management tool providing easy automatic deployment, updates and management of a large number of clients in order to be able to offer the most attractive user experience for consumers.

III Visions

Trust Management and Policy Manager

When two entities transfer sensitive information, a trust relationship is needed. Trust allows consumers to reasonably rely on the information or actions of another party. Trust can be divided into two main areas: authentication trust and authorization trust. Authentication is related to one entity, where the task is either to prove the identity of an entity or to prove that certain data has been sent by the entity. The authorization trust is related to two or more parties and their interrelationships. It is also related to the distribution of data or to actions done on behalf of the other party (e.g., controlling data distribution and billing). Privacy control is also a special case of authorization trust management.

Policies, which define the relationships that are allowed and which are not, are needed when creating the necessary trust relationships. These policies are typically in consumers' minds or in company policies. Even if trust is an intrinsic and subjective property, which may be propagated but not transferred, and is not transitive, it is possible to create distributed solutions which control trust and make it manageable.

Trust Management

Trust management is a systematic approach for managing security policies, credentials and trust relationships. A policy tells who is trusted to do what. Credentials delegate trust to somebody else. Ideally there would be a single policy, but in practice different parts of the policy come from different sources because of the delegation of authorization or different administrators for different services. Trust management is the umbrella on top of identity, authentication and authorization management binding them together. Since trust management-related information must also be distributed, trust management itself needs a management solution.

Authentication is related to one entity, and the task is either to prove the identity of that entity or to prove that certain data has been sent by the entity. Trust relationships can be set up directly between entities or through a third party or a chain of third parties which the communicating entities trust. Because authentication is related to only one entity, the trusted identity can be created before contacting or knowing the other communicating party and trust can therefore be managed by a single entity.

The Authorization trust is related to two or more parties and their interrelationships. Thus, the trust cannot be created before knowing or contacting the other party. All parties can and must define beforehand a set of rules the other party must fulfill in order to allow the trust relationship to be formed. The trust relationship can, again, be set up directly between the communicating entities or through a third party or a chain of third parties that the communicating entities trust. Note that the authorization trust relationship does not always need the identities to be trusted - it may be enough to know that the other party is the same as last time, even if you do not know who it is.

In order to keep management within reasonable limits, authorization trust shall be set directly between entities, without any trusted third party. Note that reliable authentication must be performed before creating authorization trust.

The most challenging phase of trust management is to create initial trust between entities. These entities must trust the identities as well as their capabilities to execute an agreed policy. Once this initial trust is in place, the trust relationship can be expanded according to the agreed policy. A single initial trust relationship can be expanded to cover different forms of authentication and authorization trusts, if allowed by the policy. When you deliver some information, this policy must also specify if the trusted party is allowed to distribute the information further or even sell it.

Initial trust creation means binding a business or personal agreement on an applied policy to some secret(s). The most typical example is a password shared by both entities. A more secure method is to use a random key that must be delivered in physical media because of the large amount of information. Such a key can also be a physical secure channel for information exchange. Creation of initial trust is the most critical phase of trust creation; therefore, both parties must verify the identity of the other party using the authentication methods of human society which are reliable enough for the intended use. Also, the shared secret must be passed over a reliable channel.

The trust relationship may be symmetric or asymmetric. Trust relationship creation may also be provided as a service (e.g., an end-point which delegates some service to care for certain areas of trust management). This may be related to the end-points at the same level (e.g., communication between end-points), or there may be a service broker which takes care of the trust management of consumers and services.

Trust is not automatically transitive. If A trusts B and B trusts C, it does not automatically mean that A trusts C – B must create a policy which enables A to trust C. In addition, if the trust is planned to be symmetric, a similar chain must be created in the opposite direction.

Policy Manager

The policy manager is the tool for managing and distributing policies and credentials. It can also be used to describe trust relationships and bind them to credentials. Trust relationship management cannot, in any case, be automated because it is related to business relationships. Using a systematic approach allows specification of a general language for writing policies and credentials as well as the implementation of a compliance checker to be called by applications. The language specifies actions which are operations affecting security, principals who can be authorized to perform these actions, policies defining the rules about how the principals are allowed to perform these actions, and credentials allowing entities to delegate authorization.

Product Creation Process

Providing security in products and systems is a process. One cannot just buy and introduce security into products. Every person who is involved in the development of a component of a system is responsible for ensuring that the component is bug free and does not open security holes in the system under any circumstances. In product development, security is not to be understood in terms like costs or revenues, but rather in terms of company culture, trust, reliability, sense of responsibility, consumer satisfaction and quality.

Security Awareness

Last, but not least, consumers must ensure that they are using the system's security features correctly. Consumers, as well as all other concerned parties (e.g., carriers, service and content providers), must be aware of all security-related issues, including risks and preventive actions.

The purpose of increased security awareness is to highlight the importance of creating the right atmosphere for driving down security risks. It is not about scaring consumers or complicating the creation of systems and services, but about providing information and tools on how to avoid common security vulnerabilities (e.g., denial of service, spoofing, impersonation, network eavesdropping, password account security, viruses and Trojan horses, insider breaches and social engineering).

One challenge is to address consumers' natural behavior to exaggerate the risks associated with things that happen infrequently or which they do not understand, and to underestimate the risk of things that happen frequently. Therefore, consumer devices and applications have to be designed so that consumers can always understand when and to whom they are giving critical information. Naturally, this also requires that the system is easy and convenient to use.

Security in MITA

Security is an essential element when enabling new services and applications on the Mobile Internet. For example, corporations and other organizations have to have reliable means to restrict access to their network and services; the market for consuming and especially producing digital content will not be born if copyrights cannot be respected; and when money, tickets and other valuable tokens are involved, one has to be extremely careful to prevent fakes and other crimes. Also, protecting communication, whatever it is, is important in many situations. All these and many other security needs are dealt with in the MITA security framework.

Applications and Service Enablers

Application programs use fundamentals and protocols to create security functionality a consumer can see. In most cases, applications make security visible to consumers by providing feedback on system security states. The applications and service enablers security category covers Application layer and Application framework security issues in the MITA element model as illustrated in the figure below.

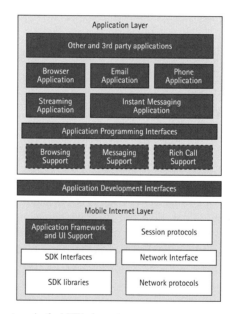

Application Security Subsystems in the MITA element

Protocols

Protocols relate to data transmission and access. The protocol security category covers Internet protocol security in the MITA element model as illustrated in the following figure.

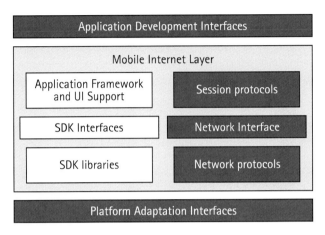

Protocol Security Subsystem in the MITA element

Fundamentals

Fundamentals are the basic components (e.g., encryption/decryption subsystem) of a device without which no security can be implemented. Device and system security has to be developed from the ground up and the fundamentals provide the basis for creating security functionality in the system as shown in the figure below.

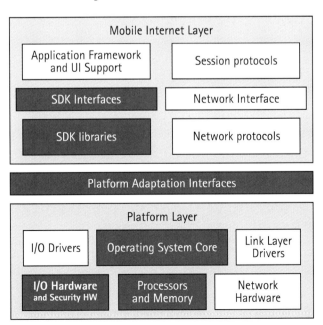

Fundamental Security related subsystems in the MITA element

Policies

If the fundamentals, protocols and applications are in place, it is a matter of policy to set the rules for how these technical components can and will be used to create and enforce system security. The importance of policies in the security landscape must be understood: in many cases it is 80% policy and 20% technology, which make security work.

Mobile Internet Interfaces

Industry generally evolves best in a business environment based on open standards and interfaces. Several vendors together can deploy parts of a system, which eventually offer new services for consumers. This is possible only when subsystem vendors agree upon subsystems and interfaces. Growth within the business environment can be boosted by forming standards and developing the maturity of subsystems and interfaces. This also enables a new development and integration paradigm, through which new services can be built by developing new subsystems that use existing subsystems as services. For the customer, this means rich and cost-effective service offered in the form of devices, services and applications.

Application development for the Mobile Internet, including service creation and integration, is maturing to the level where applications and services are built by using modular subsystems and are integrated by using open interfaces. The Mobile Internet Interfaces (MII) focuses on harmonizing and developing the maturity of interfaces and tools as well as on encouraging a high standard of identification of subsystems in the early phase of system development. The MII Framework introduces the MITA subsystem architecture and interface framework as well as processes for subsystem identification and interface evolution to open application programming interfaces.

Developer Communities

The Mobile Internet Interfaces Framework aims to be the tool for developers and service integrators to break down complexity by categorizing and harmonizing interfaces. Widely accepted interface guidelines directly benefit developer communities, but service integrators will also get their portion of the benefits. The wider the acceptance among developer communities that can be achieved, the easier the work of service integrators will be. This described evolution will be visible through the entire value chain. For example, carriers will be able to enjoy a rich offering of compatible service subsystems and a shorter time to service.

A few developer communities are listed below.

- o   C and C++ developers
- o   Application developers
- o   Java™ developer community
- o   Symbian™ developer community
- o   Forum Nokia developer community

In addition to these public communities, each company can have their own internal developer communities, which can produce new proposals to public communities. Most importantly, these internal developer communities will share the same interface guidelines as the public communities.

Developer communities are the channel for the interface work, but in finalizing the work, interface standardization is needed. The Java Community Process (JCP) is a good example of a successful interface standardization forum.

Modular Software Abstraction Levels

MITA emphasizes multi-vendor systems. Modularity is one of the ways to enable multi-vendor systems development. Several abstraction levels are needed to break down complexity to a manageable level. This chapter introduces and gives an idea of the positioning of the abstraction levels. In this abstraction the subsystem level offers open interfaces to application developers and system integrators.

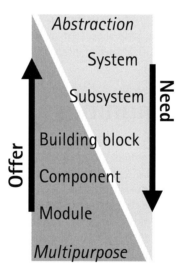

Software Abstraction Levels

The abstraction levels are illustrated in the figure above. The level of abstraction grows higher step by step from the Module level to the System level. In the same way, software modularity increases when moving from the System level down to the Module level.

System analysis is done step by step from the System Abstraction level to the Module level, whereas the lower abstraction levels function as enablers that are offered for building the next levels of functionalities. The higher the level, the less work is needed to deliver actual functionality.

There can also be different conceptual levels inside each described abstraction level. Inside the subsystem abstraction level, actual subsystems can be organized by using different conceptual levels.

A module is piece of code designed to implement the primitive functionality needed within specific features. Modules are typically sets of stateless functionality that can easily be used for different purposes and in different contexts. A module is tied to the programming language.

A component is a piece of code designed to offer the complete solution of some specific feature in a reusable manner. Components are typically state and session aware and allow simultaneous use by multiple peers. Components can be organized into a model which describes the characteristics and behavior of different component types. This model can be used to develop similar subsystems. A component is tied to the application framework and environment.

A building block is a group of components bundled together for easier management and distribution. The building block is tied to the application framework and environment.

A subsystem is a logical part of the system offering specified interfaces and functionality that can be used for system construction. A subsystem is typically able to offer complete service or a set of services to be used by other subsystems or applications. It is tied to the development environment.

A system is group of subsystems offering functionality for consumers, either directly or through some other systems. It is tied to the development environment.

The subsystem level focuses on interface functionality for external development and system integrators. From an evolutionary point of view, components grow into subsystems; i.e., natural necessary blocks of code can be offered to others to use as well, even though they were originally created for a different purpose. In some cases, a component can be even extended to the subsystem without any changes being made to it. That component can be published in a well-controlled way, and through the process described later in this framework. However, this nomination case requires that subsystem interface guidelines are used for component interface design, meaning, it is already designed like a subsystem. A modular architecture with a rich set of subsystems and well defined interfaces is an essential step on the path for Mobile Internet Interfaces. In MITA, all subsystem interfaces should follow the same framework and guidelines.

The MII framework focuses on the subsystem level. The purpose of introducing the other abstraction levels is to make it easier to understand the subsystem level, not to offer exact definitions of all levels and the relations between them. The following figure should be considered as the ideal example of relations between the levels.

III

Visions

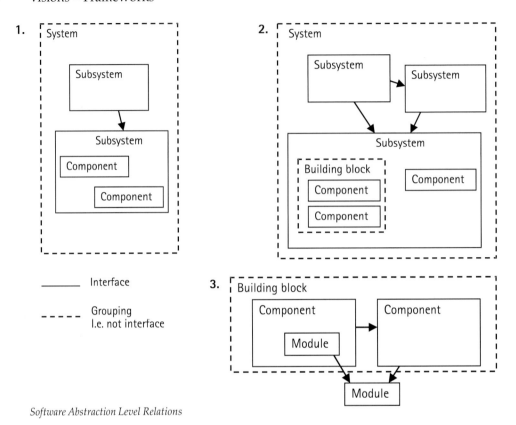

Software Abstraction Level Relations

The previous figure above describes the nature and groupings of the abstraction levels. All levels do not always offer physical interface, but exist for grouping and management purposes. The levels offering actual interfaces are the module, component and subsystem levels. The Module and the Component are implementation related levels whereas the Subsystem and the System are conceptual levels. From a developer's point of view, this model introduces three physical levels (module, component and subsystem) to deal with.

1. The system drawing at the top left corner of the figure illustrates, how the system consists of two subsystems where one is using another's services. The subsystem lower in the drawing is built by using two components, which may be used as part of other subsystems as well.

2. The system drawing at the top right corner of the figure illustrates a more complex system, where the same subsystem is used by two other subsystems. Obviously, interface design needs to take this into account. The building block is used to organize two components to be used as a one building block for several subsystems.

3. The last drawing at the bottom of the figure illustrates how primitive functionality is packaged to modules and used to build components. The module can be used to organize a component's functionality, like the module on the left, or to package primitive functionality to be used by several components, like the module between the components.

Applications can use basically all the services offered by subsystem interfaces in the previous three figures; the same interface may even be used by more than one subsystem at the same time. The application developer can decide which level of offered abstraction and functionality is best for an application by selecting the right subsystem from the hierarchy of possible subsystems.

Subsystem Architecture

The MITA Subsystem Architecture (SSA) offers an implementation view of technical architecture. MITA subsystems encapsulate a group of functionalities in the technical architecture to form independent, well-isolated subsystems. Generally, a primary requirement is that the implementation or implementation technology of any subsystem can be replaced with another implementation requiring a zero or minimum amount of modifications to other subsystems or applications that utilize the services of the replaced subsystem. This requirement makes it necessary for subsystems to have clear and well-defined interfaces. From the industry perspective, harmonized subsystem architecture is needed for analyses, definitions and interface harmonization on the practical level.

The Subsystem Architecture describes general elements in the technical architecture from the perspective of interface and application development. The SSA does not define the actual structure of subsystem internal implementation.

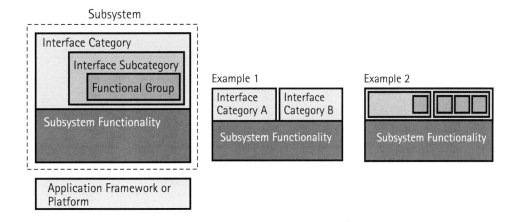

Subsystem Architecture illustration

Subsystem functionality in the figure above is an element illustrating the actual implementation and functionality of a subsystem.

The Subsystem implementation is divided into subsystem functionality and the subsystem interface. The subsystem interface is divided further into the interface category, the interface subcategory and functional groups.

III
Visions

The interface category is the top-level category of interfaces. These categories are created to organize different interfaces into different groups according to the nature and type of the interface.

The interface subcategory is the next level of the interface description. The interface subcategories are needed to make fine enough distinctions in the categorization of interfaces.

The last level of interface description is the functional group. The functional group level can be used to identify or create common functional groups between interfaces and interface categories.

These three levels make it easier to identify common functionality and fundamentals between interfaces and can make integrating new value added features to interfaces more straightforward.

The application framework or platform element are the basic services that environments can offer to subsystems. The application framework or platform element in the subsystem architecture focuses on gathering a common set of services offered to subsystems.

Interface Categories

There are two different approaches to categorizing interfaces. The first approach is to identify different types of interfaces. The Mobile Internet Interface categories are: Mobile Internet Software Interfaces (MSI) and Mobile Internet Protocol Interfaces (MPI).

The second approach is to look at interfaces based on their location in the MITA architecture. The location categorization is based on three identified segments. The location categories are: terminal, network and server.

The figure below describes the positioning of both these views and categories. Typically, protocol interfaces are located between entities, either in another segment or in the same segment.

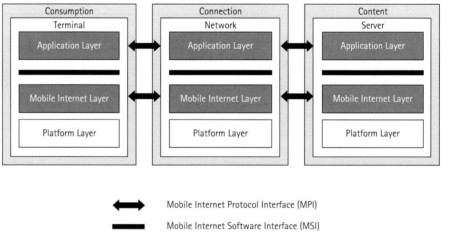

Category Positioning

In terminals, most of the open interfaces are software interfaces for application developers, whereas in servers, the open interfaces include both software and protocol interfaces, enabling fast and rich service implementation by system integrators and developers. In network elements, Mobile Internet Interfaces are mainly protocol interfaces enabling different MITA end-to-end views.

The figure below introduces a couple of typical subsystem types from the perspective of interface categories. The subsystem (1) is a typical compact subsystem on the terminal side. All the main categories of the open interfaces are present. This type of subsystem illustrates the case where standard functionality offered through MSI is mapped to a standard protocol used to connect to the network side. The subsystem type (2) provides operations between two different protocols. The subsystem (3) provides operations between the protocol based communication and the communication technology that is used between local software subsystems. Again, the operation can be simple mapping or an advanced service with information query. The subsystem type (4) illustrates the scenario where the service is built by integrating several existing services together to create one new subsystem. The subsystem type (5) is a subsystem used by an application developer to build a new service by reusing existing subsystems and services. The subsystem type (6) implements a so-called connector function. The connector subsystem enables the integration of legacy services with new services. These are not all of the possible types of subsystems, but are useful in providing an idea of the dynamics of the subsystem architecture.

III

Visions

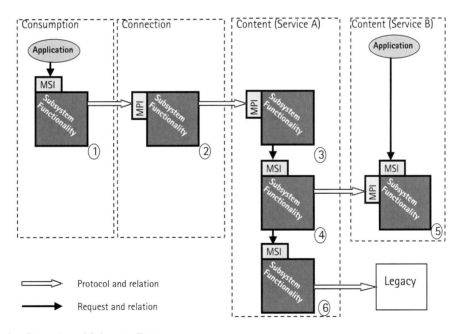

Interface Categories and Subsystem Types

Requirements

The general requirements and fundamentals that must be taken into account with all Mobile Internet Interfaces are listed below.

1. Interfaces shall allow an easy way to create applications and services. This shall be done by defining interfaces primarily from the application developer and service provider's perspective so that they are easy to learn and use.

2. Interface specifications shall be written so that they are independent from actual implementation technologies.

3. Interface logic shall be clear and straightforward so that the same semantics can be used even when an interface is implemented by using different technologies in different environments.

4. It shall be possible to implement adapters on interface implementations so that different implementation technologies can be used to access the interface. However, interfaces shall be defined in an implementation independent way nevertheless.

5. Interfaces shall be version aware. There can be several levels of intelligence with this characteristic of interfaces.

6. Interfaces shall hide implementation details and offer abstraction to the functionality, but shall not hide the functionality and capabilities available.

7. Interface and subsystem functionality shall be implementable on several different platforms (e.g., Symbian™, Linux® and Java).

8. Interface and related documentation shall be designed so that publishing and standardization will be possible.

9. Software Development Kit (SDK) development shall be possible for an interface and the implementation behind it.

10. Tool development shall be possible for an interface and the implementation behind it.

11. An interface shall be designed so that minimal changes to it will be needed in the further development of the subsystem and its functionality.

12. An interface and the functionality behind it shall be designed to allow multiple simultaneous customers.

13. Common error handling, configuration and parameter passing technologies shall be used.

14. Common interface opening and closing paradigms shall be preferred.

Mobile Internet Software Interfaces

Mobile Internet software interfaces are further divided into two interface subcategories, Application Programming Interfaces (APIs) and System Software Interfaces (SSI).

Application programming interfaces are designed for application developers to build value on top of the Mobile Internet layer. Subsystems (1) and (5) in the subsystem example figure offer application programming interfaces.

System Software Interfaces are designed for system integrators and subsystem developers to build the Mobile Internet layer for application developers and service providers.

Mobile Internet Protocol Interfaces

Mobile Internet protocol interfaces are further divided into two interface subcategories: Protocol Data Units (PDU), including protocol payload definitions, and content formats, describing presentation formats for the content.

It is assumed that all three MITA end-to-end views are supported in related MITA elements. All mandatory and most optional Internet protocols presented in MITA must be implemented.

In theory, any of the MITA Internet protocols as a whole, its PDU structures or payload formats, and/or the content formats that are carried in the payload can belong to Mobile Internet Protocol Interfaces.

General Interface Design Principles

Some valuable principles can be generally identified in interface design. These principles ensure better modularity and easier reuse later.

One-Way Dependencies

When a subsystem is communicating with another subsystem so that there is a client-server relation where the client is clearly the only active party, initiating communication and transactions, a one-way dependency exists between subsystems. The connection can be direct between the subsystems or organized by the application framework or execution environment services. The different ways to connect do not change the dependency relation.

For example, in the situation where two subsystems need to send information to each other based on events going to take a place during execution, the communication can be organized in one of two ways. One option is that both subsystems can act in server and client modes, which leads to the dependency described in the next chapter. Another option is to organize communication between subsystems so that there is a clear client-server relation; that is, through a question-answer or command-response communication originated by a client. Server originated communication from server to client can be implemented by using a notification mechanism where notifications are first requested by a subsystem acting in the client mode.

Addressing mechanisms and actual implementation need to be done so that a server type subsystem can work even if a client is not reachable.

One-way dependency as a design principle is clearly the most important factor in ensuring real working modularity and the reuse of subsystems.

III

Visions

Two-Way Dependencies

When two subsystems can communicate with each other so that both can initiate communication, a two-way dependency exists between the subsystems. In real implementations, both subsystems must exist before one can work properly. Two-way dependency is acceptable between subsystems in the same abstraction level when unavoidable or in cases when both subsystems need to exist anyway.

The risk in building two-way dependencies is that it breaks modularity, leading to situations where subsystems having this kind of relation are actually just part of the same subsystem. This is especially problematic between subsystems belonging to different abstraction levels because introducing two-way relations between the levels may confuse the abstraction model. In these cases, the definition of subsystems should be changed, so these separate subsystems can be handled as one interconnecting subsystem.

Some subsystems purposed to handle traditional communication protocols are an exception to this principle. A protocol, itself, can abstract subsystems from each other, and both subsystems are typically located at the same abstraction levels.

Notification

Notification is a mechanism to build flexible two-way communication between subsystems without breaking the one-way dependency principle. Notification is typically needed in situations where information or events are expected to come back at a later point in time. Both subsystems can be arranged to continue operating while awaiting notification. A notification mechanism can be implemented in many ways. It can be, for example, a message-based transaction or a so-called callback-function call, either made directly or over different remote call mechanisms. The essential point is that notification is requested in only one direction between subsystems, so the good one-way dependency principle is followed in notifications, too.

Firm and Solid Interface

An interface is considered firm and solid if most of the following criteria are fulfilled:

o   Not many changes are needed over time

o   There is not a way to confuse a subsystem through the interface

o   All functions follow the same procedure and logic

o   The interface clearly represents the functionality implemented by the subsystem

o   The subsystem can be improved without changing the interface

o   The interface does have minimum requirements for the deployment environment

o   The subsystem implementation technology can be changed without changing the interface.

When interfaces are firm and solid, subsystems can reach higher quality and stability. Applications and other subsystems using high quality subsystems are easier to test and integrate, and can also reach higher quality, which leads to better consumer satisfaction.

Data Types

The fewer the different data types, data formats and structures that are introduced with the subsystem, the better the interoperability that can be achieved and the easier the integration work will be between subsystems.

For example, some data structures can be split into basic data types, which can be updated by different sequential or single actions before an actual activation command.

When basic data types are used in different interfaces, they start to look and work similarly, making integration and tool development easier.

An object oriented approach should be preferred in data types regardless of the subsystem implementation technology.

Semantics

Actual implementation techniques and environments often define how interfaces are implemented. From a later reuse point of view, the most important factors are the actual logic and semantics used in interface design. A clear logical interface is always easier to integrate with a larger system because it is likely to work like similarly designed systems. Moreover, it is easy to implement adapters between different environments and implementation techniques if there is no need to change the logic of the interface. For example, the same sequence models and state charts can be followed in two different implementations of an interface even if the implementation technology is different.

Versioning

An interface version needs to be identified easily. All functionality on top of it is designed based on the feature set offered by the interface. Changes to the interface can affect the functionality built on top of it, requiring new testing for the rest of systems at the very least.

If an interface version needs to be read by other subsystems or if other subsystems need to be aware of it in some other way, the rest of the system can then be built to adapt correctly to the interface and different versions of it.

More flexibility can be offered if a subsystem can be implemented so that it can offer several different versions of the interface or environment and be able to host different versions of the subsystem.

Evolution Process

Although interfaces and subsystems can be designed for open purposes, usually open interfaces and subsystems evolve from the natural structuring of systems into smaller pieces. On the left-hand side of the following figure, the process P1 is focusing on producing high standard interfaces and subsystems to be used to implement needed system functionality. When an interface is realized to offer value as an open interface, the process P2, illustrated on the right hand side of the figure, is needed. Transforming subsystem interfaces into open subsystem interfaces is much easier if the same design guidelines are used from the beginning of interface design. Design guidelines for open subsystem interfaces should be possible for all subsystem interfaces.

This is a brief overview of the interface evolution process. At some point, a subsystem is identified and organized into a separate development activity. This process splits subsystem development into two different activities. Although the interface is clearly designed separately from actual subsystem development, it still takes lessons learned during subsystem development into account. There are two phases of review: first come workgroup reviews, which are followed by public reviews and standardization activities, although standardization can actually start during the workgroup review phase or even during system design as with the JCP. Here, standardization refers to the activities involved in finalizing a standard such as SDK and tool development based on managed releases of interface versions. The same vendor that offers a subsystem typically offers the SDK. In addition, on SDK can include various sets of tools as well. A tool vendor, who is usually not the same as the subsystem vendor, typically offers tools as shown in the process. Tools are typically offered to be used with standard or high volume interfaces and functionality. Even so, the process is used only for open interface development; a reference implementation of the actual subsystem is needed for quality purposes. Subsystem development can be done for specific purposes only, as a reference implementation for community purposes, or as a commercial product. In the case of commercial products, interoperability tests are essential. The value of the end results can be guaranteed by ensuring high quality interface design guidelines. Guidelines are developed based on input gathered from each point of the process.

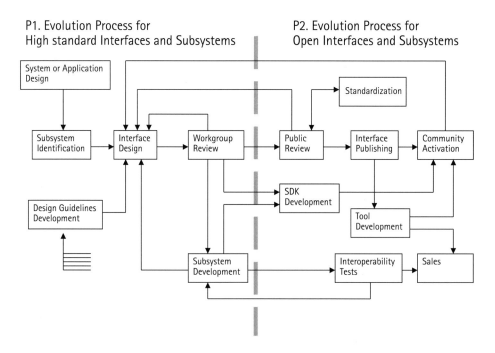

Interface Evolution Process

Quality of Service

Evolution Towards Quality of Service on the Internet

The origin of Internet Protocol (IP) is in computer communication. The basic idea of the Internet was to connect existing computer networks rather than to build a new one. The result was a best effort forwarding service for packets, rather than a connection-oriented service with well-defined quantity and quality characteristics. There were three main reasons behind this focal selection. First, the networking environment was so diverse that it was not reasonable to assume that all networks could meet any complicated quality or quantity requirements. Second, the very nature of the service was cooperation between organizations rather than a commercial service for consumers with readiness to pay for specific services. Third, the main need for communication was data communication between computers without any strict quality or quantity requirements.

Now, 30 years after the original considerations, it is evident that the decisions related to the fundamental characteristics of the Internet protocol were very successful. Further, it is amazing how well the simple principles of IP have met the changing needs of communication services - or at least no other networking technology has been more successful. The diversity of networking technologies is even more prominent nowadays due to increased mobility and new wireless access technologies. In contrast, the cooperative service model is not generally valid anymore, and various new applications with different requirements try to exploit the transmission capacity of IP networks. In particular, from the traditional telecommunication perspective it is difficult to believe and accept the fact that best effort technology can be used as a basis for serious commercial services. Moreover, the adaptability of many applications to varying conditions has proved to be better than what the designers of traditional telecommunication services have assumed.

Still, there is pressure to change the characteristics of IP in the direction of a more controlled service, because of changes in the service models and application requirements. In addition, wireless access appears to bring the need to control the sharing of resources more thoroughly than in fixed networks. Integrated Services, Differentiated Services and Multi-Protocol Label Switching (MPLS) have tried to provide tools to make IP technology more suitable for different business models and for different applications. So far, all these efforts have had only a limited effect despite the vast specification work. One reason for the lack of success is that any significant addition to the best effort model endangers the fluency of traffic between different network domains. This is a very serious risk if we remember that interoperation is the original goal of IP technology and that the main strength of the Internet is truly global coverage. Therefore, we must be very careful when designing new features even if some needs, such as improved quality of service seem to be of great importance.

Fundamental Objectives for Quality of Service

This chapter addresses the question of how a carrier should approach the Quality of Service (QoS) issue. The starting point here is the set of profound changes in the use of IP technology itself. The roles of carriers, service providers and customers are considerably different than they were twenty years ago. Actually, at the early stage of IP networks there were hardly any carriers, service providers or customers, but only a number of users and some operational personnel to manage the network. Furthermore, these changes are and should be reflected on the level of applications, flows and packets in order to be really effective. The vital question is, what will the relationship be between, on the one hand, the changing roles of service providers and consumers, and on the other hand, the treatment of flows and packets inside the network.

Let's consider this issue by defining the basic objectives for a QoS system on four levels:

1. Support the mission of the service provider or carrier

2. Serve the principal needs of consumers

3. Meet the quantity and quality requirements of applications

4. Transmit as many packets as possible

The fundamental assumption is that when defining the actions of the network, a hierarchical structure is formed where the first objective is the most important and the last objective is the least important. Each service provider may define their mission in whatever terms and all other objectives will be considered in light of that mission. In communication services, the mission most probably includes an objective to serve the needs of consumers. It should be stressed that when the needs of different consumers are conflicting, we have to look at the upper level in the hierarchy (i.e., the mission of the service provider) instead of a lower level (i.e., the applications requirements) in order to solve the conflict.

Correspondingly, if after solving conflicts between consumers there still are conflicts between different flows serving different applications, we have to look primarily at the needs of each consumer rather than trying to maximize the use of network resources. In this sense, the hierarchy appears to be imperative and universally applicable. If and only if the service provider explicitly states that the importance ordering of the objectives is different than the one described above, the structure of the hierarchy could be different. That may also mean that one (or two) of the requirements is ignored completely, for instance, because individual consumers cannot be distinguished in all parts of the network.

From this perspective, QoS is more about the mission of the service provider, that is, typically business, than the fulfillment of the special requirements of applications.

In order to meet the objectives set for QoS, the carrier has to proceed in phases:

1. Define the fundamental mission of the network operation as clearly as possible

2. Design an appropriate service model including billing

3. Build an appropriate network with enough capacity and a suitable management system

4. Use suitable mechanisms for differentiation between the packets, flows and consumers of the network operation

5. Offer additional information to consumers for adapting to varying network conditions

These phases also form a hierarchical structure. Without an explicit mission statement, all other phases of the project are vulnerable. Without a service model, it is very difficult to determine the needs for forwarding capacity and a management system. Most importantly, no QoS mechanism can rescue the service provider if the network does not have enough capacity. Differentiation mechanisms are reasonable only within an appropriate service model, and they serve the fundamental objectives set for the service model, but their ability to improve the situation in the case of insufficient capacity is limited. Finally, the service provider may decide to offer additional information about network conditions to consumers. However, this information is meaningful only if all preceding phases have been successfully implemented and any mechanisms related to the additional information do not disrupt the function of the overall service model.

In general, it is extremely important to be careful when adding new features. A widely adopted approach in IP is that the service model is based purely on the best effort principle and on sufficient capacity inside the network to transmit almost all packets. In this case, the last two phases can mostly be ignored. This alternative should always be seriously considered when more complicated systems are developed.

Realization of Quality of Service

Let us assume that a carrier wants to design a QoS system by using the results of the previous discussion. First, the carrier defines its mission to be the maximization of revenue. The service model consists of a high quality voice service over an IP network with time-dependent billing (e.g., 0.1 euros/min) and Web browsing and e-mail services for residential consumers with two flat rates (e.g., 10 euros/month and 30 euros/month (phase 2)). This implies that the service provider needs to dimension the network according to the expected number of simultaneous voice consumers plus some extra bandwidth for data services (phase 3). Further, the carrier decides not to provide any specific information about the state of the network (phase 5).

Consequently, the main issue to be addressed is the type of service differentiation rules and mechanisms which need to be implemented in order to realize the service model and to fulfill the mission (phase 4). In order to ensure that consumers are kept satisfied with the voice service, and that there is an appropriate incentive for consumers to pay extra for improved data services, the following two rules seem practical:

1. To give preference for voice flows over data flows, but only on the condition that the amount of resources used by each voice connection is strictly limited.

2. To give preference for consumers who have paid more when dividing resources among data connections.

The exact way to accomplish these tasks by means of technical mechanisms is an important issue but even this is secondary when compared to the service provider's mission and overall service model. Before going into the technical details of the implementation, we have to identify the most probable missions and service models in order to have better knowledge about the requirements set for the differentiation mechanisms.

For the sake of simplicity, let us assume that the business part of a service provider's mission is to maximize revenue, although we should also note that the target of maximization could be something other than money.

The main characteristics of a typical service provision system are:

1. Each customer has a value for the service provider. The value depends on the price paid by the consumer. In addition to a flat rate, the price may include a time-dependent or volume-based component related to some specific service elements.

2. Each consumer "owns" a number of flows, each of them consuming a certain amount of network resources.

3. The total value of the consumer is divided, according to some principle, among all the flows or packets owned by the consumer.

4. The value of each flow or packet defines how the network shall treat the flows or packets. Particularly, every flow or packet with high value shall be favored over other flows or packets with lower value.

The system forms a value chain illustrated in the following figure:

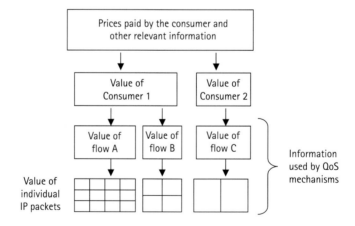

Value chain from charging information down to the value of IP packets

If these principles are implemented in an appropriate way, the most essential part of a service provider's objectives is likely to be satisfied. In order to accomplish this, there must be a clear link between consumer value and flow handling and/or packet marking in a way that all network elements are able to make reasonable decisions. Thus, the most important characteristics of differentiation mechanisms are:

1. Necessary information about consumer relationship, most notably billing and on-going traffic processes, shall be gathered and further processed in a way that the resultant data can be used by QoS mechanisms. Particularly, the data must have clear indication of the business value or importance of all flows and packets.

2. The network must have means to transmit the gathered and processed information through the network to all network elements making QoS decisions. Information may include signaling messages related to establishing new flows and specific bits in the IP packet header.

3. Network elements must have tools to make efficient discarding decisions. The business value of a flow defines its relative value when the network elements make a decision to either accept or discard entire flows. Correspondingly, the value of each packet determines whether or not it should be discarded during a congestion situation.

These are the main needs that IP technology encounters in a changing business environment and a changing relationship between consumers and service providers.

The Role of Applications in the Quality of Service System

The previous section addressed the issue of the changing business environment and its effect on the QoS system. Another part of the fundamental change in IP technology pertains to applications. Certain applications, most notably voice, have requirements that cannot always be fulfilled in a best effort network with a high utilization factor. The problems are related to transmission delay and packet loss in the end-to-end service. To understand the relationship between these characteristics and the best effort principle, we have to consider the protocol that is used to control the traffic load in IP networks, that is, Transmission Control Protocol (TCP). The basic principle of TCP is illustrated in the following figure. When a traffic source using TCP notices that one or several packets are lost, it rapidly decreases the bit rate, and then gradually increases the rate when no packet loss is observed. Thus, the load level on each link does not permanently exceed the capacity of the link and an excessive amount of re-sent packets do not overload the network. However, on a bottleneck link several percent of the packets can be lost even during normal operating conditions. In addition, viable functioning of the system requires that the network nodes are able to buffer a sufficient number of packets, which may result in a large delay variation. Consequently, both delay and packet loss characteristics of a best effort IP network are not good enough for some critical applications.

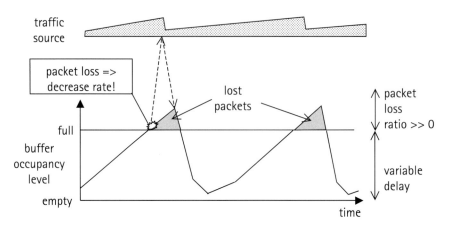

Principle of TCP control and its effect on QoS

Despite this apparent defect in IP, we have to be careful with the practical consequences. First, even though the functioning of applications is an important issue, dividing of resources is primarily a business issue. Second, almost any application can be designed to adapt to changing capacity without requiring a strictly defined bit rate. Third, in many situations the quality of service can be kept high enough even for the most demanding applications, particularly in the core network with high capacity optical links, by a pure overdimensioning of resources. Fourth, any differentiation mechanism tends to consume resources which could be used to increase packet forwarding capacity in a pure best effort network.

In conclusion, a packet's special delay requirement may be of importance inside a network, whereas bit rate and packet loss requirements related to individual applications, flows or packets are usually of minor consequence in IP networks, on the condition that the business value of the flow or packet is known and appropriately taken into account. Note that the business importance of a packet does not have a direct relationship with the quality requirements of applications. The fact that certain applications (e.g., video applications) have strict packet loss requirements does not directly imply business importance. It is imperative to make a clear distinction between the business importance and the quality requirements of applications.

Regarding the needs of applications, the main inference is that in addition to business importance, each packet may contain information about its delay requirement.

The basic approach used to satisfy the essential needs of business and of applications has been defined. Methods exist to use network resources even more efficiently, however. First, the service provider can offer additional tools for the consumer to inform the network of their own preferences. The consumer may, for instance, wish that the transmission of an e-mail should gain preference over the update of antivirus files. Note that this favoring can be effective only within the capacity available for that particular consumer, and does not usually have any significant effect on how resources are divided among other consumers. Another possibility is to give consumers or applications additional information about the probable capacity available for a new or existing flow. That information could also be conditional in the sense that the available capacity is a function of the price and/or special quality requirements.

However, according to the fundamental principles presented earlier in this chapter, this kind of information has to be considered as extra information either for the consumer or for the network, without any significant effect on the service model. In addition, it seems that without a certain level of differentiation already available inside the network, it is not possible to efficiently use such methods. It does not make sense to support consumer preferences without controlling the sharing of resources between different consumers. Also, it is somewhat questionable to offer information about the state of the network to consumers unless the network can give incentive for the consumers to adapt to the situation, because an incentive usually implies differentiation between adaptive and non-adaptive flows.

Consequences for the Mobile Internet

These considerations are basically well known, and moreover, there are various mechanisms to accomplish these tasks. What has been missing is a harmonious system covering all the necessary parts but excluding all the unnecessary ingredients. Discriminating between the necessary and the unnecessary is the key task, and a particularly hard one within the framework of the Mobile Internet. The Mobile Internet will consist of several different networking technologies, network environments and services. In some parts of the Mobile Internet the Quality of Service mechanisms and principles may be based on an approach which is not suitable for other parts of the network. For example, radio technologies often support a natural flow or connection-oriented QoS while fixed Internet has been designed for packet-based approaches. This implies that the only reasonable way to provide real end-to-end QoS must be based on a common measure, and fulfilling carriers' business goals is exactly this measure.

The necessary traffic control actions can be implemented in various ways, including the specifications made by the Internet Engineering Task Force (IETF) (e.g., Differentiated Services, Resource Reservation Protocol (RSVP) and MPLS). The key point is that the fundamental objectives of the system have to be preserved independently of the technological choices.

Let us finally outline the main characteristics of service provisioning in a network environment with four main layers: the optical core, the metropolitan region, radio access network and radio link between base station and mobile device. This hierarchical structure can be seen in the following figure. Using the example in this chapter the main technical characteristics can be as follows:

1. **Basic principles**

   The flat rate paid by a consumer defines the share of the resources available for that consumer. The consumer can increase her share by temporarily paying more, for instance 0.1 euros/min to guarantee that sufficient capacity is available for voice connections.

   In addition, flows may request a real-time service. Consumers can do this automatically for all voice connections they pay for.

2. **Wireless links and the radio access network**

   The incoming traffic of every consumer is measured in every access node. The measurement result and the share paid by the consumer are compared and the outcome defines the importance of the incoming packet - the higher the share or lower the bit rate, the higher the importance of the packet will be.

III

Visions

The quality and reliability of voice connections over the radio link are guaranteed by means of appropriate resource reservation. On the other hand, the data connections share the remaining radio capacity in a dynamic manner depending on the packet importance marking.

3. **The Metropolitan area with medium–size links and routers**

There are no resource reservations for individual flows.

During a congestion situation the packets with lowest importance are discarded first. In addition, among the accepted packets, the packets which have required real-time services are transmitted before other packets. If and when voice packets obtain the highest importance marking, they are protected from the negative effects of data connections using TCP.

4. **The Core network based on optical transmission and high–capacity routers**

The optical core network can be based on pure best-effort services with an appropriate traffic measurement and management system guaranteeing the sufficiency of network resources to transmit virtually all packets.

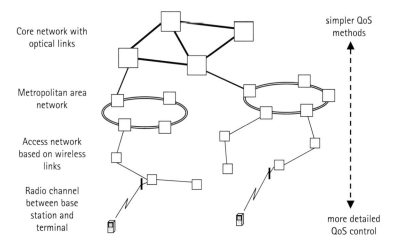

Hierarchical structure of the Mobile Internet with different QoS approaches

This kind of harmonious QoS system efficiently serves the service provider even though the technical approaches in different parts of the network are dissimilar. It should be stressed that in this framework QoS is more a business than a technological issue. Every technological choice serves the mission of the service provider; every technological choice works consistently with all other choices; and the total outcome will be cost-efficient. Thus, we do not need one universal QoS technology; instead we need a consistent and comprehensible QoS framework which is able to combine business objectives and differentiation mechanisms in an efficient way.

Quality of Service in MITA

Quality of Service is one of the end-to-end controls in the MITA models. In addition to the horizontal protocol layers and interfaces, these end-to-end controls need to be harmonized in the vertically integrated dimension. Quality of Service, together with security and privacy, is an excellent example of end-to-end controls since successful end-to-end QoS always involves vertical dependencies. After all, end-to-end Quality of Service is only as strong as the weakest link. If one protocol layer at the Mobile Internet Layer fails, end-to-end Quality of Service will be degraded.

The figure below illustrates the location of the end-to-end controls in the Mobile Internet Layer.

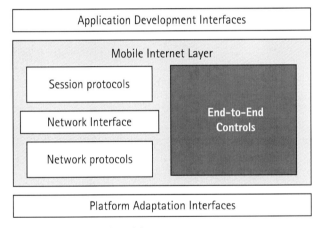

End-to-end controls in the MITA Network Model

In analyzing the end-to-end characteristics, special emphasis is put on the Interaction modes. On one hand, the Interaction modes set requirements. On the other hand, network connectivity and the access networks expose characteristic features. End-to-end controls have to take into account these requirements and characteristics while aiming to keep the system simple. This is also the basic challenge for Quality of Service.

III

Visions

IV IMPLEMENTATIONS

- o 4.1 Introduction

- o 4.2 Terminal

- o 4.3 Network

- o 4.4 Applications and Servers

PART 4.1

Introduction

o Introduction to MITA Reference Implementation

o MITA Reference Implementation Environment

o Reference Implementations in MITA Models

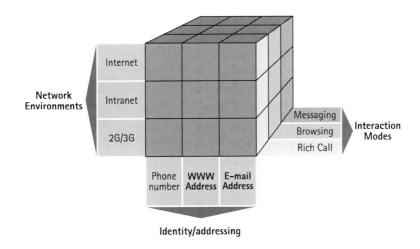

Introduction to MITA Reference Implementations

Our vision assumes that mobile networks and the Internet will converge into one unified Mobile Internet in a few years. The result will be a new environment, called the Mobile World, where the evolution paths of mobile communications and the Internet have converged. The Mobile World will require new competencies from all parties involved in the industry. Understanding mobility and the unique characteristics of the mobile business will be vital to building the networks and services of the future.

Success in the Mobile World will be about speed: speed of application and terminal development for refined consumer segments, speed of new service creation, and speed of cost-optimized network development and roll-out. The Mobile World can be perceived as a holistic, evolving environment of the future, but also as an environment on a more personal level enabling people to shape their own Mobile World through personalized communication services.

The Nokia solution addressing these demands is the Mobile Internet Technical Architecture. The technical architecture development has multiple parallel tracks: reviews of existing products and solutions, analyses of the current actions in standardization, reviews and studies of the latest research results, conceptual modeling actions and creation of technical visions and specifications. However, these tracks are more or less work-in-progress that do not make any practical implementations or references.

Combining the Mobile domain and the Web domain is by no means simple, as the resulting environment will contain many relatively complicated components. Without thorough prototyping of these building blocks, an adequate end result will be hard to achieve. The experiences obtained from prototyping can be fed quickly back to other parts of architecture development, for example, to protocol developers, which saves development time and requires less work to reach targets.

However, developing the technical architecture is more than just a question of prototyping individual components (e.g., protocols). Equally important is integrating the various components into the overall system. While integration can be made easier by the careful definition of interfaces between various layers and elements, real, hands-on experience is one of the keys to success. This is because prototyping provides a bridge between visionary work and the real implementation that is sometimes not-so-ideal and complicated. What works in theory may not work well in real products since some additional component may have an unexpected effect on the overall performance of the system. For example, two technologies can in a tightly integrated environment interact in surprising ways not foreseen by the developers of the individual technologies. Essentially, these side effects are the price of the increased complexity of future communication systems.

Thus, any far-reaching process, such as MITA, must be able to face the hard facts and draw the right conclusions at the right time. Implementations are the right tool for this, since they serve as a reality check and as insurance against unexpected problems.

For these reasons, MITA work includes a significant effort to produce so-called MITA Reference Implementations. These do not form a complete MITA system or products, but are a summary of key technologies needed to build the Mobile World. Reference Implementations and their integration is a continuous development process that adopts new technologies when they are ready to be prototyped.

The key parts of current MITA Reference Implementations are presented later in this chapter.

Objectives

The objectives of MITA Reference Implementations are to address the generic challenges described above. More specifically, the MITA Reference Implementation Environment aims to provide information about:

- o Applying MITA principles and models to state of the art technologies,
- o Implementing individual technologies,
- o Verifying interaction of technologies with each other, and
- o Integrating technologies into common test environments.

Moreover, this information will be used for:

- o Providing feedback to improve the technologies,
- o Finding missing components,
- o Eliminating unwanted interaction between technologies, and
- o Developing new opportunities and synergies in the overall system.

From the practical point of view, MITA Reference Implementation work is divided into two major parts: the development of technologies by experts in those areas; and the integration of these technologies into the common MITA Reference Implementation Environment which consists of one service network and multiple accesses.

In the present MITA Reference Implementation, the key objectives have been to verify that the same set of services can be used from different access networks, to identify the needed technologies that enable access independent connectivity, to prototype packet-based voice communication and to study Rich Call, Messaging and Digital Rights Management (DRM) technologies.

Technologies

Several key technologies have been selected and implemented for the MITA Reference Implementation Environment. These have been selected using the following criteria:

o   The technology must have a clear role in the MITA system.

o   The technology must be mature enough to allow relatively stable implementation. It does not need to be completely frozen but at least the major features must be available.

o   The technology must also provide the required functionality for testing purposes.

The list of tested technologies includes:

o   Digital Rights Management and micro payment

o   Session Initiation Protocol (SIP)

o   IPv6/IPv4 routing infrastructure

o   IPv4/IPv6 interworking

o   Mobile IPv6

o   General Packet Radio Service (GPRS)

o   3G Packet Core

o   Wireless Local Area Network (WLAN)

o   Java

o   Linux® and open source development

Demonstrations

Based on the reference implementations, a set of demonstration cases have been produced and presented in public. Some of these demonstrations include:

o   All end-points and network elements support IPv6 and are implemented in the Linux environment include.

o   The Nokia 9210 phone is used as a target device in selected demonstrations.

o   Mobile IPv6 to verify the latest IETF drafts. It also supports extensions that improve mobility management to support packet-based voice better.

o   SIP based voice over IP solution (both audio and video supported). Implementation includes terminal, proxies, gateways and a light Multiparty Conferencing Unit (MCU).

o   Support for typical call services.

o   SIP based presence and instant messaging with a content adaptation server and enhanced presence information. Both Java and native language versions are implemented.

IV Implementations

o   Content downloading and peer-to-peer distribution with DRM support.

o   Integrate SMS and SIP presence solutions enabling message and call routing based on presence information.

Conclusions

MITA Reference Implementations have produced several valuable results. Implementations have offered the verification of several key technologies. After all, the existence of these implementations is a strong statement for the feasibility of the technology.

The results on integration have been very promising. For example, the use cases have shown that it is feasible to make handovers between different access technologies while maintaining the service and connection. In addition, the MITA Reference Implementation Environment has proved that quite a wide range of technologies can work together when the architecture has been designed with interoperability in mind.

However, in the long run, the most valuable results are not related to proving concepts. The competence and experience created through prototyping will be used to develop technologies for MITA faster with less expense and more reliability.

As mentioned in the introduction of the MITA Reference Implementations section, prototyping is a continuous process. The results will be used to provide input for the next set of MITA specifications and technology development.

MITA Reference Implementation Environment

The MITA Reference Implementation Environment consists of a group of terminals with different access technologies supported. To be able to test these terminals with one and the same set of services, multiple radio access networks are integrated (via emulation or direct use) to access core networks. Two access core networks are integrated into one unified transport network enabling access to services. This installation allows different terminal types to use the same IPT service core and other associated services (e.g., browsing and streaming).

The figure below shows a simplified model of the MITA Reference Implementation Environment.

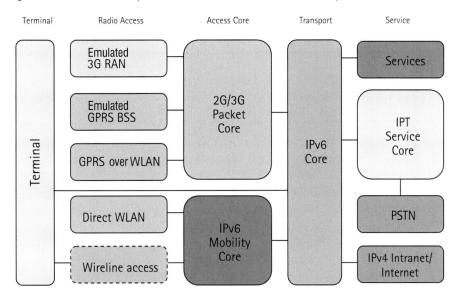

Logical architecture of the MITA Reference Implementation Environment

The architecture is divided vertically into the following conceptual building blocks:

o   **Terminal:** Single mode or multimode.

o   **Radio Access:** Emulated 2G and 3G Radio Access Networks (RANs), and two Wireless Local Area Networks (WLANs). For verification purposes, also fixed IPv6 access is supported.

o   **Access Core:** Emulated 2G/3G Packet Core network and IPv6 Mobility Core network based on Mobile IPv6.

o   **Transport:** IPv6 Core network.

o   **Service:** IP Telephony (IPT) service core network with additional messaging, browsing and streaming services, gateway to the Public Switched Telephone Network (PSTN) and access to Internet/Intranet.

At the boundary of other networks (PSTN, IPv4 Intranet/Internet), there is a significant amount of gateway functionality. 2G General Packet Radio Service (GPRS), 3G RAN and Packet Core networks are emulated networks (i.e., protocols implemented without physical layer hardware) over wireline Ethernet or WLAN.

The main focus of the MITA Reference Implementation Environment has been on terminals, the IPv6 support, service core servers and services. Each of these is described in more detail below in its own section.

Terminals

The terminals are IP-based and support both IPv6 and IPv4. The supported call control protocol is Session Initiation Protocol (SIP). There has been a separate terminal for each access scenario, however, the tested services and use cases have been the same for all access scenarios and terminals. For testing purposes, a dual-mode terminal supporting emulated GPRS and GPRS over WLAN scenarios has also been implemented.

All terminals run on the Linux operating system and are common laptop or desktop computers. In the case of WLAN, the radio component is implemented on a network access card in the same unit (laptop PC) with the signaling software. In the case of WCDMA, there are separate emulators for WCDMA radio (protocols below IP) and a laptop for IP Telephony and other signaling (protocols above IP). The terminals support storing/retrieving of general and user specific settings to/from a smart card.

The terminal has an easy-to-use graphical user interface for SIP based services, called SURF. The IP Telephony software suite (e.g., SIP stack) is called Sofia. For other services, public third party implementations are used.

Radio Access Networks

3G Radio Access Network

The MITA Reference Implementation Environment supports the emulated UMTS Terrestrial Radio Access Network (UTRAN) with a Wideband Code Division Multiple Access (WCDMA) radio interface according to the Third Generation Partnership Project (3GPP) Release 99 standard.

3G RAN logical architecture

General Packet Radio Service Base Station Subsystem

The European Telecommunications Standards Institute (ETSI) GPRS standard complements the Global System for Mobile Communications (GSM) Base Station System (BSS) with a packet-based radio interface and a new core network interface.

In the MITA reference implementation environment, the GPRS emulator implements the 2G GPRS BSS and related user and control plane protocols.

GPRS BSS logical architecture

General Packet Radio Service Over Wireless Local Area Network

The GPRS provides global mobility management and offers an authenticated and secured packet data service, using Subscriber Identity Module (SIM) card-based authentication and user data encryption.

IV Implementations

WLAN based on IEEE 802.11 provides a fast data service through a simple infrastructure. Compared with the GPRS system, WLAN based access network is easy to configure, easy to build and does not require a lot of investments. But WLAN does not really support global mobility, nor does it offer a secured user data service.

In order to take advantage of both GPRS and WLAN to offer cheaper and faster radio service with global mobility management and secured user data, an integrated GPRS over WLAN service has been considered.

GPRS over WLAN logical architecture

In the MITA Reference Implementation Environment, the GPRS emulator implements the GPRS parts of the GPRS over WLAN scenario. GPRS BSS is not used, but has been replaced with WLAN. The Interworking Element (IWE) is like a Serving GPRS Support Node (SGSN), where the lower BSS level protocol layers have been replaced with GPRS over WLAN protocols.

Direct WLAN

The direct WLAN radio access alternative maximizes the use of standard IP technologies for mobility management and for Authentication, Authorization and Accounting (AAA) in the access core. WLAN provides a wireless link layer with local link layer mobility. WLAN links provide high capacity but typically limited coverage.

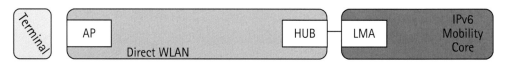

Direct WLAN logical architecture

Access Core Network

2G/3G Packet Core

The 2G GPRS core network and 3G UMTS packet switched domain are both IP networks containing SGSN, Gateway GPRS Support Node (GGSN) and Home Location Register (HLR) elements. There are also other elements (e.g., internal Domain Name System (DNS) server, Border Gateway (BG), Short Message Service Center (SMSC), and legal interception support), but SSGN, GGSN and HLR are the most relevant elements from the MITA point of view. The SGSN has an interface for a radio access network and the GGSN has an interface for external IP networks. User data packets belong to sessions are tunneled between the SGSN and the GGSN. The HLR stores subscriber data (e.g., location and services). The 3G core network also contains advanced features (e.g., better support for QoS).

The 2G/3G packet core networks can have a common GGSN, but the SGSNs are different. In addition, the HLR can be made common for 2G and 3G networks. In the MITA reference implementation environment, the GGSNs for 2G and 3G are separate.

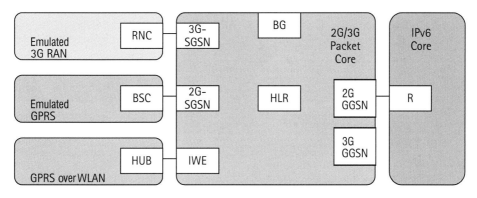

2G/3G Packet Core logical architecture

IPv6 Mobility Core

IPv6 supports mobility inherently. Mobility at the IP level means support for mobility between different link layer technologies. Mobile IP uses two IP addresses: a fixed home address and a care-of address that changes at each new point of attachment.

The IPv6 Mobility Core implements similar kind of mobility functionality to the 2G/3G Packet Core, but maximizes the use of standard IP technologies for mobility management and AAA. In this case, Mobile IPv6 takes care of mobility management.

The main elements of the IPv6 Mobility Core are the Leaf Mobility Agent (LMA), Gateway Mobility Agent (GMA) and Home Agent (HA).

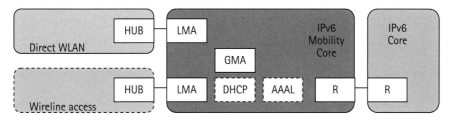

IPv6 Mobility Core logical architecture

IV

Implementations

IPv6 Core Network

The IPv6 Core network provides transport between service core elements and access networks. Both Access Core networks are integrated with the IPv6 Core. The IPv6 core also supports IPv4 for backwards compatibility. An interface to IPv4 Intranet/Internet goes via a Network Address Translation - Protocol Translation (NAT-PT) element.

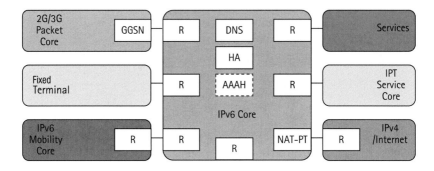

IPv6 Core network logical architecture

IPT Service Core Network

The IPT Service Core network implements IP telephony and other related services. It emulates the 3GPP Release 5 IP Multimedia Subsystem (IMS) architecture having SIP based proxies and gateways.

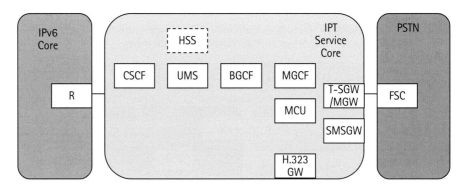

IPT Service Core logical architecture

Services Network

The service network supports the following services: multimedia sessions, SIP based presence and instant messaging, basic conferencing, group messaging between conference participants, content adaptation according to terminal type, announcements and location-based services. The service logic is centered on SIP, but a part of the services (e.g., location-based) also utilizes HyperText Transfer Protocol (HTTP) based components.

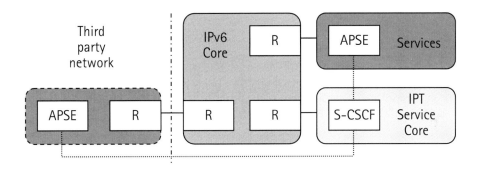

Services network logical architecture

Gateways to PSTN/GSM

The Public Switched Telephone Network (PSTN) and GSM do not support standard IP telephony call control and media protocols. Some gateway functionality is needed at the boundary of IPT service core and PSTN. The GSM network also supports mobility, but full roaming implementations between the IPT service core and GSM, while important, is beyond the scope of the MITA Reference Implementation Environment.

SMSGW allows limited presence based roaming between the IPT service core and GSM and a distributed gateway allows calls between IPT terminals, and PSTN/GSM devices.

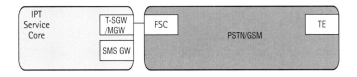

PSTN logical architecture

IV

Implementations

IPv4 Intranet/Internet

IPv4 Intranet/Internet network in MITA Reference Implementation Environment supports standard IPv4 telephony call control and media protocols. IPv6/IPv4 gateway functionality (NAT-PT) is needed at the boundary of IPv6 core networks and IPv4 intranet/Internet.

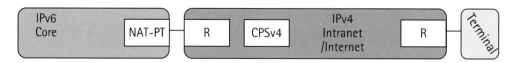

Intranet/Internet logical architecture

In the MITA Reference Implementation Environment, an IPv4 based intranet connection is possible. When the MITA terminals are used as IPv4 based intranet terminals, their IPv6 capabilities are not used. In this access scenario, the NAT-PT handles the adaptation between IPv6 and IPv4 protocols, allowing MITA terminals to access IPv6 based services from IPv4 based network.

Reference Implementations in MITA Models

MITA Reference Implementations implement various technologies needed to build the Mobile World. These have been integrated together into a MITA Reference Implementation Environment. This environment has formed the basis for various demonstrations.

The MITA models and modeling principles have been used in the creation of the reference implementation environment. The key principles for MITA modeling are:

o   The architecture divides into independent sub-architectures while fulfilling business needs,

o   The architecture is open, modular and hierarchical, and

o   The architecture can tolerate varying rates of technological change in individual components.

This involves the ideas of deploying a layered element model, layered network model, layered identities model, generic content delivery model and multiple access model.

For example, MITA Reference Implementations have been created bearing in mind the division between the Application layer, Mobile Internet Layer and Platforms layer. This has enabled a clear division of components and clarified the interfaces and distribution of functions. Application Programming Interfaces (APIs) have been developed in MITA Reference Implementations for various platforms and environments since these are essential for managing the layered structure.

Layered Element Examples

One way to achieve the MITA modeling principles is to divide a network element into layers. The layered element model makes a clear division between Platform, Mobile Internet and Application layers in network elements, as shown in the following figure.

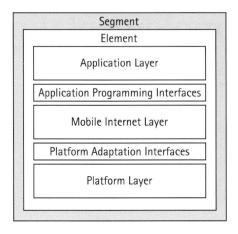

MITA layered element model

The Application layer consists of user interfaces, application logics, and related support functions. The Mobile Internet Layer allows the same applications to run on multiple platforms and provides tools for developers to implement new services. The Platform layer consists of operating system specific software and hardware.

Below are some examples of terminal and server elements.

Terminal Examples

The MITA Reference Implementation in terminals involves Session Initiation Protocol (SIP) clients which are part of the Mobile Internet Layer. This is because SIP is an Internet protocol which can be used by Application layer software to access services over the network. The Digital Rights Management (DRM) client is a part of the Application layer and DRM subsystems are part of the Mobile Internet layer since they provide support for Interaction modes (e.g., browsing).

Server Examples

In a similar way, MITA Reference Implementations on the server side include SIP and DRM components:

o   SIP Proxy

o   SIP message server

o   SIP Gateway

o   SMS Gateway

o   SIP Multiparty Conferencing Unit

o   DRM Server

The benefit of using the layered element model is that the role of a Reference Implementation becomes clear. When the scope of the software is properly understood, it is easier to implement proper interfaces and detailed functions to fulfill that role. For example, using the MITA model as the starting point, it is easy to see that various SIP components should provide support for various Interaction modes (e.g., Browsing, Messaging and Rich Call).

Layered Network Examples

The essence of the layered network model is that elements can be divided into end points and network elements. The role of the network elements is to support Access and Connectivity layers, while end-points should also support Application layer functions. More specifically, elements in the network category relay Transport, Session and Application layer protocols transparently, whereas end-points terminate those protocols. Further on, end-points can be divided into terminals and servers. The benefit of this model is that it gives a clear understanding of the functions actually needed in each element.

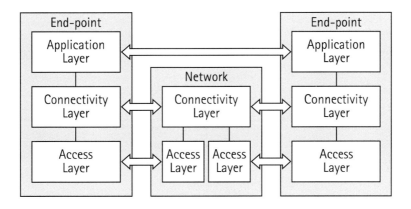

MITA layered network model

Terminal-to-Terminal Examples

Terminal to terminal demonstration cases used in the MITA Reference Implementation Environment include SIP calls and SIP messaging.

Terminal-to-Server Examples

Content download is an example of a case in which communication occurs between a terminal and a server. Typically in a content download, the terminal retrieves information from the server. Here the roles of implemented Reference Implementation entities can be clearly divided and there is no need to include any extra functions on the terminal.

IV Implementations

Server-to-Server Examples

Presence servers are an example of server to server interaction. In this case, the communicating end points are both servers exchanging information about the presence status. For example, in SIP, the messaging SIP proxy may fetch the destination terminal capabilities from the presence server and route messages to the content adaptation server when needed.

Content Delivery Examples

The MITA content delivery model essentially divides entities dealing with content to sources and sinks. Both contain a network process (either sending or receiving), control process and a content process (either creation or consumption).

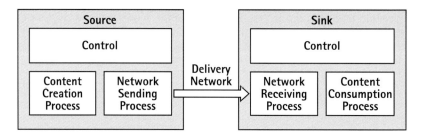

MITA Content Delivery Model

Examples of supported content delivery use cases include:

o   SIP call

o   SIP message also with content adaptation

o   Content download from server with DRM support

Conclusions

The use of MITA models has formed the basis of MITA Reference Implementations.

The use of a layered element model has lead to a clear separation of functions inside a network element. This means that the role and requirements of implemented components become clearer and it is easier to see the range of services that the individual components should provide for the upper layers. This reduces the implementation costs and enables better reuse of existing implementations.

The use of a layered network model means that the network elements in the MITA Reference Implementation Environment can be divided according to their role in network elements and end points or those in servers and terminals. The benefit here is that individual elements can only run those components that are needed for their intended role, thus reducing the probability of overdimensioning the capacities of these elements.

The use of a content delivery model means that the role of Reference Implementations and demonstrations has been divided into content sources and sinks. This introduces a clear view of the functions needed to implement in the control, network and content processes. Again, the immediate benefit is the reduced risk of wasting capacity in the network elements and better reuse of the implemented components. For example, similar content processing functions can be used with multiple applications and network protocols can be isolated from applications. Interfaces between these three roles can also be verified.

PART 4.2

Terminal

o Terminal Platform

o 2G/3G Terminals in the MITA Reference Implementation Environment

o GPRS Over WLAN Access

o Sofia – IPv6 Multimedia Communications Software

o SIP Transaction Engines

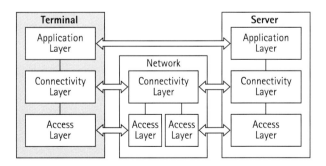

Terminal Platform

Development of the Reference Terminal Platform was initiated in order to create a flexible, adaptable and customizable platform for research activities in the area of mobile communications. The objective was to provide a terminal platform for seamless services over a wireless IPv6 network. This objective involves highly demanding requirements, considering the variety of applications which need to be supported (e.g., Web browsing and IP Telephony).

The Reference Terminal Platform described in this section realizes the Platform layer in the MITA Concept model. This entity consists of platform hardware, operating system core modules and device drivers. As a whole, it provides access to a local system and networking resources via several interfaces.

Terminal Hardware Platform

Selecting the terminal hardware platform is itself a difficult task because of the required set of functionalities. The selected platform does not only affect the form factor, but also several other issues, such as:

- o Performance
- o User Interface (UI)
- o Connectivity
- o Portability/movability
- o Operating time
- o Adaptability

The form factor category considered in this case ranges from laptop computers and Web tablets to Personal Digital Assistant (PDA) type of devices.

Performance

The performance of a terminal is a perfect example of a compromise between size and functionality. One might prefer a smaller device (e.g., a PDA) and consider it more chic and usable than a laptop computer, but one most certainly would lose in data processing performance. This is due to several factors, not only the performance of the processor itself, but also due to the type of memory used.

Thus, the selection of the terminal device has a major impact on the capability to support streaming media (e.g., IP Telephony) because it requires at least soft real-time capabilities.

User Interface

User interfaces have a very important role in terminal platforms. Perfectly good hardware can be worthless because of a poorly designed UI or a set of input/output interfaces which is inappropriate for a specific type of use.

In the form factor category, keyboard, mouse and stylus-operated devices are common, and choosing one over another sets requirements on the overall UI design. In this type of reference terminal implementation, however, it is certain that supporting a mixed, keyboard and pointer environment would be the most flexible and useful approach. As such, it provides a flexible platform not tied to strict boundary conditions.

A complete UI design also contains a display of some sort. The form factor of the terminal display is considered one of the main criteria for terminal platform implementation. Usually, the options are limited to full (640x480), half (640x240) or quarter (240x320) sized VGA displays in this category of products. It is obvious that the size of the display has a great impact on the look & feel of the device, but also on its usability, for example, in the case of Internet browsing.

Besides the form factor, displays differ from one another in their physical capabilities. For example, the frame rate and color palette of the display hardware determine whether the hardware can be used for streaming video with true colors or for black and white text editing - not to mention the different requirements these applications have on processor performance.

Integrated Connectivity

The Reference Terminal Platform preserves the option to use fixed connectivity, but the dominant methods are based on wireless technologies. The current implementation includes integrated support for the Wireless Local Area Network (WLAN). Other access technologies are emulated over Ethernet or WLAN access. This fact has been exploited in research and development activities related to optimizing communication solutions over wireless media.

Portability/Mobility

One of the fundamentals in the reference implementation has been a mobile device which can be used while moving. Thus, the requirement extends the conception of a portable terminal closer to a mobile device than to a laptop. For example, a Web tablet in this sense represents a perfect device for demonstrations: it has a big enough display combined with portability.

Operating Time

This attribute is a combination of the power consumption of a device versus battery lifetime. Unfortunately, we must always compromise between weight/size and capacity. In the reference implementation, the optimization of operating time has not been a focus area.

Adaptability

All of the above are more or less considered integral characteristics of terminal devices. In addition, terminals can have other integrated functionalities (e.g., networking) or they might provide extension capabilities with accessories. These characteristics can be highly desirable, of course, depending on how the device will be used. As with the other optimization issues, adaptability optimization has not been a focus area.

Linux Distribution

In addition to a hardware platform, the MITA Platform layer consists of operating system core modules and device drivers. These are part of the Linux distribution composed as part of the Reference terminal platform implementation activity.

The development of the Linux kernel (i.e., the operating system core) has been rapid. It has consisted of a combination of sub-projects, each concentrating on a specific topic providing enhancements or totally new features. The pace of these sub-projects varies considerably due to their varying size and nature. The area of IPv6 networking, in particular, is intriguing and challenging.

Work on the Linux distribution has included Linux kernel tuning according to the platform and system requirements. That is, the latest available 2.4.x series kernel has been tuned up to a few laptop environments with certain memory requirements and configured with appropriate features to enable required capabilities (e.g., IPv6 networking).

The configuration has also emphasized a fault tolerant platform, because the Linux distribution has been designed for research and development use. This is a beneficial characteristic when implementing device drivers, because quite often an error in the device driver is fatal and results in a crashed operating system.

There are always two approaches to implementing a Linux distribution: build one from scratch or modify an existing one. Regardless of your approach, the basic functional blocks of a distribution are still the same:

- o Kernel
- o Libraries
- o Device drivers
- o Command shells
- o Graphical UI frameworks
- o Windowing frameworks
- o Utilities

The Reference Terminal Platform is based on open technologies such as the Linux kernel, XFree86 windowing and Mozilla browser. Also, we have been following the evolution of the Linux kernel and have frequently made updates, aligning our activities with the latest Linux kernel modifications available [LinuxKernel].

Creating our own Linux distribution for the reference terminal platform has required some extra effort and generated additional costs because we had to develop new applications and tools. On the other hand, we have gained a lot from the open source community and the developments made by thousands of Linux developers.

IV

Implementations

The Reference Terminal platform is based on x86 technology, and therefore the architectural differences do not require a huge amount of work. However, supporting all the desired features with the distribution requires work in several areas:

- o   Libraries
- o   Configuration tools
- o   Installation tools
- o   Other tools
- o   Device drivers

These, combined with the basic application suite, comprise a Reference Terminal Platform based on Linux, which can be used for further research activities. Moreover, other projects can exploit this platform in order to speed up their own activities.

Mobile IPv6 in Linux

Mobile IPv6 is specified to be a mandatory feature of the complete IPv6 implementation, though currently the mainstream Linux kernel does not support it at all. Even IPv6 functionality in the Linux kernel is rather basic.

The current mainstream Linux kernel release includes an experimental IPv6 implementation, which provides basic IPv6 functionality and allows dual IPv4/IPv6 stack operation. There is enough IPv6 support to start experimenting with IPv6, though at present, the system does not support all IPv6 features. In particular, the lack of IPSec (IP Security) support can be considered a major deficiency.

Current commercial Linux distributions are ready to be used with IPv6, including kernel support, initialization scripts and configuration files. However, some patching is necessary - as with any other experimental code - if one is considering serious utilization of IPv6.

The Mobile IPv6 for Linux (MIPL) [1] project at the Helsinki University of Technology has taken an active role in addressing these issues. It aims to improve the state of Linux IPv6 implementation with Mobile IPv6 patches, and ultimately to integrate these patches into mainstream Linux kernel releases.

Mobile IPv6 for Linux (MIPL) development was started at the beginning of 2000 at the Helsinki University of Technology to provide Mobile IPv6 functionality for the Linux IPv6 stack. The MIPL source is released under the General Public License (GPL). It implements Mobile IPv6 functionality according to the Mobile IPv6 Internet Draft 15 [2], and also the parts of the IPSec protocol needed for Mobile IPv6 authentication. The MIPL implementation is actively being developed and tested by a large development community around the world and will conform to the Mobile IPv6 specification once it is finished.

Currently, the Reference Terminal Platform also incorporates Mobile IPv6 enhancements (e.g., context transfer, buffer management, header compression and regional registration). In addition to the proof of concept type of implementation work, the aim is to ensure that Linux Mobile IPv6 will conform to the specifications and be the best possible implementation of Mobile IPv6.

Device Drivers

Hardware devices require software drivers to function. Device drivers are usually executed in a so-called kernel space where all kernel code is executed. Applications are usually run in a user space and cannot usually control hardware directly; instead, they use function calls to the kernel or to device drivers. This way, ordinary applications cannot damage the hardware or the system by accidentally misusing the hardware.

Nokia has developed Linux device drivers for some of its products. Presently there is support for Nokia C110/C111 Wireless LAN cards and the D211 multimode radio card.

Linux has a good and efficient network stack, which supports all commonly used network protocols. The network stack has a zero-copy principle, meaning that packets are not copied from one software module to another. Instead, packets are passed as a pointer to data in memory. Only in exceptions do packets need to be copied from one memory location to another, a good practice since such copying is relatively slow.

The Linux kernel supports modular drivers called modules. A driver module can be loaded only when it is needed; otherwise the driver is not in memory, freeing memory for other purposes. Nokia C110/C111 and D211 device drivers are also modules; they are loaded into the kernel when the card is inserted into the PC Memory Card International Association (PCMCIA) slot and are unloaded when the card is removed.

Linux itself has been ported to many processors and platforms. It is relatively easy to port a device driver from one architecture to another since practically all the interfaces are the same in different platforms.

Nokia C110/C111 Wireless LAN Card Driver

The Linux driver for the Nokia C110/C111 card is available to all card owners at the Forum Nokia Web site. The driver supports most of the features of the card but without a graphical user interface. For the Linux system the card looks like a normal wired Ethernet card and Wireless LAN management is performed with a separate user space control program to support WLAN-specific functions.

The driver is the first Nokia product to be published under the NOKia Open Source (NOKOS) license [3]. In addition, some files in the driver package are licensed under the Nokia Mobile Phones end-user software agreement or under the Mozilla public license. An open source driver means that people can change the code themselves if they want to customize the driver or just keep up with changes in the Linux kernel interfaces.

The card itself has hardware support for multicasts. This means that the Linux kernel networking stack can set certain multicast addresses into a hardware register in the card, and the card will only listen to these registered multicast addresses. This is very efficient for IPv6 since it uses multicasts quite heavily and is not thus burdened with multicasts it is not interested in.

Benefits

Since the first release of the Reference Terminal Platform, it has provided a common platform for several research projects, aligning activities and increasing cooperation. Improved

IV   Implementations

communication and sharing a common platform have provided a good start towards the next more advanced distribution with a richer set of functionalities.

References

[1] http://www.mipl.mediapoli.com/

[2] Johnson, D., Perkins, C. Mobility Support in IPv6 (draft–ietf–mobileip–ipv6–15.txt, Nov. 2000).

[3] http://www.opensource.org/licenses/nokia.html

[Linux kernel] http://www.kernel.org

2G/3G Terminals in the MITA Reference Implementation Environment

Second generation (2G) and third generation (3G) mobile networks form one of the three basic MITA Network environments. As a consequence, the MITA Reference Implementation Environment contains 2G and 3G access network. This section describes the 2G/3G features in terminals.

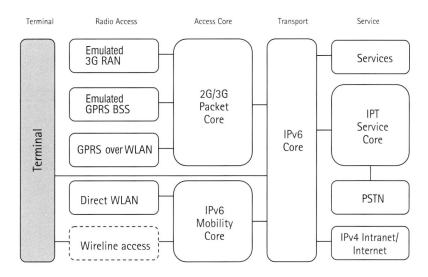

Cellular 2G/3G terminal in the MITA Reference Implementation Environment

Terminals deploy two major 2G/3G components: the User Equipment (UE) Emulator and the QoS and Session Manager. The former implements the 3GPP protocols while the latter is used for setting the QoS parameters for different types of Packet Data Protocol (PDP) contexts.

User Equipment Emulator

Terminals of the MITA reference implementation environment deploy the User Equipment (UE) Emulators for 2G/3G access. The emulators can be connected to real 3GPP Wideband Code Division Multiple Access (WCDMA) radio or to a User Datagram Protocol (UDP) socket in a demonstration environment. Physically, the UE Emulator is based on Standard PC hardware using the Linux operating system. This system enables the use of a multitude of simultaneous PDP contexts, both primary and secondary.

The UE Emulator emulates the 3GPP protocol stack of the UE, and implements both signaling and control planes. The UE contains an interface to WCDMA Terminal Equipment (TE) which is typically a laptop PC running applications. Several TEs can be connected using an Ethernet hub to UE. A real WCDMA radio interface has been replaced with a UDP socket and a real radio environment can be emulated using a Cyclical Redundancy Check (CRC) error generator.

Features of the UE Emulator

The UE emulator supports the following layer 3 packet protocols: Session Management (SM), GPRS Mobility Management (GMM) and Radio Resource Control (RRC). Implementation of Layer 2 protocols consists of Radio Link Control (RLC), Medium Access Control (MAC) and the Packet Data Convergence Protocol (PDCP).

The next figure illustrates the protocols of the UE emulator:

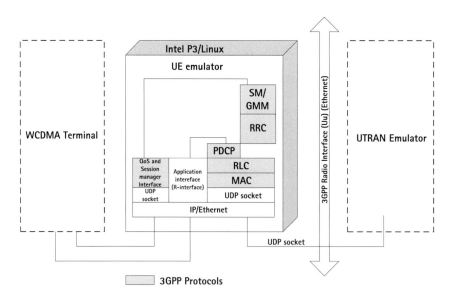

Protocols of the UE Emulator

The RLC protocol supports concatenation of several higher layers of Protocol Data Units (PDUs) into one RLC PDU and the segmentation of one higher layer PDU into several RLC PDUs. RLC has Acknowledged, Unacknowledged and Transparent transmission modes. The MAC protocol supports several simultaneous Transport Formats (TF) and a packet scheduler for prioritizing different types of PDP contexts. PDCP contains the ROHC IP header compression algorithm for compressing IPv4 and IPv6 packets.

UE supports the following signaling procedures:

o   Attach

o   Detach

o   PDP context activation/modification/release

QoS and Session Manager

It is important that the MITA Reference Implementation Environment be easy to use. This means, for example, that it can automatically start PDP context activation and deactivation procedures when some application is started or released.

The QoS and Session manager is a tool for setting QoS parameters for different types of PDP contexts. With the QoS and Session Manager it is possible to define individual QoS parameters for video call, Web browsing and other types of applications. The QoS and Session Manager communicates with applications and the UE protocol stack, and conveys session activation and deactivation requests sent from the application to the UE Emulator which in turn starts PDP context activation or deactivation procedures for the given application.

The next figure provides a general overview where applications and the QoS and Session Manager are located in the MITA Reference Implementation Environment.

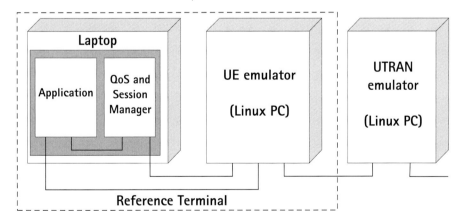

QoS and Session Manager in the MITA Reference terminal

IV Implementations

GPRS Over WLAN Access

The General Packet Radio Service (GPRS) over Wireless Local Area Network (WLAN) architecture definition and demonstrator implementation is one part of the MITA multiple access technology. The GPRS over WLAN demonstrator had a target of producing a viable integration model where WLAN would be used as a radio resource complementing GPRS in a dual-mode access scenario as effectively as possible. The work concludes that making use of the mobility, authentication and security features of GPRS over the WLAN access channel would facilitate roaming between networks and enable use of carrier services (e.g., QoS and billing).

The selected development approach can be called a *tight integration model*, in contrast to a *loose integration model* where the integration between GPRS and IP access is done on the network layer.

The loose integration alternative would usually imply IP-level integration of mobility and security, using Mobile IP and possibly IP Security protocol. As a protocol, GPRS in these cases is reduced to being a link layer, possibly with some information distribution to IP mobility management for optimization purposes.

"Loose integration model"

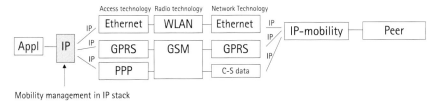

Mobility management in IP stack

"Tight integration model"

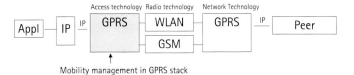

Mobility management in GPRS stack

Loose vs. Tight integration models

The main difference between these two approaches is their suitability for different business models: the tight integration is more carrier-centered and suitable for use cases such as high-speed hotspots within GPRS/UMTS public networks, whereas the loose integration is more geared towards making IP protocols the focal point of roaming, mobility and security management. The tight integration model on the link layer provides at least the following advantages for GPRS customers and carriers:

1   *Seamless handover and roaming.* As GPRS protocols are used both when roaming between access points within the WLAN access domain and between WLAN access points and GPRS base stations, roaming is as seamless as in the GPRS domain itself.

2   *SIM card-based system authentication and encryption.* As authentication and security management is done in layers above the link control in the GPRS infrastructure, these features will work on the WLAN interface without any modifications.

3   *Charging and billing infrastructure.* In the GSM/GPRS infrastructure there is existing support for charging and billing that can be applied to the GPRS over WLAN structure as well.

4   *Customer relationship.* GSM carriers have a long-standing customer relationship with the consumers of their network, and GPRS over WLAN charges can be included in the same bill as charges for GPRS usage.

5   *Value-added services.* In cases where GPRS carriers have their own value-added services, these will be available to GPRS over WLAN consumers as well.

6   *Easy deployment.* Previously mentioned points together show that the architecture is more of an evolutionary step than a new technology or service framework that has to be learned and managed (both for customers and for service providers). In fact, the tight integration model is similar to dual-frequency GSM-phone systems in that virtually nothing changes when you look at the functionality or the network from above.

7   *Network off-loading.* In some network setups network traffic in the GPRS network can be off-loaded to WLAN hot spots if GPRS over WLAN coverage is available. In this case, terminals do not necessarily see any advantage between using the native radio resource or WLAN.

Additionally, the tight and loose integration models are not necessarily mutually exclusive; they achieve different goals and may be run on the same mobile device in parallel. Both approaches can be made to hide access-specific technology issues from upper protocol layers, applications, services and consumers.

References [1] and/or [2] can be used as introductory material to the GPRS and IEEE 802.11 WLAN technologies.

A Selected Integration Point in the GPRS Architecture

In principle, there are a number of interfacing alternatives when considering how to integrate the WLAN radio resource into the GPRS architecture. In the analysis phase, we examined 16 alternatives before finally choosing to replace the Base Station Controller (BSC) with WLAN below the Link Layer Control (LLC) layer in Serving GPRS Support Nodes (SGSN) and Mobile Stations (MS).

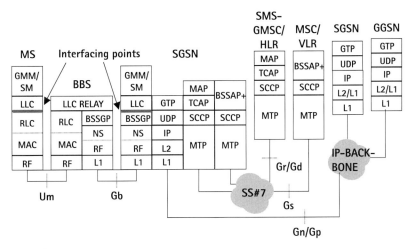

GPRS signaling plane

Mobility Management

Fine-grained, global mobility management is one of the keys to the success of GSM and GPRS. At least the same level of service should be achieved with WLAN radio access to a GPRS network. Native WLAN mobility should not be compromised if not absolutely necessary, because the WLAN radio interface might also be used for WLAN-only data services. SGSN is the heart of GPRS mobility management for every scenario in the study, so it seemed feasible to cut mobility management below that point, and add supporting WLAN functionality for micro-mobility within the area of an SGSN.

Location Management

GPRS mobility management is based on the idea that the network, particularly the Home Location Register (HLR), always has certain knowledge about the location of a mobile device once it is attached to the GPRS network. In GPRS, location management is divided into three levels of location areas: Cell, Routing Area and Location Area. When a mobile device moves, its location information is updated either with the messages Cell Update or Routing Area Update, depending on the mobility management status of the device. When using the existing mobility management in a GPRS system, the WLAN radio resource should support corresponding levels of location management. Naturally, one would think of dividing the WLAN coverage areas into Cell, Routing Areas and Location Areas as well.

If we look at the functions performed by the LLC layer (and respectively required by the layers above it), its main purpose is to convey information between layer 3 entities in the MS and SGSN. LLC includes functions for: [4]

o   The provision of one or more logical link connections (acknowledged and unacknowledged)

o   Sequence control, to maintain the sequential order of frames across a logical link connection

o   Detection of transmission, format and operational errors on a logical link connection

o   Recovery from detected transmission, format and operational errors

IV

Implementations

o   Notification of unrecoverable errors

o   Flow control

o   Ciphering

Furthermore, LLC requires the following services from the layer(s) below:

o   LLC Protocol Data Unit (PDU) delimitation to allow the LLC layer to determine the first and last octet in each LLC PDU;

o   Transport of the MS address in each LLC PDU between MS and the SGSN.

Compared to the WLAN 802.11(b) MAC, its functionality cannot by itself provide the features of the LLC layer, whereas a PDU delimiting and transport of MS address can relatively easily be achieved by adding a thin layer of logic on top of the 802.11 MAC. It also follows that the interfacing point most naturally fits below the LLC in the GPRS signaling model. In the following text, this new protocol layer is called Interworking Function (IWF).

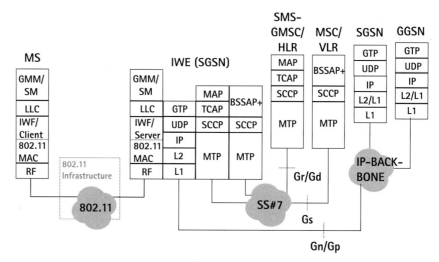

GPRS over WLAN Signaling plane

Link-Level Architecture

In order to support mobility and roaming in the WLAN network, PDU transmission and MS address transmission has to be implemented on top of the 802.11. A WLAN Interworking Protocol (WIP) was defined to provide the following functions for the LLC protocol layer: Cell Id mapping, Cell Id/AP acquisition, TLLI transporting, LLC PDU delimitation and Cell Id/AP mapping on the network side.

From a network point of view, the 802.11 WLAN is set up in a structured mode of operation, where each access point controls the network it is administering. The WIP protocol essentially defines two message types: signaling and transparent data. All messages to and from the LLC layer at the respective ends are transmitted as data messages. In addition, signaling messages are reserved for mobility management purposes as follows: client terminals run a continuous background scan during operation, where MAC addresses of currently accessible access points are revealed to clients, and stored in a cache.

Each GPRS enabled access point broadcasts a record of a) its location in the GPRS network (Cell Id, Routing Area), its current load (number of clients and/or transmitted bits/sec); and b) possibly a table of neighboring GPRS-enabled access points (MAC addresses vs. GPRS location and their load). The client terminal can also request these advertisements. At the server end, a mapping between the client MAC addresses and corresponding MS identities is kept, based on an initial *client-info* message originating from the client when it decides to attach in the GPRS sense. Elements in this table may be released when the corresponding Interworking Element (IWE) receives information that the client has roamed to another IWE or SGSN. To make the structure more practical, the IWF at the server end is divided into two parts (IWF-upper and IWF-lower) where the lower part takes care of the functionality described above and is situated in the WLAN access point, and the upper part is co-located with the Interworking Element (IWE), i.e., the modified SGSN. The two parts communicate via a TCP socket.

Since the WIP protocol uses its own Ethernet packet type, it can be used in parallel with other types of WLAN traffic such as native IP. It is feasible to build access points that simultaneously serve roaming GPRS consumers and native IP consumers, but if there are differences in bandwidth charges between these types of consumers, QoS support on the WLAN layer would be necessary.

The GPRS over WLAN load is lightweight on the radio. Discounting MAC-addressing, which is inherent to the Ethernet, the IWF PDUs and the WIP protocol add 11 bytes to a transmitted data packet. At an MTU of 1500 bytes on the Ethernet this is an overhead of less than 1 % compared to a bare data packet. For transporting small packets (e.g., signaling or voice), the overhead may grow as high as 20 %. Whether this is significant on a >10 Mbit/s channel depends on the application.

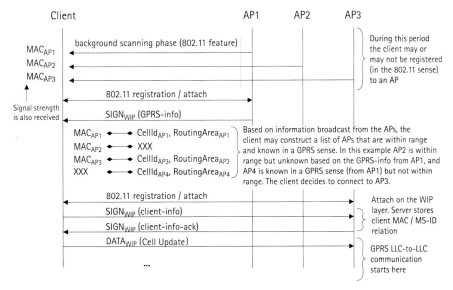

GPRS over WLAN link-level signaling

The handover mechanism in the WIP protocol is completely client-initiated. A continuously running background scan procedure combined with a list of information regarding neighboring access points provides the mobility management functionality with enough information for its decision-making processes. The client mobility management functionality consists of two modules: the Mobility Management Controller (MMCTL) and the WLAN Device Controller (WDCTL). The latter uses fuzzy-logic to find the best AP based on the two main parameters: the signal-to-noise ratio of a connection and an estimation of packet loss. The basic principle is shown in the following figure. When a new best AP is found, the MMCTL is informed of such a change and then starts a client-initiated handover.

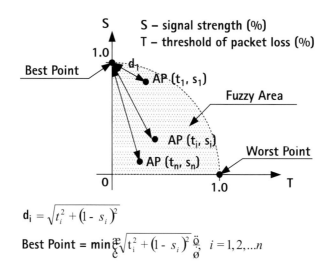

$$d_i = \sqrt{t_i^2 + \left(1 - s_i\right)^2}$$

$$\text{Best Point} = \min\left\{\sqrt{t_i^2 + \left(1 - s_i\right)^2}\right\}, \quad i = 1, 2, \ldots n$$

Best access point selection with fuzzy analysis

Dual-Mode Client

The final architectural component implemented is a dual-mode client stack, with support for both native GPRS and GPRS over WLAN. This stack has been created by adding a protocol switch at the bottom of the LLC protocol layer in the client. It selects between the RLC and IWF layers, which, in practical terms, enables roaming between the two radio interfaces. The protocol switch is controlled by the mobility management functionality in the GPRS stack. Switching between the protocol stacks must be done in coordination with the mobility management signaling, so that the signaling and user data contexts are maintained.

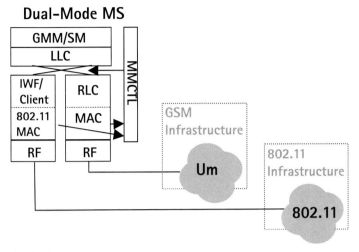

Dual-mode Mobile Station

The decision logic in mobility management can be made arbitrarily complex. The mobility management decides which access mechanism to use at a specific time, and how and when to handoff between available access points and between available network types. The decision logic may or may not include consumer input. Hence, the decision logic input parameters include:

1. Available access points and their S/N ratio

2. Cost of transmission vs. the consumer's willingness to pay

3. Energy consumption considerations

4. Available bandwidth in a specific access point vs. the current needs of the consumer

5. Handoff delays and implications

Demonstrator

LLC switching functionality and IWF were added to GPRS emulators of the MITA Reference Implementation Environment. The emulators are implemented using the C Virtual Operating System (CVOPS). In the object-oriented architecture of CVOPS, protocol layers are implemented as objects communicating using the CVOPS scheduler. The emulator also emulates the native GSM radio resource over IP; in the demonstration setup, both network accesses where tested over WLAN, with the GPRS over WLAN part as a full implementation and the native GPRS access emulated as IP transport over WLAN channels.

The server part of the demonstration system consists of eight PCs running Linux. A total of five PCs implement the GPRS access point functionality. The actual network part consists of three PCs containing two SGSNs, two BSCs and four BTSs, two IWEs, a HLR, a Gateway GPRS Support

Node (GGSN) and additionally stacks for SS7 communication. The five access points were able to be connected to any combination of the eight access variations formed by the four BTSs and include the possibility of connecting up to two APs and an IWE. The following figure shows one possible setup of the network. Two Linux laptops with dual-mode stacks and WLAN cards form the mobile station.

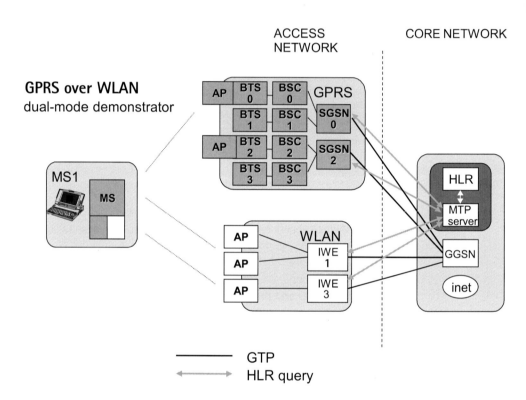

GPRS over WLAN demonstrator layout

References

[1]   Jianhua Wang: WLAN Radio Access To GPRS Network, August 2000, M.Sc Thesis, Helsinki University of Technology, Faculty of Electrical and Communications Engineering.

[2]   The Wireless LAN Alliance, http://www.wlana.com/intro/introduction/index.html "Introduction to Wireless LAN," printed on Feb. 01, 2000.

[3]   ETSI GSM 03.60 V6.2.0 "GPRS Service description"

[4]   ETSI GSM 04.64 Version 6.2.0 "GPRS MS-SGSN LLC layer specification"

Sofia – IPv6 Multimedia Communications Software

Internet telephony consists not only of transmitting speech over packet-based networks, but also includes many other aspects of communications: easy-to-remember addressing, user and service mobility, network presence, instant messaging and multimedia. In addition to peer-to-peer communications, seamless integration with Web browsing and real-time multimedia streaming are needed for a rich user experience.

Sofia is an IPv6 multimedia communications software suite developed by the Nokia Research Center. Sofia contains the basic protocols used by Internet telephony: Session Initiation Protocol (SIP), Session Description Protocol (SDP), and Real-time Transport Protocol (RTP). Other protocols (e.g., Real Time Streaming Protocol (RTSP) and HyperText Transfer Protocol (HTTP)) are also included as they are needed when providing rich multimedia services.

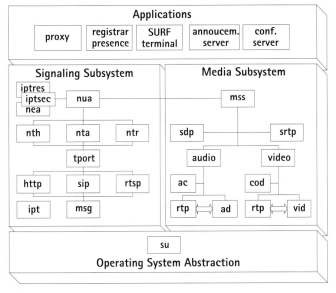

Sofia software architecture

Sofia Signaling Subsystem

The core of Internet telephony is the SIP, which is used to locate users, determine their status and communication capabilities, and finally setup and manage calls. The Sofia signaling subsystem contains modules implementing different layers of the SIP protocol, and providing other signaling-related services used by SIP entities.

The SIP specification has matured considerably over the past three years: the protocol was simplified and clarified, functionality which no one had implemented was removed, and some features were added.

The new sip-bis specification divides the SIP protocol into five layers: logical entity, application core, transaction, transport and message syntax layers. The SIP protocol layers are investigated below together with the corresponding Sofia modules implementing them.

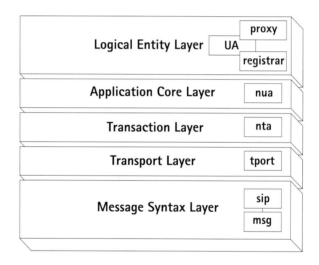

SIP protocol layers and corresponding Sofia modules

Logical Entity Layer

The SIP specification identifies six different logical entities: User Agent (UA), Stateful Proxy, Stateless Proxy, Registrar, Redirect Server and Back-to-Back User Agent (B2BUA).

The entity initiating a new SIP request is called a User Agent Client (UAC), while the entity ultimately responding to the request is called a User Agent Server (UAS). A logical entity, the user agent, is involved in both initiating SIP requests and responding to them. A terminal, gateway or network server contains a User Agent entity. In the Surf terminal, the Sofia NUA module implements the SIP user-agent functionality.

Like a user-agent, a proxy contains both server and client functionality. As a server, it accepts incoming requests, and as a client it forwards them to their destination. There are two kinds of proxies, stateful and stateless. A stateful proxy forwards transactions and contains transaction state machines. A stateless proxy does not contain a transaction layer, but instead it works directly on top of the transport layer. The Sofia proxy module works both as a stateless and a stateful proxy.

A registrar accepts REGISTER requests, and uses them to update the location service information. The Sofia registrar module implements the registrar and location service functionalities.

A redirect server provides a very straightforward routing service: upon receiving a request, it replies either with a 3XX series response redirecting the client towards the ultimate destination, or with a 404 Not Found response if the destination was not known to it. The redirect server is a very simple UAS, and it can be implemented with a few lines of C language code within the Sofia architecture. There is no separate redirect server module, but the Sofia proxy can be configured to function as one.

A B2BUA acts as a UAS when receiving a request. In order to respond to requests, it acts as a UAC and generates other requests. It maintains dialog state, and must participate in all transactions related to those dialogs it is involved in. The Sofia Multiparty Conferencing Unit (MCU) is a simple B2BUA.

These logical entities are just basic roles for the SIP network elements, for a SIP network element can play different roles depending on the services it needs to provide. For example, a proxy server can start processing a MESSAGE request as a stateless proxy, but if it discovers that the recipient is registered with it, it would switch to the stateful role. If the proxy did not know the recipient's message adaptation parameters it could act as a B2BUA and ask for the parameters using an OPTIONS request before running the message adaptation process.

Application Core Layer

The UAC core, UAS core, and proxy core reside at the application core layer. They consist of common processing functions required by respective functional entities. For example, UAS core functions are common to all different UAS servers. When describing the transaction layer, the application cores are also known as Transaction Users (TU).

Dialogs are maintained at the application core layer. A dialog is a peer-to-peer relationship between two user agents, and it is established by an initial request and a successful (i.e., 2XX class) response to it. Early dialogs are established by provisional responses to the initial request. A dialog is also associated with a route, with route management also taking place at the application core layer. Detecting merged requests (requests forked and routed over a different path to the UAS) is also related to dialog management.

The UAC core takes care of completing the request, sending transactions, recursing redirections and retrying requests with negotiated content and authorization information. It also uses special transactions to ensure reliable reception of different response messages (e.g., ACK for 2XX responses, PRACK for 1XX responses).

IV Implementations

Common tasks performed at the UAS application core layer include request method inspection, request Uniform Resource Identifier (URI) inspection, extension/options negotiation, and negotiation of content type and encoding. The UAS is responsible for resending the response messages when ACK or PRACK has not been received from UAC.

A UAS can also work in a stateless manner, so it can be implemented directly on top of transport. Such a stateless UAS never sends any provisional responses, but always replies to requests promptly with a final response. Special care should be taken in processing requests like CANCEL and ACK.

In the Sofia architecture, the NTA module takes care of some of these tasks, for instance, dialog and route management, request completion, ACK and PRACK transactions. The rest of the UAC and UAS tasks are implemented in the NUA module.

Transaction Layer

The transaction layer takes care of matching responses with requests and vice versa, retransmitting SIP messages and transaction timeouts. Transactions are a central part of the SIP protocol and every task in SIP takes place as a series of transactions. User agents and stateful proxies contain a transaction layer, which contains both client transaction and server transaction objects. A transaction object contains a state engine which processes transaction requests according to the state machines defined in the SIP specification.

The NTA module contains implementation of the SIP transaction layer, both transaction clients and transaction servers.

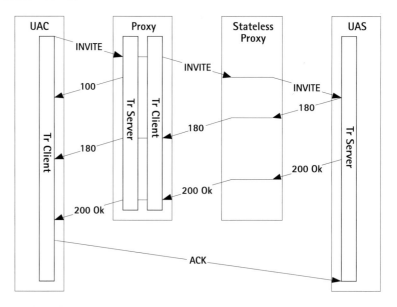

Basic SIP session initiation

Transport Layer

The SIP can be used with different transport protocols. These protocols can be reliable (e.g., Transmission Control Protocol (TCP)) or unreliable (e.g., User Datagram Protocol (UDP)), message-based (e.g., UDP) or stream-based (e.g., TCP). The transport layer is responsible for managing connections between SIP entities; it takes care of opening and closing connections, responding to network errors and reporting them to the layers above it.

The base specification defines how SIP deals with the UDP, TCP or Transport Layer Security (TLS) protocol. The SIP specification made both UDP and TCP mandatory for both SIP Proxies and User Agents.

The Sofia TPORT module contains an interface towards different transport protocols which are currently implemented within the OS kernel.

Message Encoding Layer

The message encoding layer is responsible for presenting SIP messages, requests and responses on the network using a transmission syntax understood by other SIP entities. The SIP uses text-based messages like many other Internet protocols. The basic message syntax is analogous to HTTP/1.1, where the request or status line is followed by headers, followed by an optional payload. The Advanced Backus-Naur Form (ABNF) rules specify the message syntax.

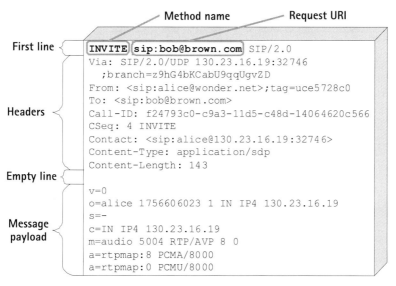

A SIP request message.

The Sofia parser is implemented with two modules: the SIP module contains SIP-specific parsing functionality while the MSG module contains generic protocol-independent parsing functions.

Routing SIP with DNS

The SIP request routing [sip-srv] is based on the DNS-like Internet e-mail protocol Simple Mail Transfer Protocol (SMTP). Internet mail routing is driven by mail server addresses and their priorities are stored in the Domain Name System (DNS) as Mail Exchange (MX) records. SIP routing, however, uses a more complex but also a more generic approach developed long after SMTP and MX. Instead of service-specific records, it is based on generic Naming Authority Pointer (NAPTR) [naptr] and service records (i.e., SRV records) [dns-srv] as explained below.

Naming Authority Pointers

When a SIP network element wants to know which protocols and services a domain can provide, it can make a NAPTR query before deciding which SRV record it will query from DNS. When UA has made a NAPTR query for a domain it is returned an answer of the format:

Domain TTL IN NAPTR Order Preference Flags Service Regexp Replacement

where

> *Domain*
>
>> is the domain name of the NAPTR record.
>
> *TTL*
>
>> is the time to live. This specifies the time interval that the resource record may be cached before the source of the information should again be consulted.
>
> *Order*
>
>> determines the order in which the NAPTR records must be processed.
>
> *Preference*
>
>> specifies preferred weight of the NAPTR records of the same order.
>
> *Flags*
>
>> defines how the NAPTR result is interpreted. Flags are single characters from A to Z or 0 to 9. For example, the flag *S* means that result would be the name of an SRV record.
>
> *Service*
>
>> specifies the service available when using this NAPTR record. The format for Service field is protocol+resolution_service, for example "SIP+D2T" means that the DNS domain name is given to Regexp, which gives the address of a host.
>
> *Regexp*
>
>> is a string containing a substitution expression, which is applied to the original query string in order to construct the query string or the URI used next.

Replacement

is the next query string or URI if no regexp is defined.

The figure below gives an example of an NAPRT record.

```
; sip services in example.com
example.com. 600 IN NAPTR 0 100 "S" "SIP+D2T" "" _sip._tcp.example.com
       600 IN NAPTR 0 100 "S" "SIP+D2U" "" _sip._udp.example.com
       600 IN NAPTR 0 100 "S" "SIPS+D2T" "" _sips._tcp.example.com
```

Example of NAPTR records

SRV Resource Records

SRV resource records are used to specify the location of the server or servers for a specific protocol within a given domain. The client gets an answer as a list of available servers. SRV allows administrators to use several servers for a single domain, to make server changes transparent, and to designate some servers as primary servers for a service and others as backup servers.

The format of SRV resource records returned from a server is

_Service._Protocol.Name TTL IN SRV Priority Weight Port Target

where

Service

is the name of the service. An underscore (_) is prepended to the service identifier to avoid collisions with names that may occur in the network.

Protocol

is the name of the desired transport protocol.

Name

is the domain this query refers to.

TTL

is the time to live. This specifies the time interval that the resource record may be cached before the source of the information should again be consulted.

Priority

of this target host. A client must attempt to contact the target host with the lowest numbered priority. Targets with the same priority should be tried in an order defined by the weight field.

IV

Implementations

Weight

> is used to select the server. The weight field gives the relative weight of the target in the group of targets with the same priority value.

Port

> is the port number of the service in the target host.

Target

> is the domain name of the target host.

The figure below provides an example of an SRV Resource Record in a DNS server:

```
;pscsf1 and pscsf2 should have equal load, TTL 600
_sip._tcp.example.com 600 IN SRV 0 100 5060 pscsf1.example.com
                      600 IN SRV 0 100 5060 pscsf2.example.com
```

Example of an SRV Resource Record in a DNS server

The figure below shows a complete dialog for resolving SIP URI <sip:user@example.com>.

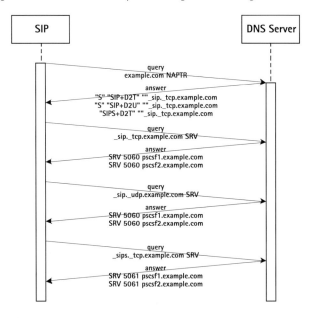

Example of a dialog when a client wants to resolve all the protocols available

Usually, a DNS server can include the SRV and A records as additional data together with the NAPTR results in the first response, so separate SRV queries are unnecessary.

Converting Telephone Numbers to URLs

ENUM [enum] takes a complete, international telephone number and resolves it to one or more URIs. A URI contains the signaling protocol, host name and the domain. ENUM uses the domain `e164.arpa` as a root of the mapping. A SIP application uses ENUM to convert telephone numbers to SIP URLs.

The following procedure is used when preparing a query for a DNS server:

1. Ensure that a telephone number is a valid E.164 number, including the country code.

2. Remove all extra characters except the leading "+". The resulting string is used as the input for NAPTR processing.

3. Also remove the leading "+" so that the telephone number consists only of digits.

4. Place dots (".") between each digit.

5. Reverse the order of the digits.

6. Append the string ".e164.arpa" to the end.

For example, if an IP telephony server wants to find out how the E.164 number +358 7 1800 8000 can be reached, it queries the DNS service for NAPTR records with the domain `0.0.0.8.0.0.8.1.7.8.5.3.e164.arpa`. The resulting NAPTR records might look like this:

```
0.0.0.8.0.0.8.1.7.8.5.3.e164.arpa.
     IN NAPTR 100 10 "u" "sip+E2U"    "!^.*$!sip:ph@nokia.fi!"      .
     IN NAPTR 101 10 "u" "http+E2U"   "!^.*$!http://www.nokia.fi!"  .
     IN NAPTR 102 10 "u" "mailto+E2U" "!^.*$!mailto:info@nokia.com!"  .
```

SIP Authentication

The baseline SIP authentication mechanism is known as an HTTP Digest, and is borrowed from the HTTP/1.1 [digest]. Because SIP and HyperText Transfer Protocol (HTTP) have quite different service models, the SIP specification has to clarify and modify HTTP Digest usage. Digest authentication is based on digest algorithms, such as Message Digest 5 (MD5) or Secure Hash Algorithm 1 (SHA-1). A digest algorithm is a trap-door function, which takes an arbitrary bit-string as input and provides a compact fingerprint, digest, of that data as output. It is very hard to find another bit-string which would generate the same digest.

When using digest authentication, the server will generate a challenge - some random-looking data known as nonce - and send that to the client. The client would take the password required by the server, the nonce sent to it, the relevant parts of the request, some random data and generate a digest. The digest would then be sent to the server within the request message. The server can then calculate the same digest using the password known by it and the same parts of the request.

IV

Implementations

The Sofia IPTSEC module contains implementation of both server and client sides of the HTTP digest authentication scheme. The implementation allows a client to authenticate its request with several proxies and servers.

Sofia Multimedia Subsystem

An Internet call consists conceptually of two parts, a signaling part and a media part, a multimedia session. The multimedia session may contain multiple mediums and connections. The Sofia Multimedia Subsystem (MSS) contains implementation for the various components of the multimedia session.

Session Negotiation

The multimedia session components are described and negotiated using Session Description Protocol (SDP) [sdp]. Despite its name, SDP is basically a description language for session components and parameters. The SDP module contains encoding and decoding functionality for SDP session descriptions.

SDP was originally intended for describing loosely coupled multicast sessions. In these sessions there are typically few senders but many receivers. In this case, SDP is used only to describe the session and not to negotiate its contents.

A separate application of SDP known as the offer/answer model [sdp-oa] was later developed to specify how sessions are negotiated using SDP. The offer/answer model describes session negotiation in a point-to-point unicast session. According to the model, one session participant offers the other a description of the session from her perspective, and the other participant answers with a description of the desired session from his perspective.

SIP user agents follow the offer/answer model when they exchange SDP descriptions and negotiate the call contents. The MSS module provides an Application Program Interface (API) used to setup and modify multimedia sessions according to the standard specification.

```
v=0
o=jari 2890844526 1 IN IP4 hews001.nokia.com
s=
c=IN IP4 172.21.41.115
t=0 0
m=audio 49170 RTP/AVP 0 96 97
a=rtpmap:0 PCMU/8000
a=rtpmap:96 AMR/8000
a=rtpmap:97 AMR-WB/16000
m=audio 51434 RTP/AVP 110
a=rtpmap:110 telephone-events/8000
a=sendonly
m=video 51372 RTP/AVP 31
a=rtpmap:31 H261/90000
m=video 53000 RTP/AVP 32
a=rtpmap:32 MPV/90000
```

Offer

```
v=0
o=- 2890844730 1 IN IP4 gw.nokia.com
s=
c=IN IP4 172.21.41.1
t=0 0
m=audio 65422 RTP/AVP 96 97
a=rtpmap:96 AMR/8000
a=rtpmap:97 AMR-WB/16000
m=audio 53354 RTP/AVP 110
a=rtpmap:110 telephone-events/8000
a=recvonly
m=video 0 RTP/AVP 31
m=video 53000 RTP/AVP 32
a=rtpmap:32 MPV/90000
```

Answer

Example of offer/answer negotiation

The figure above shows messages in a basic offer/answer negotiation. In the offer, there are a total of four media descriptions. The first audio media stream has three speech codec alternatives. The second audio media has only one codec, which is used for carrying telephone-events, such as Dial Tone Multi-Frequency (DTMF) tones. The telephone events stream is also marked `sendonly`, as the offerer is not prepared to receive events. After these two audio streams there are two proposed media streams for video, one using the H.261 video codec, another the MPV video codec.

The answer has all the media descriptions in the same order as in the offer. In the first audio media the answerer has selected two of the codecs from the offer. The payload types are the same and in the same order as in the offer. The answerer accepts the second audio as is, but marks the stream `recvonly`, as the answerer is only willing to receive events. The answerer does not support H.261, so he declines the first video stream and sets its port number to zero. The second video stream is accepted as is.

Media Transport

Speech is carried over the Internet using the Real-time Transport Protocol (RTP) [rtp]. Besides speech, the RTP can be used to carry other media (e.g., video or high-quality audio). The Real-time Transport Control Protocol (RTCP) is used to monitor media delivery, synchronize different streams and provide minimal control and identification for multimedia streams.

The RTP is not a complete protocol by itself, but provides fundamental end-to-end delivery services for real-time data. The usage of RTP features greatly depends on the application profile and the media transmitted. The RTP profile document [rtp-avp] actually describes two profiles, one for audio and another for video.

The Sofia RTP module implements both the RTP and RTCP. It follows an object-oriented approach, and is designed to provide a virtual interface for the actual media-specific implementation.

The audio codec interface AC and the audio device abstraction layer AD were designed to be interoperable smoothly with various RTP features. The Sofia Multimedia Subsystem audio stream implementation combines the AC and AD modules with the RTP module.

IV Implementations

References

[sip-bis] Rosenberg, J. et al, "SIP: Session Initiation Protocol," Request for Comments 3261, March 2002.

[sip-srv] Rosenberg, J. and H. Schulzrinne, "SIP: Locating SIP Servers," Request for Comments 3263, March 2002.

[naptr] Mealling, M., and R. Daniel, "The Naming Authority Pointer (NAPTR) DNS Resource Record," Request for Comments 2915, September 2000.

[dns-srv] Gulbrandsen, A., Vixie, P., and L. Esibov, "A DNS RR for specifying the location of services (DNS SRV)," Request for Comments 2782, February 2000.

[enum] Faltström, P., "E.164 number and DNS," Request for Comments 2916, September 2000.

[digest] Franks J. et al, "HTTP Authentication: Basic and Digest Access Authentication," Request for Comments 2617, June 1999.

[sdp-oa] Rosenberg, J., and H. Schulzrinne, "An Offer/Answer Model with SDP," Request for Comments 3264, March 2002.

[sdp] Jacobson, V., and M. Handley, "SDP: Session Description Protocol," Request for Comments 2327, Jan. 1998.

[rtp] Schulzrinne, H., Casner, S., Frederick, R., and V. Jacobson, "RTP: A Transport Protocol for Real-Time Applications," Request for Comments 1889, Jan. 1996.

[rtp-avp] Schulzrinne, H., "RTP Profile for Audio and Video Conferences with Minimal Control," Internet Engineering Task Force, Request for Comments 1890, Jan. 1996.

SIP Transaction Engines

This section provides an overview of SIP transaction engine implementations and the Application Programming Interfaces (API) they provide. The SIP transaction engines include the Sofia NTA module. The NTA module provides a SIP transaction layer for C and Java™ APIs.

Sofia Transaction API

Sofia provides two different levels of access to the SIP protocol: a high-level interface known as the NUA (Sofia User Agent API), and a low-level interface known as the NTA (Sofia Transaction API). Both APIs are specified in C. The NTA module contains implementation of NTA API.

The NTA module is the central part of the Sofia software suite, containing the fundamental components of the SIP protocol, namely, transaction processing and dialog management. The NTA module contains some functions that the SIP specification places above SIP transaction layer, namely, Uniform Resource Identifier (URI) processing and dialog management. They are included partly for historical reasons and partly in order to avoid duplicating functionality outside the NTA module.

The NTA module uses services from four low-level modules: TPORT, SIP, MSG and IPT. The TPORT module provides an abstraction layer to the underlying transport protocols: the User Datagram Protocol (UDP), Transmission Control Protocol (TCP) and Stream Control Transport Protocol (SCIP). The SIP and MSG modules provide encoding and decoding of SIP messages, and manipulation of SIP headers. The SIP module contains SIP-specific functionality while functionality in the MSG module is generic and common to the Session Initiation Protocol (SIP), Real Time Streaming Protocol (RTSP) and HyperText Transfer Protocol (HTTP). The IPT module contains functions for UTF-8 encoding/decoding, base64 encoding/decoding, generating globally unique call identifiers and other utilities.

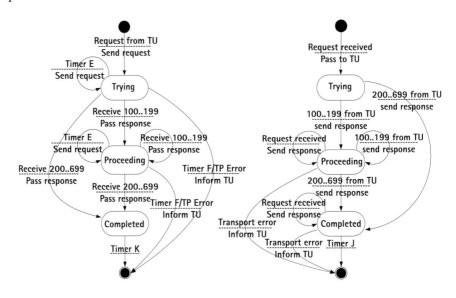

Normal SIP transaction state machines: client transaction on the left, server transaction on the right

The SIP and MSG Modules

In addition to encoding and decoding, SIP and MSG modules also provide functions for manipulating SIP headers: creating and copying them, changing their value, adding and removing them from the messages. The SIP module contains all the SIP-specific functionality, while the MSG module provides generic protocol-independent functions. The MSG module also contains functions for handling different Uniform Resource Identifiers (URI) and Uniform Resource Locators (URL).

The SIP module provides the default SIP message class object, which contains the parsing table used by the SIP. The message class is used to create SIP messages with the default layout. For special applications of the SIP parser (e.g., implementing the Common Gateway Interface for SIP (SIP-CGI) [sip-cgi]), a special SIP message class object can also be created.

Each header has its own header class object, which can be retrieved from the message class using the header name. Other parts of the message (e.g., the first line or the payload) have also header classes to represent them.

The message parsing process is fairly simple: first, the request or status line is parsed, then the headers are separated from the rest of the message one-by-one and passed to their own parsers. The way SIP messages are encapsulated varies from one transport protocol to another. Therefore, the parsing process is driven by the TPORT module. The message parser returns after an empty line between headers and message payload has been detected and the complete set of headers has been parsed; the TPORT module then decides how to cope with the payload.

The TPORT Module

The TPORT module contains a simple abstraction layer on top of various transport protocols used with SIP. Of course, the tport module can also be used with other protocols (e.g., HTTP or RTSP).

The TPORT module provides a uniform interface towards all transports, and mainly takes care of receiving and sending SIP messages. When passed a message to be sent, it first determines its destination, encodes it and then passes the encoded message to the underlying transport protocol. When receiving data, the TPORT module passes it to the parser, and when the parser determines it has completed a message, it passes the message to the application.

The TPORT module caches the connections for connection-oriented protocols, keeping them open while they are used and shutting them down when they are no longer needed. The TPORT module interprets network errors and reports them to the upper layer.

The TPORT module determines the proper transport and connection by its name tuple (containing the transport protocol name, and remote IP and port numbers). In addition to these, the data structure also contains the canonic name of the transport end-point, which can be used to avoid resolving names of frequently used destinations (e.g., the default outbound proxy).

The TPORT module provides means for enumerating active transports, so that the upper layers can deduce which transports they have at their disposal.

NTA API Objects

While the NTA API is specified using C, it follows object-oriented design principles. The API provides access to five different objects:

o   messages (`msg_t`),

o   client transactions (`nta_outgoing_t`),

o   server transactions (`nta_incoming_t`),

o   dialogs (`nta_leg_t`), and

o   agent (`nta_agent_t`).

So, in addition to the functions required to manage client transactions, server transactions, and dialogs. It is also used as a message factory. The `nta_msg_create` function creates new SIP messages with the help of a message class that is associated with the agent object.

NTA Agent

The NTA agent object is a container for transport streams, active transactions and legs. It also provides access to the stack-wide parameters. The main task of an agent object is matching incoming messages with other objects: client transactions, server transactions, dialogs and hooks. It is also a message factory: using the message class associated with the NTA agent when creating new SIP messages.

IV

Implementations

NTA Dialogs

NTA dialog objects, called *legs*, process requests belonging to a particular SIP dialog. A dialog is specified by Call-ID, local address and its tag, remote address and its tag, and by the leg's destination address. A tag is an extra identifier attached to an address making it unique, necessary because a SIP address can be bound with several user agents. When matching an incoming request with legs, the Call-ID header from the request is compared with leg's Call-ID, To header with local address, From header with remote address, and request-URI with the leg's destination address.

A leg can be underspecified, for instance, if the remote tag is not known. When matching legs, the most specific match is chosen.

As a special case, a leg can contain only the destination address. By default incoming requests can be processed by a default leg (i.e., a leg without Call-ID, local or remote addresses). Only the destination address is matched with the leg's destination address. A default leg can also be created without a destination URI, and is used to process requests which did not match a dialog leg or other default legs.

When an application creates a leg it assigns it a callback function and a context pointer. Whenever a request is matched with a leg, the leg object creates a new server transaction object, invokes the callback function and passes the new server transaction to the application.

NTA Server Transactions

Server transactions are created by NTA server transactions object when it receives a new request message. The request messages may either match a dialog leg or a default leg. A server transaction takes care of reliably sending responses to the client.

When an incoming server transaction is created, it is inserted into the hash table, whose key is a combination of the Call-ID and CSeq value. Even though the SIP specifies an optimization technique for recognizing the retransmitted requests by the branch parameter in the topmost Via header, this optimization is really only useful in proxies. That is, a UAS should recognize merged requests and reply to them with a *482 Request Merged error* response. The merged requests have the same Call-ID, CSeq, To and From headers, but a different branch value in the topmost Via. The branch values differ because a proxy has forked the request and these forked requests have arrived through different paths to the server.

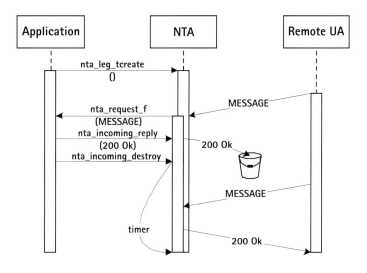

A response to a normal server transaction is retransmitted only when receiving a retransmitted request.

The newly-created transaction is passed to the application by invoking the callback function (nta_request_f). Upon receiving a new incoming transaction, the application should promptly reply to it. If it cannot answer immediately (within 200 milliseconds), it should then reply with a provisional response. The server transaction generates a 100 Trying provisional response by itself if it receives a retransmitted request before the application has responded.

An incoming server transaction is usually replied to with the reply function (nta_incoming_treply). The reply function generates a suitable response message copying appropriate headers (e.g., Call-ID, Via, From, To, and Record-Route) from the request message, and augments them with headers given by the user.

When the application is done with the server transaction, it can mark the transaction as expendable with destroy function (nta_incoming_destroy). The transaction is eventually freed by a timer after no more retransmitted requests are expected to arrive. If the application destroys a server transaction it has not replied to, a 500 Internal Server Error response is generated.

IV Implementations

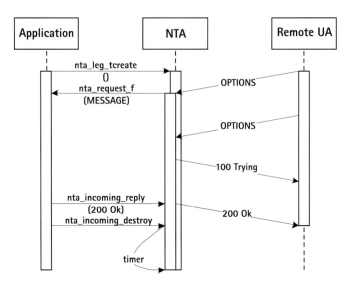

A server transaction optionally generates a 100 Trying response if the application has not generated any response.

While an application can send multiple provisional responses, only one final response can be sent. INVITE is an exception, however. It is possible to reply to an INVITE server transaction with multiple 200-series responses.

The request callback function can shortcut responding to the requests, and directly return a numeric response code. A corresponding response message is immediately generated and, if the response was final, the incoming transaction is marked for destroyal. If the response code is not valid, a 500 Internal Server Error response is sent instead. It is not possible to reply to an INVITE request with a 200-series response in this manner, 200 Ok to INVITE requires special processing from the application.

If the incoming request was an INVITE, the application should bind a callback function to it, unless it can respond immediately to it. The callback function takes care of processing the related CANCEL or ACK transactions or processing timeout if no ACK was received.

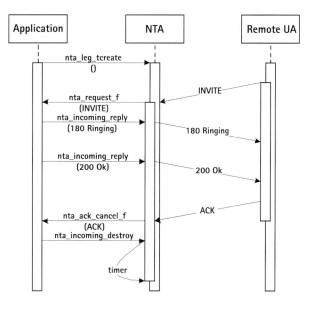

An ACK request is processed with the callback function bound to the INVITE request.

NTA Client Transactions

The NTA client transaction objects take care of transmitting SIP requests reliably. When a client transaction is created, it sends a request message to the network, then waits for responses. It then hands response messages over to the application. The transaction is completed when a final response has been received. A completed transaction is marked as expendable and is eventually freed by a timer. A completed transaction is kept alive, as it is needed to process retransmitted responses possibly still in transit.

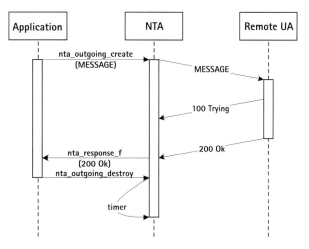

A message sequence of a normal NTA client transaction

NTA defines a straightforward API for client transactions. The application creates a client transaction with creation function (`nta_outgoing_mcreate`). The request message is sent immediately when the outgoing transaction is created.

The client transaction is added to the hash table in the agent object. The branch parameter in the topmost Via header is generated by NTA, and is used as a key to the hash table. Whenever the agent receives a response message, it uses the branch parameter to locate the client transaction. The client transaction object processes the responses, usually delivering them to the application using the callback function. The callback function, in turn, was provided by the application when the transaction was created.

A timer takes care of retransmitting the request until a suitable response has been received. For normal transactions, the request message is retransmitted until a final response is received.

INVITE and ACK transactions are special cases. The INVITE transaction stops retransmitting the request when a provisional response is received. In order to ensure reliable reception of the final response, it must be acknowledged with an ACK message. An ACK to a final error response is generated internally by NTA. An ACK to 200-series response is sent by the application, which usually just creates a new ACK transaction. Further retransmitted 200-series responses are delivered to the ACK transaction instead of the original INVITE.

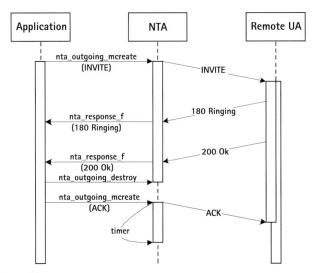

Separate ACK transaction

When the application no longer needs the transaction, it can be destroyed. Actually, a destroyed transaction is only marked as expendable, and the transaction state is not modified. If the application is not interested in the eventual response message, it can destroy a transaction at any time.

The application can select whether *proxy semantics* or *plain semantics* are followed when processing transport errors or timeouts. When using *proxy semantics*, the callback function is given an internally generated response message. When using *plain semantics*, the callback function is invoked without a response message, and the application must use discover function (`nta_outgoing_status`) to discover the error condition.

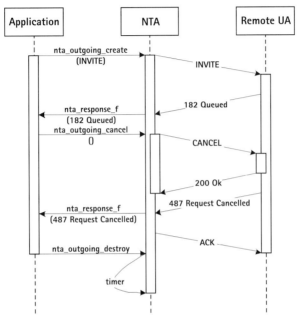

A cancelled INVITE client transaction

There are two convenience functions for canceling INVITE transactions (`nta_outgoing_cancel` and `nta_outgoing_tcancel`). With the latter, the caller can provide a transaction callback function, which is called when a response to CANCEL is received.

Note that these convenience functions do not change the state of the INVITE transaction, but rather create a separate CANCEL transaction. The transaction server completes the INVITE transaction by sending a 487 Request Cancelled response.

The ACK message is sent automatically by NTA when it receives an error response to an INVITE transaction. From the application point of view, it is part of the original INVITE transaction.

Stateless Processing

It is possible to use NTA to process some messages in a stateless manner, for example, in a stateless proxy. The NTA provides two functions for this purpose: the first function `nta_msg_tsend` forwards the messages (either requests or responses), and the second function `nta_msg_treply` responds to a request without creating a server transaction. It is also possible to discard messages with `nta_msg_discard`, or statefully process requests with `nta_leg_stateful`.

IV

Implementations

Processing Late 200 Ok

Sometimes a User Agent Server (UAS) has not received the CANCEL request even though the attempted call has been dropped. In that case, the UAS may still be alerting the user even though the User Agent Client (UAC) has already destroyed its call state. If the user then accepts the call and the UAS responds with 200 Ok, the UAC should be able to promptly either set up a proper call, or release the phantom call.

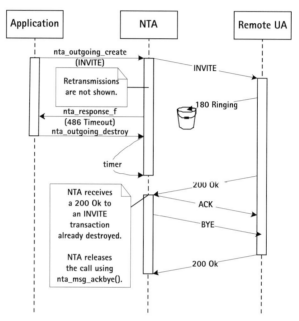

NTA can process orphan 200 Ok responses on behalf of the SIP UAC.

By default, if the application is not prepared to process messages statelessly, NTA handles these OK messages (`nta_msg_ackbye`). The NTA acknowledges the 200 Ok with an ACK transaction and immediately releases the call with a BYE transaction.

JAIN SIP API

The JAIN™ APIs [jain] are a set of Java APIs, which enable rapid development of communication and service applications on the Java platform. The JAIN API family provides APIs for different kinds of communications infrastructures, for example:

o Internet technologies

o Public Switched Telephone Network (PSTN)

o Intelligent Networks (IN)

The goal of the JAIN SIP API is to provide a means to develop SIP applications for high-end clients and network servers. The target platforms for this API are the Java 2 Standard Edition (J2SE) and Java 2 Enterprise Edition (J2EE). The JAIN SIP API provides applications access to the SIP stack, i.e., the ability to initiate and respond to SIP transactions and access different parts of SIP messages.

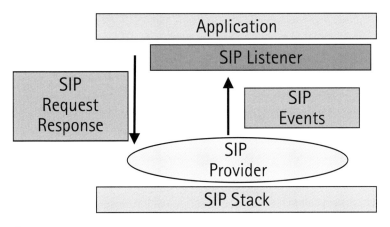

JAIN SIP architecture

The two main API components are the Java interfaces SipProvider and SipListener. A SipListener is used by applications to receive SIP events, while the SipProvider is used by applications to send messages to the network. The SipProvider interface also offers methods to manage a list of listeners. JAIN SIP API defines the following Java packages:

o **jain.protocol.ip.sip**: This package defines the main interfaces for JAIN SIP and also classes and exceptions to send and receive SIP messages, for example SipListener, SipEvent and SipParseException.

o **jain.protocol.ip.sip.address**: This package defines interfaces to represent SIP addresses, for example, SipURL and SipAddress.

o **jain.protocol.ip.sip.header**: This package defines interfaces for all standard SIP headers, for example, ToHeader and ViaHeader.

o **jain.protocol.ip.sip.message**: This package defines interfaces to represent SIP messages, for example, SipRequest and SipResponse.

IV Implementations

Here is an example of how an application can initialize a SIP stack:

```
public void initializeSipStack() throws InitializationException {
    try {
        // Get SipFactory Object
        SipFactory mySipFactory = SipFactory.getInstance();
        // Set stack provider specific path
        mySipFactory.setPathName("com.nokia.nrc");
        // Create stack
        SipStack mySipStack = (SipStack)mySipFactory.createSipStack();

        // Set stack name
        mySipStack.setStackName("NRC JAIN SIP STACK");
        Iterator listeningPoints = mySipStack.getListeningPoints();
        // Select one listening point for this application
        ListeningPoint listeningPoint = (ListeningPoint)listeningPoints.next();
        // Create SipProvider for specified listeningpoint
        SipProvider mySipProvider = mySipStack.createSipProvider(listeningPoint);

        // Set this application to listen sip events
        mySipProvider.addSipListener(this);
    } catch(Exception e) {
        // Exception handling...
    }
}
```

After an application has successfully initialized the SIP provider, it can start sending and receiving SIP messages. Here is another example of how an application can create and send a SIP message:

```
public void send Message() {
    try {
        // Create all required factory objects
        AddressFactory addressFactory = mySipFactory.createAddressFactor y();
        HeaderFactory headerFactory = mySipFactory.createHeaderFactory();
        MessageFactory messageFactory = mySipFactory.createMessageFactory();

        // Create Request      - URI
        URI requestURI = addressFactory.createURI("SIP", chris.Bouret @nokia.com );
        // Create all required headers
        FromAddress fromAddress = addressFactory.createNameAddress("Mikko Lönnfors", "sip:mikkko.lonnfors@nokia.com")
        FromHeader fromHeader = headerFactory.createFromHeader(fromAddress);
        ToAddress toAddress = addressFactory.createNameAddress("Chris Bouret", "sip:chris.bouret@nokia.com");
        ToHeader toHeader = headerFactory.createToHeader(toAddress);
        CallIdHeader callIdHeader = mySipProvider.getNewCallIdHeader();
        SCeqHeader sceqHeader = headerFactory.createCSeqHeader(1, "INVITE");

        ViaHeader viaHeader = headerFactory.createViaHeader("169.1  0.120.1", 5060, "TCP");
        List viaList = new ArrayList();
        viaList.add(viaHeader);

        // Create new Request object
        Request request = messageFactory.createRequest(requestURI, "INVITE", callIdHeader, sceqHeader, fromHeader, toHeader, viaList);

        // Send request to network
        request.send();
    } catch(Exception e) {
        // Exception handling
    }
}
```

Messages coming from the network are passed to listening applications through the SipListener interface. The interface provides three methods for this purpose:

o   **processRequest(SipEvent receivedRequest)**: This method is called when a new request has been received by SipStack.

o   **processResponse(SipEvent receivedResponse)**: This method is called when a new response has been received by SipStack.

o   **processTimeout(SipEvent transactionTimeout)**: This method is called when some SIP transaction has timed out.

SIP API for the Java 2 Platform Micro Edition

The Mobile Information Device Profile (MIDP) is a set of Java APIs which, together with the Connected, Limited Device Configuration (CLDC), provides a complete Java 2 Micro Edition (J2ME™) application runtime environment targeting mobile devices (e.g., cellular phones and two-way pagers) [J2ME]. It defines a secure platform on small devices which allows 3rd party developers to introduce new innovative services (e.g., games and messengers) more easily. IP support on 3G networks opens up even more possibilities to utilize these networking capabilities. The current MIDP 1.0 specification includes HTTP, which is good for client-server communication. By adding the SIP protocol, the possibilities expand from client-server connections to peer-to-peer connectivity [jsr180]. The SIP protocol provides the following services: user location, user availability, user capabilities, and session setup and management.

The purpose of the J2ME SIP API is to fulfill the needs of a wide range of application developers on small terminals. Potential application areas include:

o   Applications utilizing communication services enabled by SIP and other IP protocols.

o   Interactive and dynamically downloadable applications (e.g., games, chat clients, presence clients and news/sport/weather watchers)

The J2ME SIP API specification will integrate with the CLDC Generic Connection Framework pattern and take into consideration the platform's resource constraints.

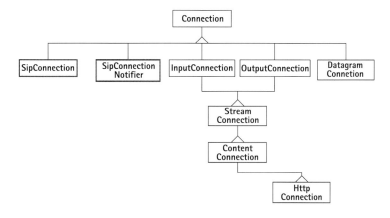

SIP in the CLDC Generic Connection Framework

IV   Implementations

J2ME MIDP/CLDC together with the SIP and HTTP provide a solid and secure platform for developers on small terminals. In conjunction with the SIP Servlet application server, it brings a dynamic environment to develop and deploy new services seamlessly. The service provider can build a new service with Java by using the SIP Servlet API on the server side and implementing a corresponding MIDlet on the client side using the J2ME SIP API. The MIDlet can be downloaded onto the terminal Over The Air (OTA) from a service provider's web site or another source.

References

[sip-bis]   Rosenberg, J., et al, "SIP: Session Initiation Protocol," RFC 3261, Proposed Internet Standard, March 2002.

[sip-cgi]   Lennox, J., H. Schultzrinne, and J. Rosenberg, "Common Gateway Interface for SIP," RFC 3050, January 2001.

[J2ME]   http://java.sun.com/j2me/index.html, J2ME Platform

[jain]   http://java.sun.com/products/jain/, The JAIN APIs

[jsr180]   Bouret, C., et al, "SIP API for J2ME," Java Specification Request 180 http://www.jcp.org/jsr/detail/180.jsp, work in progress, April 2002.

PART 4.3

Network

---

o 2G/3G Networks in the MITA Reference
   Implementation Environment

o Mobile IPv6 Core Network

o IPv6 Mobility Core

o NAT-PT – IPv6/IPv4 Translator

o IPv6 Tunnel Broker

o SIP Building Blocks

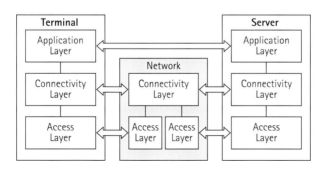

2G/3G Networks in the MITA Reference Implementation Environment

This chapter describes the features of the second and third generation radio access network and the packet core of the MITA Reference Implementation Environment.

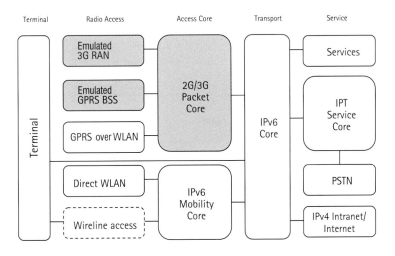

2G/3G radio access network and packet core in the MITA Reference Implementation Environment

The MITA Reference Implementation Environment deploys the UMTS Terrestrial Radio Access Network (UTRAN) and packet core emulators. These provide interfaces of Third Generation Partnership Project (3GPP) specifications so that emulators can also replace individual network elements in a real network.

UTRAN Emulator

The UTRAN Emulator contains 3GPP packet data protocol stack implementations for both signaling and the user plane. The UTRAN Emulator is based on Standard PC hardware, using the Linux operating system.

The UMTS Radio Access Network consists of two network elements: Node B and the Radio Network Controller (RNC). Node B and RNC are integrated into the emulator. UTRAN implements the Uu radio interface for the UE and Iu-ps to the Serving GPRS Support Node (SGSN) in the packet core network. The real WCDMA layer 1 in the radio interface has been replaced with the User Datagram Protocol (UDP) socket, which has a CRC error generator functionality for emulating errors.

The next figure illustrates the protocols of the UTRAN Emulator. The emulator interfaces the UE Emulator and SGSN Emulator.

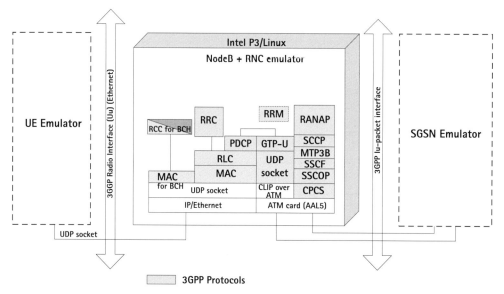

Protocols of the UTRAN emulator

Protocols and Features of the UTRAN Emulator

The UTRAN emulator contains the layer 3 protocols of RNC including Radio Resource Control (RRC) and Radio Access Network Application Protocol (RANAP). The emulator also has Radio Resource Management (RRM) containing algorithms and functionality needed to manage Wideband Code Division Multiple Access (WCDMA) radio resources under the Radio Network Controller. RRM supports algorithms and functions for handling Admission Control (AC), Load Control (LC), Power Control (PC), Handover Control (HC), Packet Scheduler (PS) and Resource Management (RM) procedures in RNC.

The user plane protocols supported in the UTRAN emulator are: Packet Data Convergence Protocol (PDCP), Radio Link Control (RLC), Medium Access Control (MAC), GPRS Tunneling Protocol for the User plane (GTP-U), User Datagram Protocol (UDP) and Classical IP (CLIP) over Asynchronous

Transfer Mode (ATM). The layer 3 protocols from Node B are Radio Resource Control (RRC) and MAC for the broadcast channel. RLC and MAC support the same features as the UE side.

Further on, the UTRAN emulator features Message Transfer Part 3 Broadband (MTP3B) and Signaling Connection Control Part (SCCP) protocols on top of the ATM protocol stack. The ATM protocol stack, in turn, consists of the Service Specific Co-operation Function (SSCF), Service Specific Connection Oriented Protocol (SSCOP) and Common Part Convergence Sublayer (CPCS) protocols. The rest of the ATM stack (e.g., ATM Adaptation Layer type 5) has been implemented on the ATM card.

The UTRAN emulator supports the following features:

o   Quality of Service (QoS) for several simultaneous Packet Data Protocol (PDP) contexts. Packet scheduling in MAC is based on priorities between simultaneous PDP contexts.

o   CRC error generator for emulating real WCDMA radio

o   ROHC header compression

o   Iu-PS to SGSN

o   The used bit rate can be negotiated during PDP context activation or modification

UTRAN supports the following signaling procedures:

o   Attach

o   Detach

o   PDP context activation/modification/release

Packet Core Emulator

The packet core emulator emulates the 3GPP packet core functionalities consisting of SGSN, Gateway GPRS Support Node (GGSN) and Home Location Register (HLR) emulators. Emulators run in a Linux® PC.

Emulators are built from protocol blocks implemented using a CVOPS protocol development platform accompanied with plain C language. It is possible to have each emulator in a separate Linux process, even in a separate Linux PC, or have them combined into one single process, depending on the use case the emulators are applied in. Each of the emulators can be replaced with real network elements and the system still works.

The Domain Name System (DNS) service required by SGSN can be provided by a Linux PC used to run the SGSN emulator. The SGSN emulator can request the DNS information from the Linux PC and if configured properly, Linux is able to provide it. The SGSN emulator also contains internal DNS implementation and therefore the use of real DNS is optional.

The emulators are able to provide the following interfaces: Iu-ps, Gr, Gn/Gp and Gi. The interfaces can be real physical interfaces or in the case of two emulators interfacing each other, the lower layer physical interface can be replaced with a UDP socket.

IV Implementations

The figure below illustrates the protocols of the packet core emulator:

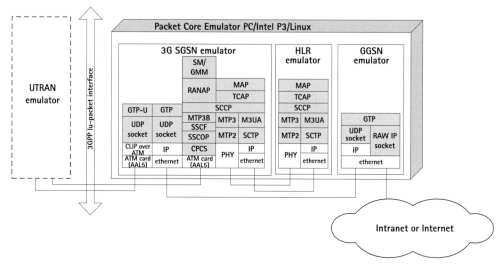

Protocols of the packet core emulator

Interfaces of the Packet Core Emulator

Interface options for the Iu-ps control plane include:

o   Real ATM transport

o   Virtual ATM transport via UDP sockets either with virtual MTP3 layer routing or point-to-point CPCS layer connection

o   SIGTRAN

Interface options for the Iu-ps user plane:

o   Classical IP over ATM package for real ATM

o   Standard UDP sockets over any transport. Both IPv4 and IPv6 are supported.

Interface options for Gr:

o   Real PCM transport

o   Virtual MTP3 layer transport via UDP sockets

o   SIGTRAN

Interface options for Gn/Gp:

o   Real IP transport, both IPv4 and IPv6 supported

o   Tunnel endpoint ports configurable in order to support multiple SGSN/GGSN network elements in a single host

Interface options for Gi:

o   Access to the global Internet via a raw socket. Every IP address allocated to PDP contexts will appear in this interface as a single IP host. Both IPv4 and IPv6 are supported.

Features of the Packet Core Emulator

SGSN is able to support any number of RNC, HLR, SMSC, SGSN and GGSN network elements. A separate ATM switch is required if more than one ATM endpoint is needed.

In its default configuration, SGSN supports 40 mobile devices and 80 PDP contexts, but this can be easily increased. Throughput is mostly CPU limited: with a 1 GHz Pentium processor the core network achieves 50 Mbit/s throughput in the 3G environment.

Quality of Service (QoS) policies are partially implemented. Core network elements do not apply any QoS policy mechanism themselves; negotiated QoS parameters are mapped onto Differentiated Services Code Points (DSCPs) and this is assigned to every GPRS Tunneling Protocol (GTP) payload packet in the Gn and Iu interface. It is up to the IP platform whether this information is used at all.

Core network emulators basically support every procedure in Iu, Gr and Gn/Gp specified in 3GPP Release 99 specifications. These include:

o   GPRS attach

o   Detach

o   Purge

o   Authentication

o   Identity check

o   PTMSI reallocation

o   Routing area update with all variants

o   Serving SRNS relocation

o   Service request

o   Subscriber management procedures

o   Paging

o   PDP context activation, modification and deactivation

o   Secondary PDP context activation, modification and deactivation

o   User payload, including IPv4 and IPv6

IV   Implementations

The GGSN will open a raw socket to read/send IPv4/IPv6 traffic from/to the external interface. The GGSN will monitor the external interface and whenever it detects a packet to the GPRS mobile device, it will capture it and send it on, correcting the GPRS device. Uplink packets are handled in the opposite way. If packets are going to an external network behind the IP subnet that the GGSN is handling, the GGSN emulator will need the assistance of an external router to deliver the packet.

Mobile IPv6 Core Network

Network Components

With the exception of some specific service and configuration nodes, all nodes in the network support IPv6 and have complete IPv6 connectivity with global addresses but without IPv6 Internet connectivity. As in IPv4, IPv6 routes consist of a combination of Routing Information Protocol (RIPng) and static routes relying mainly on the former. Address allocation is based on host address autoconfiguration, but static aliased addresses are also assigned to routers and servers. The IPv4 connectivity is based on assigning dynamic addresses from the Dynamic Host Configuration Protocol (DHCP) private address pool, as well as on using static addresses. IPv4 routes consist of a combination of a routing information protocol and static routes.

The following figure provides a look at the MIPv6 network components.

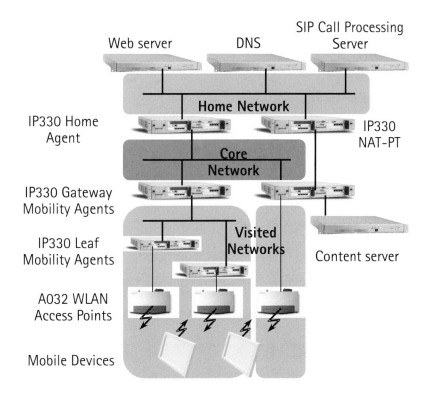

MIPv6 Network layout

Mobile Device

The mobile device used in this scenario is a 700 MHz laptop equipped with a Pentium III processor, 256 MB of memory and a 20 GB HD, running Linux with dual IP stacks, i.e., they are able to connect to the network using both IPv4 and IPv6. The Linux kernel is a slightly modified version of the default 2.4 series kernel, in order to use the Mobile IPv6 and its features. The device is connected to the network using a Personal Computer Memory Card International Association (PCMCIA) Wireless Local Area Network (WLAN) card providing an 11 Mbit/s connection.

Routers

The routers are NOKIA IPSO series 330, but could also be another IP series platform (e.g., 440, 650 or 740). They have dual stack capabilities, i.e., they are able to route both IPv4 and IPv6 traffic. In addition to these, other routers with Linux OS were also tested.

The routers have a different role depending on their location in the network. Leaf Mobility Agents (LMA) are routers on the edge of the network, directly connected to an access point providing access to the network for a mobile device. A Gateway Mobility Agent (GMA) exists logically between routers and acts as a regional top-level mobility agent. The Home Agent (HA) is a MIPv6 node in the mobile device's home network maintaining information on the mobile device's topological location.

Servers

The servers are industrial PCs with 512 MB of memory and a 20 GB hard disk, running Linux with dual IP stacks. The kernel version is the same as is in the mobile nodes, though the difference from the point of view of MIPv6 is that the nodes are configured to act as corresponding nodes.

Name resolution uses local name information for maintenance purposes, but is based on the use of IPv6 DNS servers of the type BIND9. One master DNS server serves the whole network, though individual sub networks may also have separate DNS servers.

Demonstrations

In order to demonstrate MITA MIPv6, a portable version of the MITA MIPv6 network was also built, possessing essentially the same functionality as the fixed network. The following sections cover the functionality and features tested and demonstrated in the MIPv6 test network.

Interoperability

Interoperability can be deployed using tunneling, dual stacks or network address and protocol translation. Of these, the latter two are in use in the MIPv6 network. In the network all routers, mobile devices and core nodes are dual stack entities. Additionally, the network has a Network Address Translator - Protocol Translator (NAT-PT) installed. Interoperability has been demonstrated (e.g., with Web browsing) which is possible since the NAT-PT has a HyperText Transfer Protocol (HTTP) application layer gateway.

Mobile IPv6 Roaming

The basic feature is to show how Mobile IPv6 maintains a session when a mobile device roams between WLAN access points. There is no reason for the mobile device to automatically change access point if the access points are close enough to each other. In order to ease testing and demonstration it was necessary to create a simulated manual handover, so the C110 cards in mobile devices were forced to connect to a specified C111 MAC address. However, if roaming takes place naturally, without manual handovers, and one desires to avoid the 1-3 sec scanning latency, a non-standard mechanism called hidden scanning should be used. This means that the WLAN driver periodically scans for information on the access points while joined to the current access point and before roaming. In a manual handover, an inter-frequency hard handover was used when the mobile node changed access point, i.e., it also changed the channel. A hard handover means that the old radio links are abandoned before the new radio links are established, thus simulating a situation where the link-layer can not predict the handover.

After assigning itself a new care-of address the mobile device immediately sends a binding update to the home agent and core node. A variety of factors can delay the sending of the binding update: joining a new access point, possibly performing wired equivalent privacy authentication and establishing IP layer connectivity, and assigning neighborhood discovery procedures including duplicate address detection. This delay might be noticed as glitches in a video/audio stream.

MIPv6 Enhanced

In a fast handover, the objective is to demonstrate a handover with low delay. The demonstrations considered the speed of handovers when routers a priori know where the mobile device is going to go. A mobile device may signal the router, which then communicates with the new router and informs back to the mobile device. In the demonstration, the mobile device chooses a new router and informs the current leaf mobility agent to make preparations while the mobile device does the handover.

The mobile device then makes a handover to a new leaf mobility agent and can handle traffic immediately on arrival with the new care-of address that was prepared in advance, thus avoiding duplicate address detection. In summary, the fast handover works strictly between leaf mobility agents while features, such as the regional registration6, works with routers) including routers towards the core network. Where regional registration6 eliminates signaling latency and load to the distant core node and home agent, the fast handover eliminates edge traversal latency when moving to new edge routers.

In a smooth handover, the aim is to minimize packet loss. Together, the fast handover and smooth handover form a seamless handover. A smooth handover is possible with, e.g., context transfer.

Managing buffers and header compression belongs to the Context Transfer Framework.

IV Implementations

IPv6 Mobility Core

IP-level mobility management builds on traffic indirection. A packet addressed to a host which has moved away from its home network needs to be rerouted to the mobile node's current topologically correct address. Mobile IPv6 handles this indirection by specifying a new functional component, called a Home Agent, and a set of processing rules and related signaling for the mobile node, home agent and the correspondent node. A mobile node is globally reachable through one or more addresses allocated from the same subnetwork where the home agent resides. Applications, then, start sessions with a remote end-point based on the identifying home address and continue using this address transparent to the movements of the node. Session continuity between communicating applications requires that a communication end-point abstraction (e.g., a socket) contains the same end-point address even though the underlying topological address might be changing as a function of the node's movement. A node moving away from its home network can register its current topologically correct address with the Home Agent, which then maintains the association between the care-of address and the home address. In order to achieve fully smooth and uninterrupted application behavior, it is necessary to provide some extra support in access routers in the visited network. If this is done, however, the mobility functionality can also handle traffic with strict timing constraints, as well as efficient network access control.

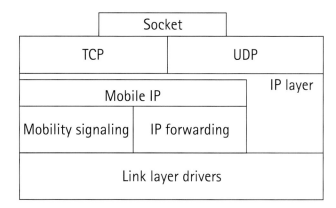

Mobile IP within the TCP/IP stack

Mobile IPv6 introduces additions and modifications to standard IPv6 stack message parsing and data forwarding as shown in the above figure. This chapter discusses mobile IPv6 implementation issues as well as enhancements in a mobility friendly network for efficient, robust, secure and real-time traffic as implemented in the MITA Reference Implementation Environment. We also describe how network access authentication has been used for the Mobile IPv6 protocol.

Mobility Signaling

When a mobile device moves to a new link with a prefix different from its previous on-link access address prefix, it needs to form a new care-of address from this link and register it with the Home Agent. If the mobile node is actively connected to the correspondent nodes, it needs to update their bindings as well. The signaling that conveys the mobility management messages (such as binding update and binding update acknowledgement) is an IPv6 protocol carried in the IPv6 extension headers.

Base line mobility management signaling [mipv6sup] has two parts: 1) authentication and authorization; and 2) actual traffic indirection which updates the binding associations. The Mobile IPv6 contains a method called Return Routability for authentication and authorization. This method introduces two tests to verify that the mobile node owns both the home address (home test) and the care-of address (care-of address test) it is claiming. Authentication and authorization is required for route optimization, where the mobile node and the correspondent node communicate directly with each other. Otherwise data is routed through the Home Agent.

The following diagram shows a Mobile IPv6 signaling sequence where a mobile node is binding with a correspondent node.

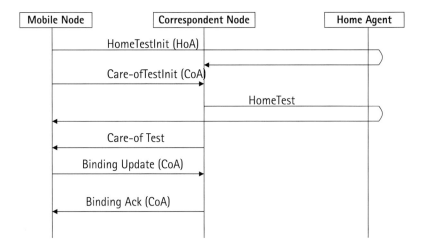

Since home agents can be deeply off-path from the optimal route between the communicating peers, it is important to be able to route packets between the peers along the optimal route. This shortens the total path length of traffic with mobile nodes, and also increases robustness by eliminating the home agent as a required intermediate point of traffic. This level of efficiency is achieved by the route optimization scheme of Mobile IPv6.

The mobility signaling of Mobile IPv6 integrates with the extension header processing of the standard IPv6 stack. Mobility signaling is carried in specific mobility headers. When the IPv6 header parsing finds a mobility header it calls a routine for the corresponding message. Return routability message handling creates the needed authentication data for the subsequent binding update messaging that controls the creation of binding cache entries.

IP Forwarding

Mobile IP adds two new data structures (binding cache and proxy neighbor cache) to standard IP forwarding, which are used as part of next hop route lookup. Each IPv6 node maintains a binding cache data structure that associates a mobile node's home address with the signaled care-of address. In addition to the home and care-of address, a binding cache entry contains a lifetime value indicating how long the binding is in effect. When a binding cache entry is created or changed the related signaling needs to be authenticated and authorized. For this purpose the binding cache stores a binding security association.

When a node forwards an IP packet, it looks in the binding cache for an entry matching the destination address. If an entry is found, the packet is given to the Mobile IPv6 modules for modification. If the node was the packet's originator (Correspondent Node), a router header is added to the packet, with the home address stored in the routing header and the care-of address as the destination address of the packet. If the node is a home agent proxying and intercepting the packets meant for the mobile node, it adds an IP-in-IP tunnel to the packet, with the outer IPv6 header containing the home agent's address as the source address and the mobile node's care-of address as the destination address.

Route Optimization

When the nodes communicate via the home agent, it is necessary to maintain bi-directional tunneling through the home agent during the whole session. To increase optimization, Mobile IPv6 includes route optimization for direct peer-to-peer mobility signaling. It allows for nodes to send and receive packets directly through the optimal route, thus also fully using the routing fabric.

To fulfill the requirement that no security infrastructure is needed for route optimization signaling protection, the binding update process is preceded by an infrastructureless binding authentication method, minimally a return routability test. It uses the routing fabric as a means of indirect verification that the sender of the binding update is where it claims to be. The correspondent node sends a message (Home Address Test (HoT)) via the home address and a second message directly to the claimed care-of address (Care-of Address Test (CoT)) to the mobile node. These messages carry cookies that need to be combined for message authentication and authorization of the binding update message. The return routability test could be replaced with stronger binding update authentication methods if and when they become available.

The routing infrastructure does not need extra support for route optimization; this is an issue only for the mobile node and its peers. However, to strengthen the security of the return routability test, IPSec should be applied for signals between the mobile node and the home agent.

For packet forwarding with route optimization, the home address is a required component in data packets sent between the mobile node and its correspondent nodes. The home address is inserted both ways into the packet in a way that allows for other nodes and intermediate filtering firewalls to be sure that these packets cannot be reflected from either end node to third parties. A firewall can drop the normal, type 0 routing headers without affecting route-optimized mobility traffic. Route-optimized traffic towards mobile nodes contains the home address in a special routing header, which is never forwarded out of the receiving node thus preventing misuse. This routing header is added to the Mobile IPv6 forwarding path as explained

IV Implementations

previously based on a matching entry in the binding cache. When a mobile node has successfully created a binding with a correspondent node, it updates the binding update list with the correspondent nodes address. When forwarding IP packets the mobile node checks if the correspondent node has an entry in the list and adds a home address option to the packet which conveys the mobile node's home address. The correspondent node does not accept a home address option without verifying that a binding cache entry exists for the home address.

Home Agent Implementation

The home agent is a forwarding node which defends the home address of a mobile node by means of proxy neighbor discovery support. This support allows the home agent to perform neighbor discovery [RFC 2461] operations on behalf of another node. For the indirection to work via the home link, the home agent provides the basic functionality of defending the home address of the off-link mobile nodes with home addresses from this link. The binding cache of a home agent differs slightly from the ones in the mobile node and the correspondent node, however. The binding cache in the home agent supports multiple routing prefixes on the home link and therefore several home addresses for a single mobile node.

Packet forwarding must occur transparently to the neighboring nodes and routers, and it must not alter the forwarded packets in order not to disturb end-to-end packet data communication. It uses its binding cache information to forward the packets to the off-link location of the mobile node. The home agent tunnels all packets to the mobile node using IPv6 encapsulation [RFC2473]. The destination of the encapsulating header is set to the mobile node's care-of address found in the binding cache. The source address of the encapsulating header is the home agent's own address.

If the mobile node and the correspondent are not using routing optimization, all traffic from the mobile node needs to be reverse-tunneled to the home agent where it is decapsulated and forwarded to the destination. Home registration signaling is secured by IP Security [IPsec]. Additional security support for route optimization makes it necessary for the home agent to have security gateway functionality. This functionality allows for looking into a packet and protecting signaling with an added outer encapsulation packet of IPv6 in IPv6 tunneling and an Encapsulating Security Payload (ESP) [EnSePa] header, based on the inner packet.

As the following figure shows, home agent functionality encompasses mobility signaling, IP forwarding and extensions to router discovery, and the ICMPv6 modules of an IPv6 router. A home agent advertises its services through router advertisements. In addition, home agent discovery and home network renumbering support are part of ICMPv6 message handling.

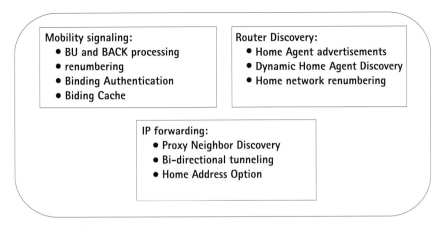

Home Agent functionality

Dynamic home agent discovery provides redundancy. There can be multiple home agents on the home link, from which the mobile node can allocate a home agent for itself by performing a dynamic home agent discovery-signaling exchange with its home link.

Optimizations for Real-Time Transport Support

With the basic mobile IPv6 scheme, it is not always possible to provide full transparency from the mobility layer to the applications. When traffic has stringent timing characteristics (e.g., rich calls) it becomes important that inefficiencies caused by mobility are eliminated. With mobility, each movement of the mobile node may cause a short pause in traffic for several reasons. For example, the latency of disconnecting from the old point of attachment to connecting to the new point of attachment, or the latency of frequent signaling with peers or the home agent can be significant. Furthermore, the bandwidth consumption of signaling can cause inefficiencies in the network and in the nodes processing this signaling. The bandwidth consumption of the data traffic may also cause congestion in links, especially those with limited-bandwidth wireless capacity, which are typically used as the last hop to the mobile node. These inefficiencies may cause a combined effect producing observable errors in delay sensitive traffic.

To support the more stringent performance requirements of rich calls, several optimizations for mobility can be supported in the routing fabric. These can be categorized as access router functionalities and other functionalities usually, but not necessarily, at the access routers.

Fast Handovers

The latency of disconnecting from the old point of attachment to connecting to the new point of attachment, or handover latency, has two components. The first component is due to the link layer specific signaling needed to establish a new link and relinquish the existing one. This latency could be significant in cases where the node disconnects from its old access point before connecting to the new access point. The second component is due to the operations required at the network protocol layer, where the mobile node has to acquire a new IP address and update its correspondents about its new location. Address acquisition with Duplicate Address Detection [RFC2461, RFC2462] can cause a latency of up to about two seconds.

The fast handover [fastmip] protocol provides network layer optimization by allowing a mobile node to acquire a new IP address prior to attaching to the new access router. This significantly reduces address acquisition latency. The fast handover protocol also establishes a forwarding path from the mobile node's previous access router to the new access router even before the mobile node attaches to the latter. This allows a mobile node to send the route update at a non-critical time, thus providing a continuous flow of packets. The fast handover protocol needs to know the target access router. This information can be obtained from a table which associates access point identifiers with access router IP addresses. The table itself could be configured manually, or it could be populated using a suitable access router discovery protocol.

Fast handover introduces binding caches into the access routers and modifies their neighbor discover process by bypassing duplicate address detection. The binding cache entries are managed by fast binding update and fast binding acknowledgement messages. The created binding cache entries are used for forwarding packets addressed to the old Care-off-Address (CoA) to the new CoA. Fast handover message handling introduces corresponding routines in destination option parsing of the standard IPv6 stack.

Context Transfers

Typically, an access router creates a state as a result of providing secure access. For instance, it could create a state corresponding to AAA access authentication. Furthermore, the access router may also create a state when providing support for such features as QoS and header compression. This state, henceforth referred to as context, is created using appropriate signaling [conttra].

When a mobile node undergoes handover, its context needs to be re-established at its new access router. Context transfer allows contexts to be re-established without the mobile node having to re-create them from first principles. This has many advantages, including preserving the scarce link bandwidth from signaling overheads, alleviating the susceptibility of context establishment to link errors and higher round-trip times, and allowing seamless operation of transport protocols so they receive uninterrupted service.

Context transfers are complementary to handovers. For instance, performing context transfer synchronized with fast handovers offers maximum performance benefits. When such a predictive transfer is not feasible, context transfer could be performed reactively after the mobile node configures its new IP address along with Mobile IP signaling.

In a context transfer implementation, each access router maintains a data structure, a feature cache, which contains the context state on a per-mobile or per-session basis. Sample feature states can be router-side packet buffering, typically as a per-mobile state, or robust header compression for data going over the access link, typically as a per-session state. When the context transfer takes place, the previous router traverses all feature cache state for a mobile node, and assembles a context transfer message for the new access router. There, a similar action installs the feature state to a feature cache, to be used with the new address on the new link.

The following diagram shows how IP forwarding, fast handover message processing and context transfer modules interact in the MITA Reference Implementation to implement reactive context transfers. Here a Context Transfer Initiate message is included in the Fast Binding Update message as a destination option.

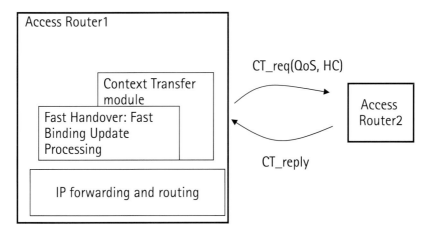

Fast Handover and Context Transfers

Localized Mobility

Localized mobility management schemes were developed to reduce signaling overhead created by fast-moving mobile nodes frequently changing their points of attachment. According to the baseline Mobile IPv6 specification, a mobile node should update its home agent and correspondent nodes each time it changes its primary care-of address. Local Mobility Management (LMM) solutions restrict the region of signaling to the visited domain, reducing the amount of signaling external to that domain. They provide smaller packet loss due to shorter route update times compared to classical end-to-end MIPv6 operation [mipv6sup].

Scarce air interface resources also favor the reduction of extraneous signaling. In the baseline Mobile IPv6 implementation, the mobile node should send a binding update to all of its correspondent nodes and the home agent. In the case of localized mobility management, the mobile node sends only one regional binding update to create a binding between the new care-of address and the externally visible regional care-of address. This binding is maintained within a mobility agent that is located in one of the routers in the visited domain. These schemes require only one binding update in a localized mobility domain per change of subnetwork. Registering the regional care-of address with the home agent and with the active correspondent nodes is needed when the mobile enters a new domain.

The MITA Reference Implementation Environment currently supports Mobile IPv6 regional registrations [regreg]. In this scheme, the mobile node acquires its regional care-of address from a top-level mobility agent, called the Gateway Mobility Agent (GMA), and registers this address with the correspondent nodes and the home agent with standard Mobile IPv6 messaging.

When the mobile node continues to move on, it compares the prefix information announced by the access routers to determine if it will still remain within the same domain of the particular GMA. If so, the node would only make regional bindings having a local effect.

Authentication, Authorization and Accounting

Currently, network access technologies are closely integrated with link layer technologies. Most wireline access networks deploy Point-to-Point Protocol (PPP) for network access authorization, whereas IEEE 802.11 is developing an authentication scheme for the WLAN environment. Diversity of customer devices and access technologies require a more general authentication solution which can be used in a wide range of use scenarios. Moreover, these solutions must thwart the inherent vulnerabilities of multi-access mobile environments.

The MITA Reference Implementation Environment applies the envisioned Authentication, Authorization and Accounting (AAA) architecture from the IETF. This AAA-based approach allows for an infrastructure of domains to be interconnected in such a way that a third party could authorize network access on-demand for mobile nodes. The main two functional elements of the AAA-architecture are home and local AAA servers. The local server, also know as an attendant, is an AAA-server in the visiting network where the mobile node roams. These two elements exchange authentication and authorization messaging using the DIAMETER protocol.

The existence of a large number of SIM modules with an associated trust infrastructure provides a widespread existing mechanism for scalable trust delegation. Introducing totally new mechanisms for IP-based trust delegation is expensive and undesirable. Moreover, leveraging an existing SIM-based mechanism for Mobile IPv6 can be achieved by a simple extension of the AAAv6 [aaaipv6] protocol. These protocol extensions for AAAv6 [sim6aaa] can be used for network access authentication as well as for security association creation between a mobile node and home agent and between other services. It requires the access router to have AAAv6 local attendant functionality and the mobile node to have a hardware-based SIM module in addition to AAAv6 signaling capability. The network should have access to an authorization center which processes SIM credentials.

In this scheme, the access router requests the mobile node to start SIM-based authentication. If the authentication succeeds, the access router programs appropriate filters in the routing engine allowing the authenticated mobile to receive and send IP-packets with the current care-of address as a source address. The filter settings are in effect as long as the authentication is deemed valid.

Reference Network

The router functionalities described in this chapter have been implemented on a robust multiprocessor router platform running the Nokia IPSO operating system.

Nokia uses different types of mobile devices as mobile nodes in Mobile IPv6 demonstrations. A typical mobile device is a laptop with a WLAN card. In this case, the operating system would be Linux.

A typical reference network is shown below. Here the access routers were IP330 series Nokia routers, the home agent was a Nokia IP650, the mobile nodes were mobile IPv6 enabled Linux laptops, and the correspondent node an ordinary mobile device in a Global System for Mobile Communications (GSM) network. Mobile IPv6 handovers with context transfers and header compressions have been demonstrated successfully with a Session Initiation Protocol (SIP) call from a Mobile IPv6 capable laptop to a GSM phone, with satisfactory customer perception. The call to the GSM phone was routed through a SIP call-processing server located overseas.

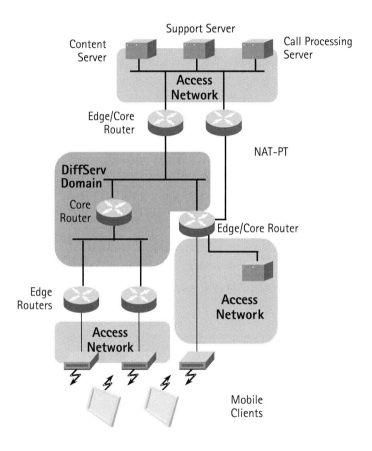

IPv6 Mobility Core Architecture

IV   Implementations

References

[mipv6sup]   Johnson D., Perkins C. "Mobility Support in IPv6" (work in progress). Internet Draft, Internet Engineering Task Force, March 2002.

[fastmip]   Dommety G., Yegin A., Perkins C., Tsirtsis G., El-Malki K., Khalil M., "Fast Handovers for Mobile IPv6," draft-ietf-mobileip-fast-mipv6-04.txt, Internet Engineering Task Force, March 2002.

[conttra]   Koodli R., Perkins C. "A Context Transfer Protocol for Seamless Mobility," draft-koodli-seamoby-ctv6-03.txt, Internet Engineering Task Force, February 2002.

[sim6aaa]   T. Kniveton, J. Malinen. "SIM Authentication EAP extension over AAAv6 (SIM6)" (work in progress). Internet Draft, Internet Engineering Task Force, June 2001.

[aaaipv6]   N. Asokan, Patrik Flykt, C. Perkins, T. Eklund. "AAA for IPv6 Network Access" (work in progress). Internet Draft, Internet Engineering Task Force, March 2000.

[regreg]   J. Malinen, F. Le, C. Perkins. "Mobile IPv6 Regional Registrations" (work in progress). Internet Draft, Internet Engineering Task Force, March 2001.

[IPsec]   S Kent, R. Atkinson. "Security Architecture for the Internet Protocol." RFC 2401, Internet Task Force, November 1998.

[EnSePa]   S Kent, R. Atkinson. "IP Encapsulating Security Payload (ESP)". RFC 2406, Internet Task Force, November 1998.

NAT-PT – IPv6/IPv4 Translator

Since the 1980s, Internet Protocol version 4 (IPv4) has been the main network protocol on the Internet. Although advanced for its time, IPv4 has some limitations, so Internet Protocol version 6 (IPv6) has been designed as the next generation Internet protocol to replace IPv4.

It is doubtful that millions of IPv4 hosts will upgrade to IPv6 overnight, so during the transition period it will be necessary to keep the IPv4 infrastructure working, and IPv4 and IPv6 nodes will need to coexist and communicate. In order to be compatible with IPv4 hosts and routers, IPv6 hosts and routers should implement a set of mechanisms known as transition mechanisms.

Some mechanisms may be adequate for an early stage of transition while others are more appropriate for intermediate or final stages. We also believe that some mechanisms will be applied in all stages. In addition, different transition mechanisms may be used during different phases of the transition. In principle, transition mechanisms can be classified into three main categories [RFC2893]: dual stack, tunneling and translation.

Methods in translation mechanisms attack the communication problem by translating an IPv6 datagrams into an IPv4 datagrams and vice versa. This translation can be performed by means of header conversion, transport relay or application proxy. The goal is to enable connection between native IPv6 nodes and IPv4 nodes with a common feature - using a translator to convert packets between two completely different protocols.

In terms of the translation mechanisms, header conversion refers to converting IPv6 packet headers to IPv4 packet headers, or vice versa. Network Address Translation - Protocol Translation (NAT-PT) [RFC2766] is a method of header conversion, by which IP addresses are mapped from one address administration to another in order to get hosts in IPv6 and IPv4 domains to communicate. NAT-PT helps IPv6 applications work with IPv4 targets just as it works with IPv6 targets, or vice versa. This scheme is based on a combination of the address translation theme as described in [RFC2663] and IPv6/IPv4 the protocol translation theme as described in [RFC2765].

The motivation behind NAT-PT is to enable communication between IPv6 and IPv4 nodes. NAT-PT enables customers in IPv6 networks to use the services in a IPv4 network and vice versa, which is essential during their period of coexistence. Compared to other translation schemes, NAT-PT is unaware of the applications traversing it, as it only looks at the IP headers. This permits multiple end-points to share and appear as a single IP address.

In order to promote and support gradual transition to IPv6, Nokia has implemented NAT-PT as a key step in transition mechanisms. In the following, we will provide a detailed discussion of the NAT-PT mechanism as well as its implementation.

NAT-PT

Work Scenarios

As depicted in the following figure, NAT-PT normally is placed at the border of IPv4 and IPv6 networks.

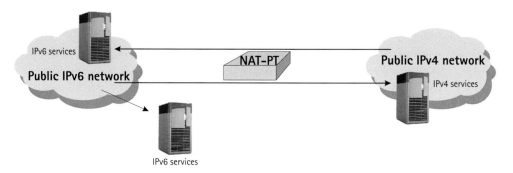

NAT-PT usage scenario

In order to let IPv6 nodes communicate with IPv4 nodes, NAT-PT has to assign an IPv4 address to an IPv6 node; this address can be used to identify the IPv6 host in an IPv4 network. Similarly, an IPv6 address should be used to identify the IPv4 host in the IPv6 network. To realize this functionality, NAT-PT needs to manage an address pool of IPv4 addresses and then assign an IPv4 address to an IPv6 host when required in a dynamic way. On the other hand, IPv4-mapped IPv6 addresses can be used to identify IPv4 hosts in the IPv6 network.

The NAT-PT mechanism can be used when an IPv6 application running on an IPv6 host must communicate with an IPv4 application running on an IPv4 host. This mechanism enables the initiation of the communication in either direction. Specifically, the work scenarios of NAT-PT can be classified into two types of communication:

o   Communication is initiated from an IPv6 machine, meaning that an IPv6 client wants to visit a server on an IPv4 network.

o   Communication is initiated from an IPv4 machine, meaning that an IPv4 client wants to visit a server on an IPv6 network.

In the first case, when an IPv6 host wants to visit a server in an IPv4 network, it initiates a communication with its IPv6 address as the source address and IPv4-mapped IPv6 address as the destination address. When an IPv6 packet is received by NAT-PT, NAT-PT translates the IPv6 packet into IPv4 by replacing the original IPv6 source address with the assigned IPv4 address, and extracting the IPv4 address from the IPv4-mapped IPv6 destination address. NAT-PT will record these address relationships in a record table. When NAT-PT receives the IPv4 packet back from the server, NAT-PT will translate the IPv4 packet to IPv6 by doing address lookup and mapping.

In the second case, the translation procedure is similar. If NAT-PT has to work in conjunction with DNS it will use the IPv6 hostname to look up the IPv4 address. In this case, NAT-PT will register the assigned IPv4 address for the IPv6 machine in the DNS server.

Such address translation requires that one IPv4 address is assigned to each IPv6 machine communicating with an IPv4 machine, but this is not efficient or even applicable due to the scarcity of IPv4 addresses. Therefore, NAPT-PT extends the notion of translation one step further by also translating a transport identifier (e.g., Transmission Control Protocol (TCP) and User Datagram Protocol (UDP) port numbers, Internet Control Message Protocol (ICMP) query identifiers). This allows the transport identifiers of a number of IPv6 hosts to be multiplexed into the transport identifiers of a single assigned IPv4 address. NAPT-PT allows a set of IPv6 hosts to share a single IPv4 address. Note that NAPT-PT can be combined with Basic-NAT-PT so that a pool of external addresses is used in conjunction with port translation.

For packets outbound from the IPv6 network, NAPT-PT would translate the source IP address and the source transport identifier, which can be either a TCP/UDP port or ICMP query ID. For inbound packets, the destination IP address, destination transport identifier, the IP and transport header checksums are translated.

Protocol Translation

TCP and UDP are essentially the transport protocol above the IP layer; its protocol stack should be independent of IP packet transmission. However, since TCP and UDP use IP sources and destinations in the pseudo-header checksums, a change of IP address results in the recalculation of the TCP and UDP checksum. Moreover, the ICMPv6 includes a pseudo-header checksum which does not exist in ICMPv4, so the checksum in ICMP messages needs to be modified by the translator. ICMP error messages contain an IP header as part of the payload; thus, the translator needs to rewrite those parts of the packets in order to make the receiver understand the IP header [RFC2463].

Furthermore, since the definitions of ICMPv6 error messages are different in ICMPv4, ICMP error messages need to be translated.

Fragmentation Issues

Fragmentation issues are a main concern: since Maximum Transmission Unit (MTU) discovery is mandatory in IPv6, only end-to-end fragmentation is allowed in the IPv6 protocol, in contrast with IPv4, where MTU discovery is optional. So if the originating IPv4 node performs MTU discovery, which it can do easily enough end-to-end across the translator, no problems would arise. But if the originating IPv4 node does not perform MTU discovery, the translator must ensure that the packet does not exceed the MTU on the IPv6 side of the path. This is done by fragmenting the IPv4 packet into a 1,280 byte IPv6 packet, the minimum packet size required in IPv6.

Because the minimum MTU required for IPv6 is larger than the one required for IPv4, end-to-end MTU discovery is not appropriate, as it may result in an MTU lower than acceptable for the IPv6 starting point. If the IPv4 path MTU is smaller than the minimum required for IPv6, the translator must then fragment these packets to fit the IPv4 MTU.

Application Level Gateway

As mentioned previously, NAT-PT is transparent to applications; it is unware what applications are transmitting packets. However some kinds of applications carry IP addresses in their payload, thus NAT-PT must concern it with changing the IP address in the payload as well. To achieve this, an application-specific Application Level Gateway (ALG) is needed to allow an IPv6 application to communicate with an IPv4 application. Specifically, ALG is inserted between application peers, though some applications embed addresses within the IP packet payload to simulate a direct connection when some intervening protocol or device prevents direct access. ALG is used when translation of header packets is not enough. For example, the File Transfer Protocol (FTP) carries IP address and TCP port information within its payload; an FTP-ALG is required to translate this address. Normally, the ALG is used in conjunction with NAT-PT to provide support for this type of application.

ALG imposes extra performance penalties: it stops the transport protocol, and may modify the data stream before forwarding it. NAT-PT, by contrast, is application unaware and does not stop the payload. If the ALG is appended, it depends on the demand of the application. Its benefits are that it can be applied without modifying the client or server stacks and, compared to others, the specification is more stable.

Another example is DNS-ALG, which can theoretically develop a mechanism to automatically update DNS records when NAT-PT updates the internal translation tables. Furthermore, it will translate DNS "A" lookups to "AAAA" references. DNS-ALG would translate addresses from IPv6 to IPv4 addresses given to it by NAT-PT.

Inherence from Network Address Translation

NAT-PT works as a state sensitive device. It generally requires a table to list the active sessions. A session is a queue of packets with the same source host and port, destination host and port, and transport protocol type, even with successive sequence numbers. A session may be unidirectional or bi-directional, plus the quantity of packets can be unmatched to bi-directional during a session. The information of a session is recorded in a table, starting from the beginning of a session. The NAT-PT should watch every session's status for its <Start>, <Refresh>, <Revive> and <Close>. For each session, the particular bindings and translations are stored. Sessions are either removed explicitly through packets, or are timed out after an extended period.

It is mandatory that all requests and responses pertaining to a session will be routed via the same NAT-PT router. One way to guarantee this is to have NAT-PT based on a border router that is unique to a stub domain, where all IP packets either originate in this domain or are destined to return to the domain. More complex network scenarios must be evaluated. For Traditional-NAT-PT, it is not possible to have two redundant NAT-PT devices connecting an IPv4 with an IPv6 network in order to be router fault-tolerant.

NAT-PT uses a pool of IPv4 addresses to be assigned to IPv6 nodes on a dynamic basis as sessions are initiated across the IPv4-to-IPv6 boundary. The IPv4 addresses are assumed to be globally unique, as this requires no changes to end nodes and IP packet routing is completely transparent [RFC2663] to end nodes. It does, however, require NAT-PT to track sessions that support and mandate the inbound and outbound datagrams pertaining to one session's traversal of the same NAT-PT router.

By combining Stateless IP/ICMP Translation Algorithm (SIIT) protocol translation with the dynamic address translation capabilities of NAT and the appropriate ALG, NAT-PT provides a complete solution that would allow a large number of commonly used applications to interoperate between IPv6-only and IPv4-only nodes.

Impact of Limitations

Topology Limitations

It is mandatory that all requests and responses pertaining to a session should be routed via the same NAT-PT router. It is a generic problem with NAT and is fully described in [RFC2663].

Impact of Address/Protocol Translation

A number of IPv4 fields have changed meaning in IPv6 and translation is not straightforward. For example, NAT-PT does not translate some option headers significantly some in IPv6. NAT-PT creates a single point of fate in the device which maintains connection state and dynamic mapping information. NAT-PT complicates the use of multi-homing by a site in order to increase the reliability of its Internet connectivity.

NAT-PT places constraints on the deployment of applications that carry IP addresses (e.g., FTP and Session Initiation Protocol (SIP)) in the data stream, and they operate on the assumption that each session is independent. Applications or protocols like these assume the end-to-end integrity of addresses and will fail when traversing a NAT-PT. NAT-PT may also need to assemble fragmented datagrams to enable translation of the application stream, and then adjust TCP sequence numbers, prior to forwarding. MTU should be negotiated when the connection is established.

While NAT-PT support is limited to TCP, UDP and other port multiplexing types of applications, NAPT-PT solves a problem inherent in NAT-PT. That is, NAT-PT would fall flat when the pool of

IPv4 addresses assigned for translation purposes is exhausted. Once the address pool is exhausted, newer IPv6 nodes cannot establish sessions with the outside world anymore. NAPT-PT, on the other hand, will allow for a maximum of 63,000 K TCP and 63,000 K UDP sessions per IPv4 address before having no TCP and UDP ports left to assign.

Lack of End-to-End Security

The great disadvantage of NAT-PT is that problems appear when end-to-end security mechanisms are broken for IPv6 to IPv4 communication. End-to-end network layer security is not possible due to the intervention of NAT-PT at the header level. Also, application layer security may be broken if an ALG is used to translate embedded addresses used in the application layer. NAT-PT should only be used when there is no way of communicating by tunnel, and when security is crucial. NAT-PT limits simultaneous access to multiple services with a network, and makes a single point of failure.

NAT-PT inhibits implementation of IP Security (IPSec). One of the most important limitations of NAT-PT is the fact that NAT-PT breaks the flexible end-to-end model of the Internet. Also, transport and application layer security may not be possible for applications that carry IP addresses to the application layer. Independent of NAT-PT, end-to-end IP based security is not possible across different address realms. Two end-nodes seeking IPSec network level security must both support either IPv4 or IPv6.

Part of IPSec functionality is maintained by the translator. Packets with Encapsulating Security Payload (ESP) format can be translated since ESP does not depend on header fields prior to the ESP header, but the correctness of the Authentication Header (AH) is not always preserved through a translator.

Domain Name System Translation and Security

There is an issue in the scheme involving the translation of DNS messages. It is clear that this scheme cannot be deployed in combination with secure DNS, i.e., an authoritative DNS name server in the IPv6 domain cannot sign replies to queries originating in the IPv4 world. As a result, an IPv4 end-node which demands that DNS replies be signed will reject replies that have been tampered with by NAT-PT.

The good news, however, is that only servers in the IPv6 domain that need to be accessible from the IPv4 world will pay the price for this limitation, as IPv4 end-nodes may not access IPv6 servers since DNS replies are not signed.

Also, note that zone transfers between DNS Security (DNS-Sec) servers within the same IPv6 network are not impacted. Clearly, until DNS-Sec deployment in DNS servers and end-host is resolved, the scheme will not work.

Applicability Statement

In a traditional NAT-PT mechanism, scaling problems are not usually relevant since the number of IPv4 addresses in the pool is usually significantly smaller than the total number of IPv6 customer hosts. A bi-directional-NAT-PT mechanism in the stateful configuration mode does have scaling problems, however. For larger networks, the number of look-up table entries strongly penalizes its management cost and delay performance.

This makes NAT-PT a useful tool to IPv6-only stub networks that need to be able to maintain connectivity with the IPv4 world without the demand to deploy servers visible to this world.

NAT-PT combined with a DNS-ALG provides bi-directional connectivity between the IPv6 stub domain and the IPv4 world, allowing sessions to be initialized by IPv4 nodes outside the IPv6 stub domain. This makes NAT-PT useful for IPv6-only stub networks that need to deploy servers visible to the IPv4 world.

Implementation

Features

Let's assume that NAT-PT resides in an IP router situated at the boundary between an IPv4 and IPv6 network, with the following specifications:

o   Operating system with dual stack support.

o   At least two network interfaces, one connected to the IPv4 network and the other to the IPv6 network.

o   The NAT-PT device must be located on the default router for the IPv6 network. Alternatively an IPv6 address prefix must exist by which hosts will route packets to the NAT-PT machine.

o   Some virtual device interfaces to filter the various packets must be installed, as the main NAT-PT module manages to capture the IP packets arriving from IPv6 and IPv4, including Ethernet Address Resolution Protocol (ARP) requests/responses and neighborhood discovery requests/responses to discover the destination host's address.

Architecture

NAT-PT architecture is based on NAT implementation, and consists of two parts: kernel and daemon. Of course, the daemon can be built into the kernel, making it more efficient and easier to compute the IPv6 MTU, but it would be more difficult to implement.

IV   Implementations

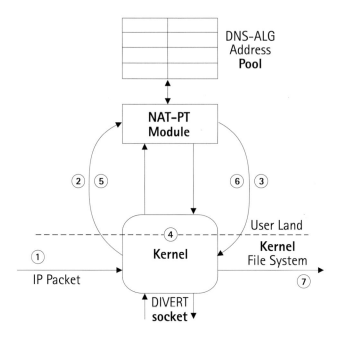

Packet flow

The previous figure shows packet flow. When an incoming packet is just arriving before routing (1), the kernel calls the NAT-PT module (2) with the packet stored in memory. The NAT-PT module examines the packet and does IP header translation if the packet matches the NAT-PT rule. Next, the translated packet is returned (3) to the kernel for routing under another IP. The kernel treats the translated packet in turn as a normal incoming packet (4). The translated packet is then given back to the kernel for further processing, which means the device driver sends it out on the interface (7). The same happens to all outgoing packets (5/6) which are routed and generated locally, just before they are transmitted out and just before any address resolution is done.

Modules
Divert Socket
NAT-PT operates within the kernel and picks up IPv4/IPv6 packets as requested by a daemon. Within this framework, the recommended practice is to use RAW sockets of the DIVERT type to minimize related development work. A DIVERT-type socket intercepts all IP packets before a route module handles these incoming packets in the IP layer routine. Then it pushes all the data in an IP packet intact up to the daemon. After an IP packet has been translated into the other IP version in the daemon, all the data of this translated IP packet should be poured back into the DIVERT socket directly. The DIVERT socket will then arrange the translated packet into an outgoing queue in the IP layer routine as an entire IP packet.

Daemon

The daemon works in user mode to process the translation of IP packets. It consists of two threads and a common library. The two threads are responsible for communicating to read/write packets from the kernel buffer. One is for reading from IPv6 and writing back to IPv4; the other is for the opposite direction. A common library provides some interfaces of application programs to fulfill the real translating functions. Therefore, if the developer wants to upgrade the implementation, it can easily keep the program style and enhance its capability, minimizing the development workload.

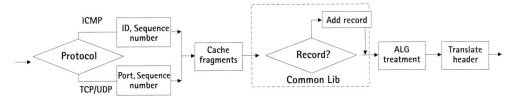

Daemon architecture

Daemon Framework

The daemon framework manages resources, dispatches modules and operates two threads, as described above.

The daemon framework gets information from system initial configuration about the IPv4 address pool, specifies address prefixes of compatible IPv6 addresses for NAT-PT as well as all policy data of the administrator. It also negotiates with the system core about MTU, and advertises the MTU to the router in order to lessen the chance of fragmentation. It creates two DIVERT type RAW sockets to communicate with the kernel for both IPv4 and IPv6. It also initializes the dispatch for threads. It hooks ALG modules into the correct status, according to the user policy. The user will demand that NAT-PT provides different services according to different situations, but ALG is not flexible to applications. So, whether different ALGs are hooked on or off will affect the efficiency of the whole NAT-PT service.

The framework is also responsible for initializing the session table and reserving a sufficient amount of successive memory space. It also periodically does housecleaning, to remove expired session records. It will adjust the distribution of links in the record table to maintain highly-efficient look-ups of the desired record. It will configure the route agent module with information on network topology so that NAT-PT can work in the default route for both IP sides. When quitting the daemon, the framework will release each resource allocated since the daemon began running, and reset the flags of relative parameters.

In terms of security, the daemon will provide a log file for packet translation as a system option, according to whether the user desires a log file.

IV Implementations

Threads Work With a DIVERT Socket

Here we will just describe one thread, read from IPv6 and write back to IPv4, called the 6_4 thread. The opposite process is handled by the 4_6 thread.

When the 6_4 thread is dispatched into start status, it first scans the socket buffer to see if data is ready at the DIVERTv6 socket. If not, the 6_4 thread temporarily releases the resources and control of the system, and changes from start status to waiting status while the other threads take a turn. If there is data in the DIVERTv6 socket buffer, the 6_4 thread copies data from this socket to the allocated successive memory buffer for later translation. Next, the 6_4 thread checks the integrity of the IPv6 packet. If the integrity is not OK, it will discard the data and quit as previous description. If the integrity is OK, it calls the IP header translator module.

With the result of the IP header translator module, a new IPv4 packet is reassembled and returned to the 6_4 thread with the data. If it needs a log file, it now writes the history of the packet onto one. Then, the 6_4 thread delivers the new IPv4 packet to the socket DIVERTv4 with the specified information of NAT-PT. The DIVERTv4 socket can reconstruct route information with the handed-down information of NAT-PT and the information in the IP header, and will next go into the standard process of sending an IPv4 packet. After this, the 6_4 thread finishes one cycle of work and quits as previously described, so other threads get their turn.

Translation of the IP Header

This module converts each field between two IP heads, according to their differences. These are shown in the following figure, the relationship between IP header fields.

IPv Header		
Vers: HD	TOS	Payload length
Fragment ID		Fragment Information
TTL	Protocol	Header Checksum
Source Address		
Destination Address		

IPv6 Header		
Vers: Class	Flow Label	
Payload length	Next hdr	Hop Limit
Source Address		
Destination Address		

Differences:
IPv4 header is 20 bytes IPv6 header is 40 bytes
Address increased from 32 to 128 bits
Fragmentation fields moved out of base header
Header checksum
Time to Live replaced with "Hop Limit"
Protocol replaced with "Next Header"
TOD replaced with "Flow Label"
Alignment changed from 32 to 64 bits

The relationship between IPv6 and IPv4

In translating the IP header, IP addresses in the header are assigned as described above, and the checksum of the IPv4 header and TCP/UDP pseudo header, respectively, are adjusted. The content data of the TCP/UDP packet is kept intact, except for ALG modification.

Address Assigned in Pool or With Specified Prefix

This module will communicate with DNS on the dynamic assignment of IPv4 addresses in the address pool to any DNS inquiry for IPv6 service from IPv4. By means of this module, load balance can be deployed on the NAT-PT matrix.

Session Management Table

While every packet traverses via NAT-PT from both IPv6 and IPv4, the daemon will record the following information for every session: destination/source IP address, destination/source port, flow identify, protocol type, arriving time, and expire time to fill a record table. Some records can be linked to construct a hash table, whose index is similar to the index of such a table in NAT.

If the daemon wants to find a record of a session in the table, it first enters a link in the table by an index algorithm with the addresses and ports of the session. It next checks whether there is a record of this session in this link. If there is such a record, it returns a pointer to the record. If there is not, it returns a NULL pointer.

If the daemon wants to add a record of a session into the table, it first checks to ensure that no record already exists. Then, it inserts into the selected link a new record item with information on the current session. If there is such a record, it refreshes it, giving it a timestamp and expiry time.

After a fixed interval, the daemon should go through the whole table and refresh every record with expiry times. If the expiry time of a record becomes zero, this record should be removed from its link.

Application Level Gateway

Because there are some protocols or applications that carry address/port information in their content, NAT-PT has to work with ALGs to process these cases. An ALG changes the IP address/port in the payload according to different protocols or applications, and NAT-PT translates the IP header of the packet and adjusts the checksum of each header.

In some situations, an ALG not only changes the IP address/port in the packet payload, but also needs to add another record in the session table for some specific usage. For example, FTP is such a protocol: after the original control session between the two ends, another session begins to transport data. So FTP-ALG replaces the IP address in the packet payload, adjusts the sequence number to match the size variant of the payload between successive packets, and increases a session record filled with information derived from the original session.

IV

Implementations

References

[1] [RFC1631]: RFC1631, The IP Network Address Translator (NAT);

[2] [RFC2663]: RFC2663, IP Network Address Translator (NAT) Terminology And Considerations;

[3] [RFC2765]: RFC2765, Stateless IP/ICMP Translation Algorithm (SIIT);

[4] [RFC2766]: RFC2766, Network Address Translation - Protocol Translation (NAT-PT);

[5] [RFC2775]: RFC2775, Internet Transparency;

[6] [RFC2893]: RFC2893, Transition mechanisms for IPv6 hosts and routers.

IPv6 Tunnel Broker

The features of IPv6 [IP VER6] show a great deal of improvement in network scalability, routing, security, mobility and address autoconfiguration, when compared to IPv4. Unfortunately, IPv6 is incompatible with IPv4, so we will need a transition period to IPv6 in order to allow IPv4 hosts and the network to gradually upgrade.

The key to a successful IPv6 transition is the ability of IPv6 to interoperate with the large IPv4 network. One challenge is that the transition should have no order dependencies. In other words, carriers should be able to upgrade their hosts first and then their routers, or their routers first and then their hosts. They should even be able to upgrade some hosts, some routers, and leave the rest alone. As a result, different transition schemes may be used at different stages of the transition. In principle, beside the straightforward dual stack strategy, the transition schemes can be classified into two categories: translation [NAT-PT] and tunneling [TRANSITION]. Tunneling is a way of connecting two IPv6 clouds by encapsulating IPv6 packets into IPv4 and transmitting IPv6 packets over an IPv4 infrastructure.

Compared to the other alternatives, tunneling retains the integrity of TCP/IP protocol suites, and thus is preferred by most network administrators dealing with IPv6. IPv6-over-IPv4 tunnels have to be explicitly configured, which creates a heavy load of dull and error-prone work for network administrators. To make things worse, newcomers to IPv6 are often confused by the concept of tunneling and therefore make the wrong configurations.

To reduce the management workload for configured tunnels, lots of schemes (e.g., automatic tunnels [TRANSITION], 6to4 [6TO4], 6over4 [6OVER4] and IPv6 Tunnel Broker [BROKER]) have been proposed to assist in the configuration. These schemes try to achieve automatic tunneling in a number of ways and for different usage scenarios. Among these, the Tunnel Broker aims at providing common IPv6 users with connectivity to IPv6 backbones via IPv6-over-IPv4 tunnels. The Tunnel Broker system is thus an attempt to solve as many problems concerning IPv6/IPv4 tunnel configuration and administration as possible. In particular, the Tunnel Broker is suitable for a large-scale network, and makes it easy for service provider to allocate addresses to clients. Nowadays, the Tunnel Broker is being widely used in 6bone [6BONE] and other IPv6 trial networks (e.g., CSELT Tunnel Broker [CSELT TB]).

Tunnel Broker System

The Tunnel Broker is basically a mechanism to obtain configured tunnels in an automatic way. The Tunnel Broker manages tunnel requests coming from consumers, and accomplishes tunnel configuration and administration.

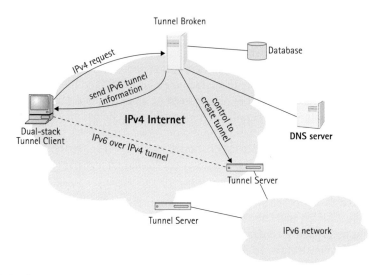

Tunnel Broker System

As illustrated in the above figure, the tunnel broker system consists of several elements: Tunnel Broker, Tunnel Servers, Tunnel Clients and a Domain Name System (DNS) Server. The Tunnel Broker can provide a service to Tunnel Clients to automatically establish tunnels between tunnel clients and tunnel servers. Here, the tunnel client can be a dual-stack IPv6/v4 host or a dual-stack machine on behalf of an IPv6 subnet, while the Tunnel Servers are dual-stack routers at the border of the IPv6 and IPv4 network.

Functionally, Tunnel Brokers can be seen as virtual IPv6 Internet Service Providers (ISPs), providing IPv6 connectivity to consumers already connected to the IPv4 Internet. A Tunnel Server can be regarded as a relay center for a group of Tunnel Clients. Each Tunnel Client has a default route to the other part of the IPv6 world via the Tunnel Server. Moreover, a Tunnel Broker manages an IPv6 address space, allocates IPv6 addresses or addresses blocks to Tunnel Clients from its address pool and registers the addresses in the DNS server in order to provide permanent DNS entries for hosts. In order to perform automatic tunneling and address allocation, a Tunnel Broker has to interact with other entities. Normally, Tunnel Broker and other entities are located in the same administration domain, but a Tunnel Broker needs to have a trust relationship with other entities so that it can configure tunnels on Tunnel Servers and Tunnel Clients. It is preferable that communication between a Tunnel Broker and others is performed with a security guarantee.

Obviously, the Tunnel Broker mechanism is stateful. A Tunnel Broker needs to maintain a database to record user registrations, tunnel end point addresses and tunnel states. It administers a group of Tunnel Servers, which provide a tunnel virtual link to the Tunnel Clients.

Furthermore, the Tunnel Broker is not designed for backbone networks, nor is it a tool for configuring IPv6/IPv4 tunnels between ISPs. The workload in these circumstances is not heavy and all the configuration work has to be done manually for security and stability.

Tunnel Configuration Procedure

Normally, a Tunnel Broker is operated or used by two kinds of users, Tunnel Broker service providers and common IPv6 users. Tunneling requests (e.g., registering, adding or deleting an IPv6/IPv4 tunnel, querying and deregistering) are sent from the Tunnel Client to the Tunnel Broker. On the other hand, the configuration of a Tunnel Broker (e.g., address space, DNS server, Tunnel Servers for tunnel broker system) is done by network administrators. These configurations are normally performed when setting up a Tunnel Broker in a network.

The usage scenario of a Tunnel Broker can be described with reference to the previous figure. To use the Tunnel Broker service, consumers need to have an IPv6/IPv4 dual stack computer as a Tunnel Client. This computer can send a request to the Tunnel Broker and apply to establish a tunnel to access an IPv6 network for a single host or a small sub-IPv6 network. The Tunnel Broker assigns IPv6 addresses to clients from its address space, automatically updates the DNS and sends the configuration to the Tunnel Server and Tunnel Client to establish an IPv6-over-IPv4 tunnel.

The basic procedure for automatic tunnel establishment consists of the following steps:

1. The dual stack client sends a registration request to the Tunnel Broker letting it know it needs tunnel establishment.

2. When the Tunnel Broker receives this request, it assigns IPv6 addresses to clients from its address space and automatically registers the corresponding host name in the DNS server.

3. After this step is completed, the Tunnel Broker can perform the tunnel creation procedure at the Tunnel Server and Tunnel Client; this can be realized by sending a create tunnel request and tunnel configuration information to the Tunnel Server and Tunnel Client.

4. The Tunnel Broker can then set up the tunnel through interaction with the Tunnel Server and Tunnel Client. After the tunnel is established, the Tunnel Client can communicate with the remote computers in the IPv6 network.

IV

Implementations

Implementation

Design Requirements and Features

The implementation of a Tunnel Broker system should conform to the basic concepts and architecture described above. As mentioned above, the Tunnel Broker service helps the clients establish a connection to the IPv6 network and alleviates the workload of the carrier. Thus, the implementation of the system should make it easy for the clients to access it and for network administrators to manage it.

Automatic and Dynamic Tunnel Setup

The Tunnel Broker sets up or releases IPv6/IPv4 tunnels at the Tunnel Server and Tunnel Client automatically according to requests from the Tunnel Client. A lifetime will be assigned to the tunnel, and the tunnel can be released in a dynamic way.

Automatic Management

Besides the automatic tunnel setup, the Tunnel Broker should also provide the functionality for administrating configured tunnels. The service must keep track of all tunnel parameters and their state. These tunnel parameters and states are kept in a Tunnel Broker database; network administrators can supervise the states of each tunnel and obtain statistics about client tunnels. Additionally, the tunnel broker can automatically remove tunnels whose lifetimes have expired.

Web Management User Interface

The Tunnel Broker provides an interface to let IPv6 clients register and request IPv6 connectivity. To ease this operation, consumers can visit the Tunnel Broker via a Web browser. Information about a tunnel request is sent to the Web server running on the Tunnel Broker.

Hostname and IP Address

The service should provide long-term IPv6 addresses, which will remain unchanged regardless where the host is connected to the Internet. Every tunnel administered by the service should have a name registered in the DNS. The IPv6 address and host name should be the same throughout the lifetime of the tunnel.

Moreover, the Tunnel Broker can allocate IPv6 address blocks of various sizes. The assigned addresses are not only for consumers but also for clients who would like to expand their IPv6 connectivity to others with an IPv6 network which they can control themselves. For example, the Tunnel Broker can assign /48 or /64 blocks based on the client's request. The Tunnel Broker's ability to allocate various-sized IPv6 address blocks is configured by network administrators and normally performed when setting up a Tunnel Broker.

The diversity of IPv6 address allocation is maximized. Administrators can determine an address allocation policy (e.g., how many IPv6 address pools can be used, what these address pools are, which Tunnel Server is in charge of a given address pool, what sizes a given address pool's IPv6 address blocks can be).

Client/Multi-Server Architecture

Multiple tunnel servers can be deployed in an entire Tunnel Broker service system. A Tunnel Broker, at least one Tunnel Server, and a DNS coordinator are indispensable components for running a Tunnel Broker model. Physically, however, it is possible for one Tunnel Broker to manage more than one tunnel server, so that some means of Tunnel Server redundancy and load balancing can be achieved. In some cases, the Tunnel Server and Tunnel Broker functions can be placed in the same equipment.

Dynamic IPv4 Address Support

The system should allow the IPv4 address of the client to change while the IPv6 address and hostname stay the same. This brings about support for dynamic IPv4 addresses in the Tunnel Broker System. It is designed so that no static IPv4 addresses are required for clients; rather, the consumer's IPv4 address is determined when s/he submits a request for tunnel construction. This feature also makes the Tunnel Broker system useful for dial-up consumers who are assigned global IPv4 addresses through the Dynamic Host Configuration Protocol (DHCP) [DHCP]. Furthermore, this service adds support for roaming consumers to the Tunnel Broker model.

A domain name would be a good way to determine the IPv6 address given to the client and used to manage and update the tunnel.

Secure Communication and Access Control

Communications between the Tunnel Broker, Tunnel Clients and Tunnel Servers may require access control and secure communication. Secure HyperText Transfer Protocol (S-HTTP) can be used to provide access control or secure communication for Tunnel Clients, while IPSec may be the best choice to grant confidentiality and authentication to the traffic between the Tunnel Broker and Tunnel Servers. Additionally, the service can provide some mechanisms to differentiate the access level of consumers based on the IPv6 address and hostname.

In conclusion, the key features of the implementation include:

o   Client/server architecture

o   Web management interface

o   Automatic tunnel setup or release on the server and client side

o   Various-size IPv6 address block allocation to Tunnel Clients

IV

Implementations

o   Domain name assignment for each client

o   Dynamic IPv4 support

o   Authentication and Security of consumer access

System Architecture

The Tunnel Broker System consists of several components, which have to cooperate together to provide IPv6 address allocation and IPv6/IPv4 tunnel configuration. The detailed structure is illustrated in the figure below.

Each component in the following figure is an independent entity able to reside on a separate machine, though some entities can be placed in the same equipment.

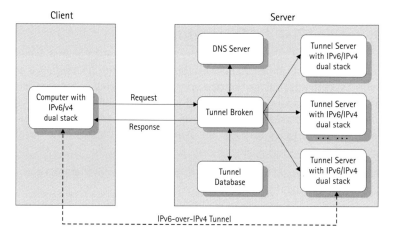

System Architecture of a Tunnel Broker

Tunnel Clients and Tunnel Servers have to be dual-stack machines. Other entities in the system must be IPv4 capable machines. They can also be IPv6 capable but this is not mandatory.

Component Design

Tunnel Server

In the implementation, the Tunnel Server can be a daemon process running in the background and communicating with the Tunnel Broker via a single TCP connection. It also maintains a table of currently existing IPv6-over-IPv4 tunnels in a file so that whenever it is restarted it can restore its previous status.

The process of tunnel addition on a tunnel server can be:

o   Deleting a previous tunnel if it exists

o   Adding a tunnel

o   Bringing up the tunnel interface

o   Adding a route to the client

Tunnel Database

The Tunnel Database stores most of the Tunnel Broker data (e.g., information on clients, allocated IPv6 address blocks, existing tunnels and configurations). For implementation, MySQL [MYSQL] can be used as a database. If the Tunnel Broker interacts with Tunnel Database via the standard MySQL APIs, no daemon processes are needed on the Tunnel Database.

DNS Server

There should be a DNS Server in the Tunnel Broker system which supports DNS Dynamic Update [DNS UPDATE] and IPv6 record type [DNS IPV6]. The DNS Server is in charge of the domain of all domain names allocated to clients; Tunnel Broker will update the record of IPv6 machines in the DNS server when it creates, modifies or deletes a tunnel. The implementation can choose BIND9 [BIND9], which satisfies the above-mentioned requirements.

Tunnel Broker

The Tunnel Broker is the central part of the Tunnel Broker system and acts as the glue which holds all components of the Tunnel Broker system together. Its major functionality includes: interacting with consumers to take their requests; turning to the Tunnel Database for most of the information it needs; sending Dynamic DNS Update requests to the DNS Server when necessary; and sending commands to the Tunnel Server to setup or release the actual IPv6/IPv4 tunnels. Since there are many Tunnel Servers, load balance between them is necessary. The simplest policy is to choose a Tunnel Server for a user randomly.

Tunnel Client

The Tunnel Client (TC) can use a simple executable program to automatically perform IPv6/IPv4 tunnel configuration on the client side. It gets the necessary information from its configuration file and command line when invoked, sends requests to the Tunnel Broker via the HTTP, and does all the necessary local configuration of the IPv6/IPv4 tunnel. The purpose of this program is to reduce the work which consumers must do to the minimum. With the help of the program running on the TC, even those who have very limited knowledge of IPv6 and IPv6/IPv4 tunneling should be able to accomplish the configuration work successfully.

IV   Implementations

A Tunnel Client can execute the following functionalities:

o   Get server status, (e.g., the IPv6 address of a usable DNS server and the available prefix lengths)

o   Register with the Tunnel Broker

o   Change User Provided Information

o   Deregister

o   Activate/Deactivate the Tunnel

o   Get information on a consumer

Reference Implementation

The test environment is established as illustrated in the following figure. In the test system one Tunnel Client and one Tunnel Broker are allocated to the IPv4 network, while two Tunnel Servers are located at the border of the IPv4 and IPv6 networks. This test system can be used to test the basic functionality of the Tunnel Broker and illustrate how an IPv6 host accesses an IPv6 network.

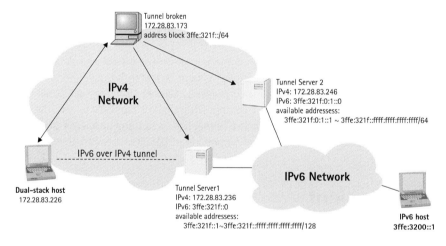

Tunnel Broker Demonstrator layout

References

[IP VER6]   S. Deering and R. Hinden, "Internet Protocol, Version 6 (IPv6) specification," RFC 2460, December 1998.

[NAT-PT]   G. Tsirtsis and P. Srisuresh, "Network Address Translation - Protocol Translation (NAT-PT)," RFC 2766, February 2000.

[TRANSITION]   R. Gilligan and E. Nordmark, "Transition mechanisms for IPv6 hosts and routers," RFC 2893, August 2000.

[6TO4]   B. Carpenter and K. Moore, "Connection of IPv6 Domains via IPv4 Clouds," RFC 3056, February 2001.

[6OVER4]   Carpenter, B. and C. Jung, "Transmission of IPv6 over IPv4 Domains without Explicit Tunnels," RFC 2529, March 1999.

[BROKER]   A. Durand, P. Fasano, I. Guardini, and D. Lento, " IPv6 Tunnel Broker," RFC 3053, January 2001.

[6BONE]   http://www.6bone.net.

[CSELT-TB]   http://carmen.cselt.it/ipv6/tools/ipv6tb.

[DHCP]   R. Droms, "Dynamic host configuration protocol," RFC 2131, March 1997.

[MYSQL]   http://www.mysql.org.

[DNS UPDATE]   P. Vixie, Editor, S. Thomson, Y. Rekhter, and J. Bound, "Dynamic updates in the domain name system (DNS UPDATE)," RFC 2136, April 1997.

[DNS IPV6]   S. Thomson and C. Huitema, "DNS extensions to support IP version 6," December 1995.

[BIND9]   http://www.isc.org/products/BIND/bind9.html.

SIP Building Blocks

Sofia Proxy

The Sofia Reference Implementation includes a SIP proxy which provides presence and message adaptation in addition to the basic SIP routing functions. The proxy is modular, and its functionality consists of six parts: proxy core, configuration module, registrar module, presence server module, message adaptation module and authentication module. This section mainly discusses the proxy core functionality and its interfaces with the other modules.

The proxy is implemented directly on top of the NTA module; there is no separate proxy core module. However, proxy services can be extended using its scripting function.

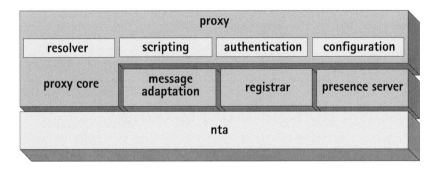

Functional composition of the Sofia proxy

Configuring the Proxy

The configuration module reads and parses the configuration file which determines which modules to activate, which SIP addresses identify the proxy, and whether the proxy should process requests in a stateless or stateful mode. The proxy can also be configured to keep call state and record-route requests. The configuration also includes static routing entries.

Proxy Initialization

When the proxy is started, it binds itself to the specified contact address, activates the authentication module, the registrar module and the presence server module. Next, it activates the timer and starts processing incoming messages.

The proxy timer terminates transactions not completed during the configured time, with a default timer value of two minutes. Usually, only INVITE transactions are active that long.

Stateless Proxying

When in the stateless mode, the proxy processes incoming requests directly without creating transaction objects. It does this by simply forwarding the requests to the ultimate destination.

The forwarding process first checks the Max-Forwards header, then the Proxy-Require header. The next step is route processing; the requestURI is replaced with the Uniform Resource Identifier (URI) taken from the Route header.

A stateless proxy can also check for authentication in the Proxy-Authorization header. Since clients do not support authenticating CANCEL or ACK requests, they are passed through unauthenticated by default.

If it is necessary to respond to an ACK request with an error code the proxy must instead discard ACK requests.

When proceeding to forward the request, the proxy first searches for a static route which is used to redirect requests to other destinations. Finally, the proxy decrements the Max-Forwards value, optionally adds itself to the Record-Route header and sends the request.

Processing responses is pretty straightforward in the stateless mode (`proxy_response`). The response is just forwarded using the NTA module. Only authentication is complex: if authentication is required, the proxy adds its own Proxy-Authentication header to the 401 or 407 responses.

Transaction Stateful Proxying

The proxy processes all the requests destined to its own URIs at the transaction layer. Such URIs include not only the URIs specified in the configuration but also all URIs added by the registrar.

Just as in the stateless mode, the proxy first checks the Max-Forwards header field, then Proxy-Require, then Proxy-Authorization.

Next, the static routing table is consulted. If a route is found, the request is simply forwarded without consulting the local location database.

If necessary, the location database is searched next. Besides contact URIs, the location database can also contain scripts. If a script is found, it is allowed to process the transaction. The script can, for example, forward the request, or modify the contact list or message contents. Currently the only supported script format is a message adaptation filter.

After scripts have been processed the proxy invokes the default routing function. Depending on the configuration and caller preferences, the proxy can either forward the request or act as a redirect server and return the contact list to the client. Multiple destinations can be tried simultaneously using a process known as forking. For each destination, the proxy creates a separate client transaction.

If the request cannot be forwarded, the proxy immediately returns an appropriate response to the client. If the user binding was not found in the registrar database, the client is returned a 404 Not Found response. If the binding was found, but the proxy decided against forwarding the request, 302 Moved Temporarily is returned. If the desired service was not available, but bindings to other services exist, a 380 Alternative Service is returned. If the user was present in the location server, but had no valid bindings registered, 480 Temporarily Unavailable is returned.

Proxy Transaction

All information related to a proxied transaction is kept in the transaction object. It contains the incoming server transaction, the original request message, requestURI, a list of relevant contacts, a list of alternative contacts, current status and corresponding best response, and finally a list of slots, each containing a fork.

Processing Responses

The responses are processed by the proxy according to the SIP specification. Provisional responses are forwarded. If recursion is enabled in the proxy configuration, contact addresses in 3XX responses are tried. The best response is saved until all forks have returned a response, or a 2XX-series response is received and the best response can be forwarded upstream towards the client.

If a 2XX series response is received and the proxy is processing INVITE, incomplete forks are cancelled. Likewise, if the proxy receives a CANCEL for an incoming INVITE transaction while it is processing it, it will CANCEL the outstanding forks and return the current best answer or 487 Request Cancelled.

Session State and Session Timers

In addition to the transaction state, the proxy can also keep the call or session state. When configured to include the session state, the proxy creates a session object (`proxy_session_t`) whenever an INVITE transaction is completed. The session object contains two dialog legs, one upstream and another downstream. The session object and associated dialogs are kept active until the session is terminated with a BYE request or when the session expires.

Sessions are kept alive by periodical refresh requests, re-INVITEs. Whenever an INVITE transaction is completed, the session lifetime is extended.

Sofia Registrar

The Sofia registrar module contains a very simple implementation of SIP registrar server functionality. A SIP registrar accepts REGISTER requests and updates its location database according to the processed requests.

The Sofia registrar module can use the authentication module in order to authenticate the clients registering with it. The location database is available for queries initiated by outside modules. It is also possible to link the registrar with other modules, which closely follow the registration data. Whenever the registrar updates its location database, it invokes the given callback functions with updated location information as its parameters.

```
                 Address of registrar server         Address of registration record

REGISTER sip:sip03.example.com SIP/2.0
Via: SIP/2.0/UDP [3ffe:1200:3012:c000:210:a4ff:fe8d:6a46]:5061
   ;branch=z9hG4bKOFLmunvFakr
From: <sip:[3ffe:1200:3012:c000:210:a4ff:fe8d:6a46]>
   ;tag=u27c7cf2a
To: <sip:joe@example.com>
Call-ID: dff6a48c-5093-11d6-b287-0010a48d6a46
CSeq: 1 REGISTER
Contact: <sip:[3ffe:1200:3012:c000:210:a4ff:fe8d:6a46]:5061>
   ;expires=1800
User-Agent: Surf/1.3 nua/2.0 nta/1.3
Content-Length: 0
```

         Duration of registration   Address to bind with sip:joe@example.com

A REGISTER request binds the URI in the To header (also known as AOR, address-of-record) with the address listed in the Contact header.

Initializing the Registrar

When the REGISTRAR module is instantiated the registrar initializes the authentication module, creates a timer, initializes the registrar database, and installs REGISTER URIs onto the NTA module. The location database is currently memory-based. All changes are written onto a journal file, however, so the registrar can restore the database contents whenever it is restarted.

The registrar timer periodically removes expired bindings from the database. When removing these bindings, the timer routing notifies the modules linked with the registrar.

Processing REGISTER Requests

The registrar is activated by NTA module to process incoming REGISTER transactions. A REGISTER request contains an address-of-record in the To header, and a list of addresses which are bound with the address-of-record in the Contact header. First the registrar does the usual User Agent Server (UAS) processing: it checks extensions, validates content type, checks authorization and then proceeds to update the database.

Next, the registrar determines if the REGISTER request is actually an unregistration. Next, it searches the location database for the URI it is supposed to update. A new entry is created if an existing one is not found.

Next, the entry is updated. The registrar adds, updates or removes contacts associated with the address-of-record URI. These contacts can either be SIP URIs or other URIs. SIP URIs are stored temporarily in the database; that is, they expire and are removed from the database unless they are refreshed periodically. The non-SIP-URIs do not expire, but have to be explicitly removed from the registrar.

After the update, the updated bindings are reported back to the registering client. Also, an internal notification is sent to the other modules linked with the registrar.

Publishing Service Data

In addition to the location information found in the Contact header, the Sofia registrar supports publishing content. Here, content is service-related data, such as call processing scripts or presence documents. Note that this method was never standardized, and alternative methods are being developed for publishing service data.

The registrar update function (`registrar_update_contents`) updates the contents associated with the input URI. The Content-Disposition header specifies the disposition type and action for the REGISTER content. The disposition type describes the purpose of the content, i.e., how the content should be processed. The action specifies whether the content is stored or removed. For each type, there can only be one document stored in the location database.

In addition to the *script* and *sip-cgi* disposition types, two new types have been used: *message-script* defines processing rules for a message adaptation service and *presence* contains the consumer's presence document. The type or file format of the message contents is specified with a Content-Type header.

```
REGISTER sip:sip03.example.com SIP/2.0
Via: SIP/2.0/UDP [3ffe:1200:3012:c000:210:a4ff:fe8d:6a46]:5061
  ;branch=z9hG4bKo+39kuAuziK
From: <sip:joe@example.com>;tag=u27c7cf2a
To: <sip:joe@example.com>
Call-ID: 345b57fc-5094-11d6-b287-0010a48d6a46
CSeq: 3 REGISTER
Contact: <sip:[3ffe:1200:3012:c000:210:a4ff:fe8d:6a46]:5061>
  ;expires=1800
User-Agent: Surf/1.3 nua/2.0 nta/1.3
Content-Type: application/xpidf+xml
Content-Disposition: presence;action=store
Content-Length: 338

<?xml version="1.0" encoding="ISO-8859-1"?>
<presence>
  <presentity uri="pr:joe@example.com"/>
  <atom atomid="IHmBiv6/v2rrp9q55lD+lg==">
    <address uri="sip:joe@example.com">
      <status status="open"/>
      <class class="business"/>
      <mobility mobility="mobile"/>
      <note>Smug</note>
    </address>
  </atom>
</presence>
```

A register request may also contain presence data.

The registrar does not validate the purpose or type of the register payload, but rather stores it along with the payload in the location database. It is up to the users of the location database to validate and interpret the contents.

Searching the Location Database

The location database can be searched (`registrar_find` and `registrar_find_all`). The first function (`registrar_find`) returns a pointer to the list of contacts associated with the input URI. The second function (`registrar_find_all`) is more versatile: the caller can specify what kind of information is needed. A memory home pointer parameter is used to duplicate the information retrieved from the internal database.

IV

Implementations

Announcement Server

The announcement server (AS) is a network element which can provide announcements for callers. Announcements are sent as one-way Voice over IP (VoIP) streams through the network.

Announcement media can be basic tones, pre-recorded announcements (e.g., those used in the ordinary telephone network) or can be tailored to specific occasions. Examples of announcements would be:

o   "The user is not available; please call again."

o   "The user does not want to receive calls; please send an instant message."

Calls can be redirected to an announcement server from several locations. The usual case would be the redirect server which knows the status of the called party. The redirect server will try to locate the call destination based on the information in the registrar. If the call destination cannot be reached or the callee does not want to receive calls, the caller can be redirected to an announcement server. This server then provides an informative announcement on the status of the callee.

Implementation

The basic announcement server implementation only has a minimal set of features: it is only able to receive calls, and it plays the announcement whose name is defined on the user part of the SIP address. The server supports several codecs and normal Session Description Protocol (SDP) Offer/Answer negotiation.

AS was implemented as a server process on a Linux computer and supports IPv6. The announcement server was implemented on top of the Sofia SIP signaling subsystem and Media Subsystem (MSS). Implementing this kind of service is very straightforward, and can be based on a basic UA implementation. The number of concurrent sessions is limited only by the processing power of the host processor.

Multiparty Conferencing Unit

A Multiparty Conferencing Unit (MCU) provides a conferencing service, which can handle any media (e.g., audio and video). The purpose of the server is to group all the participants of a conference together and distribute the combined media stream to all of them.

In the case of audio, the voice signals of all participants are mixed together. Alternatively, only the active speaker's voice is sent to the other participants, but it can sometimes be difficult to detect the active speaker.

Video mixing is more complicated. Basic mixing options would include one of the following:

o   Show only one picture, for example, the active speaker

o   Show all participants in one mosaic picture; in practice, a combination of four pictures is the upper limit

o   Send each video stream separately, so that the receiver can decide which stream to show and how to include it on her screen

o   Enable control signaling for the consumer to select the stream

Implementation

An audio-only MCU was implemented using the Sofia signaling and media subsystems. The MCU runs on a single Linux computer and supports IPv6, just as the other Sofia components. The MCU supports multiple concurrent conferences. When accepting a SIP call the MCU can decide which conference the caller wants to join by examining the user part of the SIP URI.

```
sip:conference1@mcu.nokia.com
```

Everyone who knows the conference name can join it. A password can be included in the user part of the URI, but effectively this just makes the conference name harder to guess.

The MCU decodes all incoming audio streams and mixes them together. After mixing and gain control, the result is encoded for each recipient separately. Before encoding, the recipient's own voice is subtracted from the mixed audio in order to avoid an echo. This kind of echo cancellation is essential to achieve the best possible audio quality.

The MCU also supports SIP instant messaging. A user can send an instant message to the conference Uniform Resource Locator (URL), and the MCU distributes the message to all conference participants. The MCU also notifies all conference members when someone joins or leaves the conference by sending an SIP instant message containing the participants' SIP URIs.

PSTN Gateway

A gateway is a network server which provides real-time communication between two or more terminals. The purpose of a gateway is to convert either signaling or media, or both, from one format to another. In this case, a conversion typically happens between a Switched Circuit Network (SCN) and an IP network.

A gateway can be a single device or its functionality can be decomposed into three functional elements each of which can be in a separate device: the Media Gateway Controller (MGC), the Media Gateway (MG) and the Signaling Gateway (SG). The architecture of a decomposed gateway is shown in the following figure.

IV

Implementations

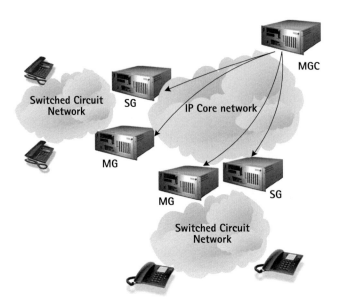

Basic decomposed gateway architecture

The main reason for decomposing a gateway is that, in such a scheme, multiple media and signaling gateways can be connected to a single gateway controller. The components can be distributed to different parts of the network and they can be purchased from different vendors. One advantage of decomposition is scalability. A media gateway can be a carrier class device handling thousands of simultaneous calls or a residential gateway handling just two calls. A media gateway is much more processor-intensive than a signaling gateway or gateway controller. A controller based on regular PC hardware can easily handle hundreds if not thousands of calls, but handling tens of calls with media transcoding requires specialized hardware with considerable Digital Signal Processor (DSP) capacity. Since converting voice data from a circuit switched domain to an IP domain uses bandwidth more efficiently, it is beneficial to locate the media gateways at the edges of the network, near the origin of the call. Decomposing the gateway makes this possible.

A protocol for media gateway controlling called Megaco/H.248 was designed in cooperation with the International Telecommunication Union (ITU-T) and Internet Engineering Task Force (IETF). Megaco/H.248 will most likely be the predominant protocol used between the gateway controller and the media gateways.

The signaling gateway receives the SCN native signaling. The SG may relay, translate or terminate the signaling, and works in conjugation with MGC. The signaling information is transferred on top of the IP network from SG to MGC using a suitable transport protocol. The Stream Control Transmission Protocol (SCTP) defined in RFC 2960 is one such protocol. RFC 2719 defines a framework for signaling transport using SCTP.

Implementation

Decomposed gateway software including MGC, MG and SG was developed for, and integrated to a part of the MITA Reference Implementation Environment. The MGC runs on a Linux computer, while MG and SG are separate processes on a Windows NT® computer. Because ISDN signaling uses the same PRI as voice traffic, MG and SG share the same physical unit but they are separate logical entities from the MGC point of view. All these elements support IPv6.

MGC uses a Sofia SIP stack for terminating VoIP calls. The architecture of the MGC is scalable, allowing it to control several SGs and MGs. The MGC itself performs a relatively light task, at least when compared to MG.

The signaling between MGC and SG is transported over a proprietary protocol basically transmitting Network Signaling API (NSA) primitives. The Q.931 signaling events are translated into NSA messages and transported between the MGC and SG using the UDP.

The MGC and MG communicate using a proprietary protocol called the Network Gateway API (NGA). The functionality required of this API closely resembles the Real Time Streaming Protocol (RTSP), and is a precursor of the MSS API. The SDP is carried over NGA without needing modifications by the MGC.

The MG is implemented using Sofia media subsystem modules. Since the MG operates as a transcoder, it must run codecs in this implementation. The host processor executes speech codecs instead of the digital signal processors on the interface card.

Converged Application Server

An important aspect of a communication infrastructure is programmability. The purpose of the SIP Servlet Application Programming Interface (API) is to standardize a Java™ platform for delivering SIP based services. The SIP Servlet API defines a similar functionality to develop SIP applications as has previously been used to create dynamic Web services using the HyperText Transfer Protocol (HTTP) servlet API [servlet]. These specifications define how servlet applications are developed and deployed and how servers hosting these applications should behave.

Goals of the SIP Servlet API have been:

o **SIP signaling:** The ability to perform a fairly complete set of SIP signaling

o **Converged applications:** It is important that servers support multi-protocol applications, for example, applications mixing Web, telephony, and presence.

o **Third party application development:** The servlet model supports third party application development.

o **Simplicity:** Underlying servers handle extra complexity (e.g., managing network listening points, CSeq, Call-ID, and Via header). Application developers are not necessarily SIP experts.

IV   Implementations

The servlet development model assumes that there can be three different roles in the application development and usage cycle. An application developer produces a SIP application. His output is a set of classes and supporting libraries. An application assembler takes the work done by the developer and ensures that is a deployable unit. The output of the assembler is a SIP application archive. The deployer takes one or more SIP application archive files and deploys the application in a specific operational environment. An Extensible Markup Language (XML) formatted deployment descriptor is used to communicate application information from the application developer to deployers.

Main Concepts

The SIP Servlet Container is a part of the application server, which provides the networking functions to send and receive SIP messages. The container decides which applications should process incoming messages. The servlet container is also responsible for managing application-related security, which it can do by using the permission architecture defined by the Java 2 platform. The container is ultimately responsible for making sure that all applications honor SIP protocol rules.

There are many different ways the SIP servlet container can be implemented. One option is to implement it as a stand-alone component. The servlet container can also be built as an add-on component onto existing SIP network elements via their native APIs.

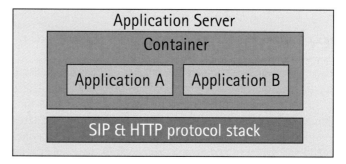

Converged server architecture

A SIP Servlet is a Java-based application component managed by a container, which performs actual SIP signaling. Servlets are platform independent Java classes which are compiled as platform neutral byte code. The byte code can be loaded into any SIP application server and run there. All servlets implement the servlet interface, which can be done either directly or by extending a class which implements the interface. The servlet interface defines three methods of managing the servlet lifecycle and passing received messages to servlets.

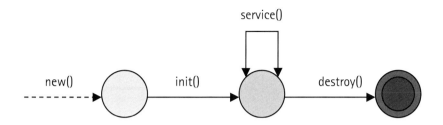

Servlet lifecycle

The servlet container loads the servlet class, instantiates a servlet object and invokes the init method on it, passing along servlet configuration information in the form of a ServletConfig object. After successful initialization, the servlet can be invoked to process received messages by invoking its service method, which takes a received request or response as an argument. When the container has no use for a particular servlet it invokes the destroy method.

Many applications consist of multiple SIP sessions/dialogs and inside these sessions there may be a need to send multiple messages. This requires that application servers keep some kind of state information associated with these sessions. Like SIP dialogs, servlets themselves do not contain any state information. The SIP Servlet API provides two objects to help with this problem, the first a SipApplicationSession, which represents an application instance and the other a SipSession, which represents a protocol session. Application sessions are specific to application instances. They can contain a number of protocol sessions (e.g., SIP and HTTP) and can also store application specific data. Protocol sessions (e.g., SipSession and HTTPSession) represent protocol-specific session information. All protocol sessions always belong to one application session. A SipSession basically corresponds to a SIP dialog.

The SIP Servlet API provides an application developer with an opportunity to make servlets behave either as a SIP User Agent (UA) or as a SIP proxy. SIP UA functionality contains two parts: client and server. Acting as a SIP UA means that servlets can send requests and receive responses to those requests. Servlets can create a new request using a SipFactory object. The SipFactory interface provides two methods for this purpose:

```
SipServletRequest createRequest(SipApplicationSession appSession,
                                String method,
                                SipAddress from,
                                SipAddress to);

SipServletRequest createRequest(SipApplicationSession appSession,
                                String method,
                                String from,
                                String to);
```

The returned SipServletRequest belongs to a new SipSession which in turn belongs to the specified SipApplicationSession. The container is responsible for creating and adding all other required SIP headers (i.e., Cseq and Call-ID). If the servlet wants to create a new request to an existing SIP dialog, the servlet must use the following method provided by the SipSession representing that dialog:

IV Implementations

```
SipServletRequest createRequest(SipApplicationSession appSession,
                                String method,
                                SipAddress from,
                                SipAddress to);

SipServletRequest createRequest(SipApplicationSession appSession,
                                String method,
                                String from,
                                String to);
```

Call-ID, CSeq, From, To and Route headers are inserted by the container based on the dialog information. When acting as a UA server, the servlet may generate a number of provisional responses and a single final response to a received request. A response skeleton can be generated by invoking the following method on the received request:

```
SipServletRequest createRequest(String method);
```

The servlet can then modify a returned response (e.g., add content, insert some headers) and then send the response by invoking the send method on the response object.

Proxy operation is controlled via a Proxy object that can be obtained from an incoming SipServletRequest object. Proxy behavior can be controlled via a number of different

```
SipServletResponse createResponse(int statuscode);

SipServletResponse createResponse(int statuscode,
                                  String reasonPhrase);
```

configuration flags:

o   A recurse flag indicates whether the container will automatically recurse or not. If this flag is set, the container will automatically proxy to the contact address received in the redirect response.

o   A recordRoute flag indicates whether the application server will stay in the signaling path or not.

o   A parallel flag indicates whether the container should proxy to all multiple destinations in parallel or in sequence.

o   A stateful flag indicates whether the proxy operation should be performed transaction statefully of transaction statelessly.

o   A supervised flag indicates whether the servlet should be invoked to handle responses received to a proxied request.

SIP Applications

SIP servlet applications are collections of servlets, class files and other resources needed to complete an application. SIP applications can be packaged and signed into a Servlet Archive (SAR) format file using standard Java archive tools.

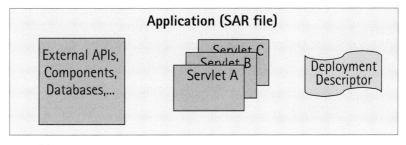

Application composition

Deployment descriptors are XML files used to convey elements and configuration information about a particular servlet application between application developers, application assemblers and deployers. Every application built using servlets has to have at least one deployment descriptor containing at least the following information:

o   Application and Servlet initialization parameters

o   Session configuration information

o   Servlet definitions

o   Information on mapping incoming messages to different servlets

An example of a deployment descriptor might look like the one below, which introduces a SIP application called *Test Servlet Application*. The container and servlets are given one run-time parameter. The example introduces a servlet called `RegisterServlet` and also specifies that this servlet should be loaded when the server starts. At the end of the descriptor file is a sample mapping of all REGISTER requests to the `RegisterServlet`.

```xml
<?xml version="1.0" encoding="ISO-8859-1"?>
<web-app>
    <display-name>
        Test Servlet Application
    </display-name>
    <description>
        This is a test application to test NRC Servlet server
    </description>
    <context-param>
        <param-name>db_url</param-name>
        <param-value>jdbc:mysql://169.21.41.174:3306/SIP</param-value>
    </context-param>
    <servlet>
        <servlet-name>
            RegisterServlet
        </servlet-name>
        <servlet-class>
            com.nokia.sip.servlets.RegisterServlet
        </servlet-class>
        <load-on-startup/>
    </servlet>
    <servlet-mapping>
        <servlet-name>
            RegisterServlet
        </servlet-name>
        <pattern>
            <equal>
                <var>request.method</var>
                <value>REGISTER</value>
            </equal>
        </pattern>
    </servlet-mapping>
</web-app>
```

Sample deployment descriptor

Implementation

A SIP servlet application server was developed to test Java APIs ability to create and manage SIP services. Therefore, the implementation concentrated only on SIP-related applications.

The server implementation was built on top of a SIP stack supporting the JAIN™ SIP API, and was done using Java™ SE 1.4. The implementation is divided into the following packages:

o   **Core:** This package provides all server core functionalities, and most of the servlet container components are located in this package.

o   **Address:** This package contains implementations for all addressing related classes (e.g., URI and SIP URI).

o   **Message:** This package provides implementations for SIP requests and response objects.

o   **Session:** Provider's classes to manage SIP sessions

o   **Mapper:** Provider's implementations for mapping requests to the correct servlets according to mapping rules provided in the deployment descriptor.

o   **Util:** Provides utility classes for other server components (e.g., parsers for the deployment descriptor and class loaders).

o   **Sdp:** Provides classes to parse SDP payloads and access different components of SDP messages.

To test server functionality some example applications were developed:

o   **Registrar:** This application implements most of the SIP registrar functionality. It can receive and process SIP REGISTER messages and store a consumer's registration information on an external database server. The implementation includes one servlet and utility classes to manage database access.

o   **Presence:** This application implements the SIP presence service. It works together with the registrar application to get information about a consumer's presence status. The service can receive a SIP SUBSCRIBE message and send SIP NOTIFY messages.

o   **IM relay:** This application acts as a proxy for SIP MESSAGE messages. It can also route incoming messages based on registration information. The application consists of one servlet to process SIP MESSAGE messages and other classes to manage connections with an external database.

IV   Implementations

References

[servlet]   http://java.sun.com/products/servlet/, Java Servlet Technology

[sip-bis]   Rosenberg, J. et al, "SIP: Session Initiation Protocol", RFC 3261, Proposed Internet Standard, March 2002.

[reg-pl]   Lennox, J., and H. Schulzrinne, "Transporting User Control Information in SIP REGISTER Payloads", Internet-Draft draft-lennox-sip-reg-payload-01, October 2000 (expired in April 2001).

PART 4.4

Applications and Servers

- o Browsing

- o Streaming

- o SIP User Agents and Terminals

- o Presence and Messaging

- o Mobile DRM

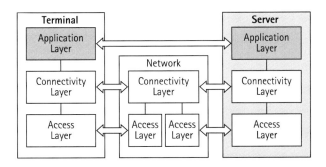

Browsing

The browsing aspect of the MITA Reference Implementation Environment was represented by basic Web client and server support. The basic objective was to test the usual browsing services made with publicly available software (i.e., no special browsers or servers were developed). The target was to affirm that they run as expected in the MITA Reference Implementation Environment over IPv6. Another target was to demonstrate interoperability between IPv4 and IPv6 using browsing services.

The tests related to browsing utilized the setup illustrated in the following figure.

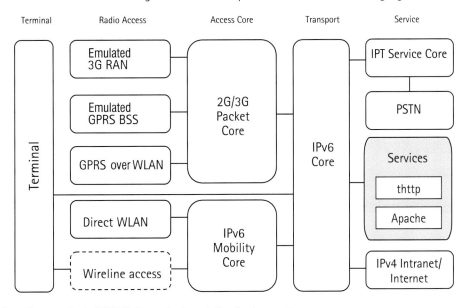

Browsing setup in the MITA Reference Implementation Environment

During a typical test setup, a couple of Linux servers in the network were running HTTP server software. The hardware platforms deployed as HTTP servers were regular PCs with no special configuration. The operating system was Linux supplemented with a kernel supporting IPv6 and Mobile IPv6.

Two different HTTP server software programs were tested. One was thttpd (Tiny HTTP daemon) [thttpd], which supports IPv6 natively and was very easy to configure. As the name proposes, this software is relatively small in size and implements the minimum requirements of HTTP/1.1. The software can run in most UNIX-like operating systems.

The other server software package tested was Apache [apache], which is the most used HTTP-server on the Internet. Apache is an HTTP/1.1 compliant Web server that runs in most of the popular operating systems. To get IPv6 support for older stable 1.3-versions of Apache, it was necessary to apply patches into Apache sources. The current Apache 2.0 version supports IPv6 natively.

The browsing features of the MITA Reference Implementation Environment also enabled the use of IPv4 browsing servers with IPv6 clients. This was done using an Apache server acting as a proxy between IPv6 and IPv4 networks. In this method, the IPv6 client basically connects to the proxy which then contacts the IPv4 server. The server returns the page to the proxy which forwards it to the IPv6 client. This kind of Web proxy usage will allow us to take advantage of the IPv6 address space when expanding the network while still offering support for legacy IPv4 terminals.

Mobile terminals, which were running on the Linux operating system and using only IPv6 for network connectivity, used a Mozilla™ browser [mozilla] for Web access. One of the reasons for selecting Mozilla was its native support for IPv6. Terminals deployed the X-window system-based graphical user interface.

Browsing features were used to validate the smooth operation of browsing services. One problem encountered was lack of support for secure Web connections using Secure Sockets Layer (SSL) over IPv6. These SSL-connections are essential to many browsing services (e.g., banking). However, it is expected that support for SSL over IPv6 will eventually be implemented. Regarding normal Web browsing, no special problems were encountered during the tests. The results show that the MITA Reference Implementation Enviroment was able to support most of the standard browsing services.

References

[thttpd]   http://www.acme.com/software/thttpd/

[apache]   http://httpd.apache.org/

[mozilla]   http://www.mozilla.org/

Streaming

Streaming refers to delivering different media as a real-time stream utilizing IP protocols. The content could be music files, real-time Internet radio broadcasts or movies. Streaming differs from the download-and-play type of retrieving, as it needs no local storage for the content. The streaming protocol conserves the order of packets, which allows content playback while the rest of the content is being downloaded. Therefore, it frees system resources, especially memory and storage capacity. It allows the user to acquire larger media content as well as live services with much less delay than if downloading the whole content as a single block.

To keep the media playing continuous and smooth, a need for buffering exists. The need for application memory, moreover, is linearly dependent on the buffer size. In mobile devices the memory and wireless bandwidth are limiting factors. Some low-bandwidth codecs with good quality media streams, e.g., Advanced Audio Coding (AAC) and Moving Pictures Experts Group (MPEG) version 4, offer one solution.

The following sections will cover audio and video as well as Real Time Streaming Protocol (RTSP) streaming.

Audio and Video

Audio streaming is the most popular form of streaming today. There are thousands of commercial 24h Internet radio stations offering varying quality audio streams depending on the bandwidth of the listener's connection. The general protocol used by such media is the Real-time Transport Protocol (RTP).

Some major bands have already offered live concerts on the Internet. It is quite obvious that delivering a live show directly to all fans would be nearly impossible. Luckily, multicast technology helps here. Multicast offers group addresses to which the stream is sent, similar to a radio with the receiver tuned to the frequency of a public broadcast station. Multicast is different from broadcast because it is a two-way channel, so group members can send data to one, some or all the other multicast group members. This is an appealing arrangement for new services and for getting immediate feedback.

Implementation

The implementation goal was to demonstrate a customer application utilizing a Mobile IPv6 network with seamless handovers. Streaming was used as part of the testing, since audio/video streaming during handover gives visual and audible confirmation that the network is functioning properly. Streaming was also an ideal application for public demonstration purposes, and was used in a number of exhibitions when the portable version of the Mobile IPv6 demonstration network toured around the world in 2001 as illustrated in the next figure.

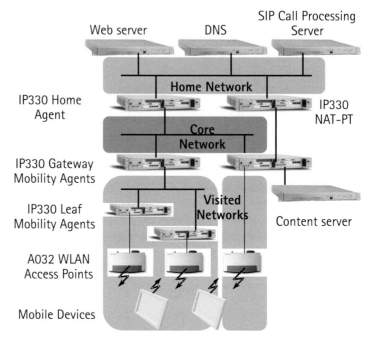

Streaming Demonstrator Layout

Streaming Session

The streaming session is initiated from a Graphical User Interface (GUI) running on a mobile device. The phases are as follows:

1. The GUI runs a script that requests a stream from the content server using HTTP/1.0 and a GET command.

2. The HyperText Transfer Protocol (HTTP) operates at the application level and assumes a connection-oriented transport protocol. In our implementation, the content is requested and downloaded from the HTTP port of the server with IPv6 enabled client.

3. On the server side, an HTTP server initiates an MPEG encoded stream to the client.

    The HTTP server does not know that it is a stream, because the client is simply requesting more and more of the content at the same rate as it presents the already fetched content to the consumer.

4. The received stream is piped to a player with a shell redirect.

The stream used in the demonstrations takes roughly 3 Mbit/s of the bandwidth including headers so the 11 Mbit/s air interface between a mobile device and the network is adequate. The content server in the previous figure is located in the home network but network services can be situated anywhere in the network. The streaming server could also be located in another mobile device in the network.

Real-Time Streaming Protocol

Most streaming technologies are based on the Real-Time Streaming Protocol (RTSP) [RFC 2326] which offers a way of controlling the media with several streams.

The RTSP differs from the SIP in being specified for controlling the presentation (i.e., seeking and pausing) whereas the SIP is used for initiating the sessions. They share many common features (e.g., both are text based protocols and partly use the same headers). The SIP has call-legs for enclosing a phone call under one state, whereas the RTSP has states for media streams called sessions. Both protocols use the Session Description Protocol (SDP) as the media descriptor but there is no offer-answer media negotiation in RTSP in the sense of SIP.

Methods

Some of the methods are stateless, as there is no need for a session for these requests. Other methods are session-dependent and can be applied after a session is created.

Method Name	Description
OPTIONS	Stateless and specified for determining requirements and options associated with a resource, or server capabilities.
DESCRIBE	Used for retrieval of a presentation from a server identified by the request Uniform Resource Locator (URL.) The response from the server contains a description of the requested presentation, and further session initialization is based on this information. One of the supported payload formats is SDP.
ANNOUNCE	Used for posting the description of the presentation to the server. The server can also send the ANNOUNCE message to the client and update the session description in real-time. The presentation description can be fetched from the server with DESCRIBE.
SETUP	Specified for setting up the transport of a media stream. In media initialization, this is the first stateful message and is used to allocate state for a session. The method is applied to every stream presented in the payload of a response to DESCRIBE.
PLAY	When all the stream transports are initialized, the PLAY request is sent to the server, which will command the server to start playing the streams. Playing can begin at the start or in the middle of the presentation.
RECORD	Similar to PLAY except the client starts sending the streams and the server will record and store the presentation.
PAUSE	Pauses the streams sent. The presentation is continued with PLAY or RECORD.
TEARDOWN	When the presentation is to be closed, the client sends a TEARDOWN request to the server indicating that the allocated resources can be freed and the session destroyed.
SET_PARAMETER	The request is specified for setting a parameter specified in the request URL. The format of the request is implementation-specific.

GET_PARAMETER Specified for retrieval of presentation parameters. The format of the payload is loose and implementation-specific.

REDIRECT   For any reason (e.g., load balancing) the server might redirect the client to retrieve the presentation from some other URL.

Implementation

The RTSP stack is divided into three modules as shown in the following figure. The MSG module interface handles generic message parsing and is also used with SIP. The RTSP module is similar to the SIP module and has functions for encoding and decoding header strings for structures and vice versa. The protocol machine is in the Transaction API for RTSP NTR module which is similar to the Sofia Transaction API. NTR has agent and session objects which manage the sending and receiving of messages. The Media Subsystem (MSS) module controls the media processing the top layer of the stack, though in the figure below it is purely for protocol control.

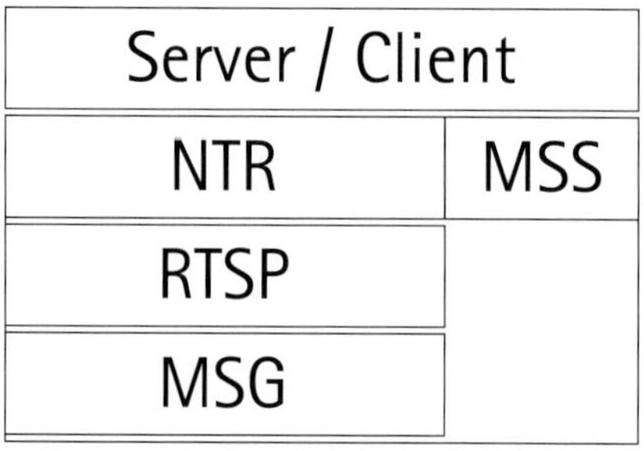

Server / Client	
NTR	MSS
RTSP	
MSG	

RTSP stack with media module

RTSP Parser

The following code example presents a function for decoding a message sequence number header, which is of the form `Cseq: <number>`.

```
rtsp_sequence_number_decode(rtsp_header_structure,
     character_string)
{
 Get the CSEQ header structure;
 Get the sequence number from the character string;
 Insert the sequence number to CSEQ header structure;

 Return;
}
```

The NTR module contains the RTSP protocol engine which is used in a similar fashion as the NTA module. The NTR agent is the core of the engine, which binds to a network port. Every incoming message is accepted or discarded depending on whether it is a valid RTSP message. If the message is stateless it is passed directly to the upper layer by a callback function. If the message is session-dependent, NTR tries to find an existing session based on the Session-Id in the message. The pointers to the sessions are stored in a hash table. If a new session is to be created, a callback function is called. A new session is created and inserted into the hash table. The engine is used in both server and client implementations.

Client

Client implementation is a straightforward application of NTR. Callbacks are used to continue the execution of presentation initialization. After a response to a message sent, a callback is called and the next message sent. In the example below, an outgoing message is created and after receiving a response to it, a callback function is called. The media part is initialized in the start of the application. The local capabilities are determined after receiving a successful response to DESCRIBE. The local media port numbers are retrieved in the SDP and sent to the server in SETUP request.

Server

The server is initialized by the creation of an NTR agent. The callback presented below handled messages which are not part of any current session. For example, the message "SETUP a new session" is created in `handle_setup_msg`. Media initialization happens as follows: the server media port numbers are got from SDP returned by `mss_describe`. The port numbers are then returned to the client in response to SETUP.

```
/* Callback for incoming messages (not part of a session) */
int rs_message(rs_t *rs,
 ntr_agent_t *agent,
 ntr_msg_t *msg,
 rtsp_t *rtsp)
{
 /* If the request was a response */
 if (rtsp->rtsp_status) {
 ntr_msg_discard(agent, msg);
 return 0;
 }

 /* Handle methods separately */
 switch (rtsp->rtsp_request->rq_method) {
 case rtsp_method_describe:
 /* describe, always stateless */
 if (handle_describe_msg(rs, msg, rtsp) < 0)
```

```
break;
return 0;
}
case rtsp_method_setup:
/* setup, for setting up a new session */
if (handle_setup_msg(rs, msg, rtsp) < 0)
break;
return 0;
  …
}
```

After receiving the SETUP request, a new session is created. The `handle_setup_msg` allocates the resources needed and NTR adds the session to the hash table. The parameters are the server structure, the message structure and the structure containing the RTSP headers in the current request.

```
/** Create a session */
int handle_setup_msg(rs_t *server, ntr_msg_t *msg, rtsp_t const *rtsp)
{
  rs_session_t *session;

  /* Allocate and initialize the session */
  session = rs_session_create(server, NULL);

  /* Add session to the NTR hash table and proceed the message handling */
  session->rss_session =
  ntr_msg_session(rs->rs_ntr_agent, /* Server agent */
  msg, /* message object */
  rs_incoming, /* Callback for session */
  session, /* Server session structure */
  0); /* no any options */

  /* If the NTR session couldn't be created */
  if (session->rss_session == NULL) {
  printf("RSERVER: Cannot create a session.\n");
  rs_session_destroy(session); /* Destroy it. */
  return -1;
  }

  return 0;
}
```

Media SubSystem

The MSS module scales flexibly to both server-side and client-side implementations. The following figure depicts the message flow between the client and server. The client initiates the presentation by sending the DESCRIBE method. The successful response payload contains a SDP description of the presentation streams and their parameters. The parameters include the codec RTP uses for streaming. After receiving the response, the client starts setting up the session by initializing its own media. The local RTP port numbers are returned in a SDP and included in the SETUP request. The server then allocates a session after receiving the SETUP message, initializes its media and responds by sending the RTP port numbers for the media streams.

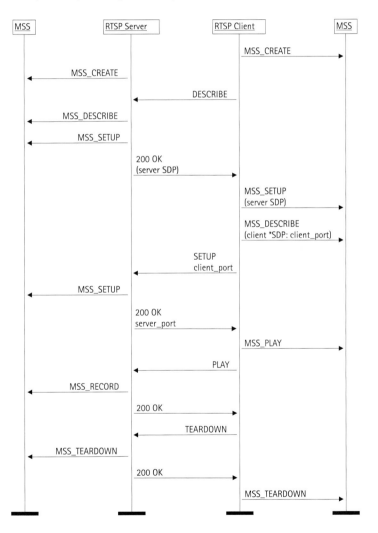

Sequence diagram of successful presentation streaming

IV

Implementations

SIP User Agents and Terminals

This chapter discusses the implementation of SIP user agents, including audio and video processing.

SIP User Agent Library

The Sofia User Agent (NUA) Application Programming Interface (API) provided by the NUA module contains high-level telephony functions for User Agent applications like terminals and gateways. The NUA API takes care of protocol details and lets application programmers, for example, make a call with a minimal number of steps. The module uses many lower-layer modules (e.g., NTA and MSS) to provide its functionality.

The main functions of NUA include call management (establishing, modifying and tearing down calls), registration management (registering the consumer with a registrar, refreshing the registration at regular intervals and removing registrations when the application exits), and subscription management (subscribing to an event server, relaying event notifications to the application, and refreshing the subscription when needed).

Using the NUA API

The NUA API is asynchronous and lets the main application thread, for example, update the user interface without disturbing the protocol engines or media processing underneath it. Feedback from the protocol engines takes place in the form of enumerated events, which are delivered to the application either asynchronously or when the application polls for them. The NUA API events are delivered to the application with a callback function it provides.

The NUA function calls and events follow a simple naming convention. The application initiates a client operation (e.g., sending an instant message) by calling the associated function (nua_message). The responses to the operation are relayed back to the application using an event (nua_r_message, "r" stands for response). Similarly, when the protocol stack receives an instant message request it sends an indication event (nua_i_message, "i" stands for incoming) to the application.

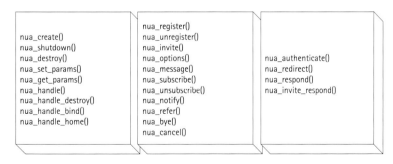

NUA API functions divided into three groups

Another important concept of the NUA API is the NUA handle, which represents the internal objects of the NUA module, be they telephone calls, chat sessions, registrations or subscriptions. Either the application or the NUA protocol engine allocates these handles. All protocol activity is related to a particular handle, and handles can also be associated with application objects.

The NUA implementation is divided into two parts, an upper part run in the context of an application thread, and a lower part run by a separate signaling protocol thread. Currently, the signaling protocol thread also takes care of some media processing. Information is passed between them using asynchronous messages.

Internally, the protocol engine contains multiple state machines, each dedicated to a particular protocol action. For each SIP operation, a separate state machine exists. In addition to SIP operations, there is a separate state machine for controlling media through the Media Subsystem (MSS) API.

Using Tagged Arguments

Different applications use a varying number of parameters with the NUA API. For example, while the simplest application provides no more than the destination Uniform Resource Identifier (URI) when making a call, a sophisticated application can include many other parameters, ranging from Call-Info containing rich caller identification to the media configuration for the call. The NUA API therefore needs to provide a flexible way to include optional parameters in function call parameters.

The approach chosen in the NUA API is named or tagged parameters. Each tagged parameter is specified by a special macro expanding to a special tag/value pair. For instance, the tag item macro `SIPTAG_SUBJECT_STR(sub)` expands to tag `siptag_subject_str` and `string_sub`. Outside parameter lists, the tag and the value are stored in a data structure called a tag item. The tag is a pointer to a special structure specifying the name of the tag and the type of tag value.

For example, initiating a call with a given subject, a couple of rich caller identification URIs, and a special media configuration would look like this:

```
nua_invite(nh,
        NUTAG_ADDRESS(uri),
        SIPTAG_SUBJECT_STR(subject),
        SIPTAG_CALL_INFO_STR(icon_url),
        SIPTAG_CALL_INFO_STR(calling_card_url),
        NUTAG_MEDIA_PATH(sdp_name),
        TAG_END());
```

NUA Example

Let us take a closer look at a detailed example of NUA usage beginning with the SIP MESSAGE [message] operation, probably the simplest operation that NUA provides. The MESSAGE method is used to transmit instant messages with SIP.

When the application wants to send an instant message, it first creates a handle or reuses an existing one. When created, the handle is usually associated with a destination address:

```
nh = nua_handle(nua, op,
                NUTAG_ADDRESS(uri),
                SIPTAG_TO(to),
                TAG_END());
```

For the instant message contents, the application can either construct a payload structure or pass it on as a C string. The latter method is applicable only with text content. The MIME type of the contents should also be specified (e.g., *text/html* or *image/jpeg*.)

```
nua_message(nh,
            SIPTAG_CONTENT_TYPE_STR("text/plain"),
            SIPTAG_PAYLOAD_STR(msg),
            TAG_END());
```

The upper part of NUA then passes the request to the SIP protocol engine, which invokes a MESSAGE transaction to the intended recipient. The responses are reported back to the application using the callback function and the associated event.

```
case nua_r_message:
  cli_r_message(status, phrase, nua, cli, nh, op, sip, tags);
  return;

...
```

A status code 200..699 informs the application when the message transactions have completed.

IV Implementations

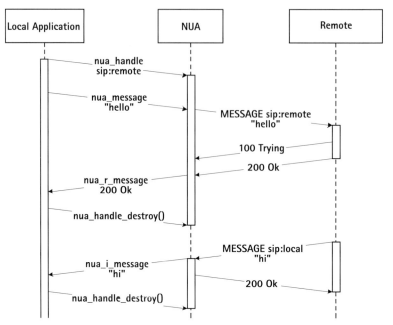

Sending an instant message with NUA

User Agent Client Tasks

The message function (nua_message) passed the request to the lower part. The request arguments are copied and the message function returns after waking up the protocol engine thread running in the lower part of NUA. The protocol engine first does some basic checks and then initializes the handle.

The processing continues by performing the common SIP UAC tasks as follows:

o   Create a nta_leg_t dialog object if needed,

o   Create and populate a request message,

o   Include Support and Required in the message headers if needed, and

o   Include authentication headers if needed.

The protocol engine then creates a new client transaction object.

Responses to the MESSAGE request are also processed by the NUA protocol engine. The engine first checks if the request could be restarted (e.g., if the request was missing authentication, if the recipient redirected me to another URI) and then proceeds to pass the response back to the application.

User Agent Server Tasks

The NUA module also takes care of common UAS tasks when it receives SIP transaction requests from the network. The basic tasks are performed as follows:

o   Check required extensions, returning a 420 Bad Extension if it is not supported,

o   Check the incoming method, returning a 405 Bad Method if it is not allowed, and

o   Check To tag for requests outside established dialogs, returning a 481 Call Does Not Exist if an unexpected To tag was found.

Responding to requests and executing method-specific operations is left to the function responsible for each method. The MESSAGE requests are handled by the message processing function, which just does the bare minimum. It creates a handle if it does not yet exist, passes the request message up to the application, and replies to the request with the 200 Ok response code.

Controlling Media

The purpose of the SIP UA is to establish media sessions. The NUA API uses the Media Subsystem interface to control the media session associated with the call. Since the MSS readily provides the semantics of the Session Description Protocol (SDP) [sdp] offer-answer model [o-a], this task is relatively straightforward.

Whenever the NUA call engine is required to send an SDP offer, it calls setup and describe functions, encodes the resulting SDP description and includes it as the payload of a SIP message. When the NUA call engine has sent an offer, it considers incoming SDP payloads as answers, and passes them to the Multimedia Subsystem. If no offer was sent, the incoming SDP payload is considered an offer, and the corresponding answer is retrieved from the Multimedia Subsystem.

Sofia Media Subsystem

This section describes the MSS implementation, part of the Sofia software distribution responsible for media transport and session control. The Media subsystem collects all media-related tasks under a single interface, which is designed to be flexible and extensible but still easy and straightforward to use.

The MSS was originally developed for Voice over IP (VoIP) applications but has also been extended to other application areas. The media subsystem supports both audio and video. It is utilized in several of the MITA Reference Implementation Environment elements (e.g., the SURF VoIP terminal, PSTN gateway, announcement server, conferencing server and streaming server). All these services share the same code base for media processing.

IV   Implementations

The MSS media subsystem is written in the C language to achieve the best possible performance and a degree of portability. The main development environment is Linux, although MSS can be compiled and run in other environments as well. For each operating system dependent part, there is an abstraction layer to allow portability.

The MSS is divided into modules with clean interfaces. Modularity eases maintenance and allows for easier reuse of code. Each of the modules is designed to be extensible without change in the interface.

MSS Interface

The MSS module implements the MSS interface and the subsystem logic. The MSS module includes Session Description Protocol (SDP) negotiation implementation according to the offer/answer model. Subsystem logic takes care of configuring, creating and destroying sessions. Each of these sessions is described with the SDP.

The MSS API is provided for using the media subsystem services. The interface methods and their semantics are similar to Real-Time Streaming Protocol (RTSP) [rtsp] methods. The interface is designed to be flexible and extensible yet straightforward and easy to use. These design requirements may sound hard to achieve, but in this case they were.

The interface can be used in a similar fashion to control very different kinds of media services. For example, the interface is used to control the Public Switched Telephone Network (PSTN) gateway and media sessions of a Surf audio/video terminal, two applications at opposite ends of the spectrum when considering application requirements.

As the interface closely resembles RTSP semantics, implementing an RTSP server and client on top of the interface is easy, and one-to-one mapping can almost be used. The interface thus allows remote control of the media, a feature which could be utilized with a distributed gateway in which the Media Gateway Controller (MGC) controls the Media Gateway (MG) remotely via an RTSP protocol. Within the media gateway the RTSP protocol would be directly mapped onto the MSS interface.

```
mss_create:     create a mss object
mss_destroy:    destroy a mss object
mss_get_status: get status
mss_announce:   set local SDP
mss_describe:   get local SDP
mss_setup:      setup a session with a local and remote SDP
mss_play:       start playing
mss_record:     start recording
mss_pause:      stop play / record
mss_teardown:   destroy a session
mss_event_bind: bind the event handler
mss_event_send: send an event
```

MSS API methods

Of these MSS interface methods, the methods announce, describe, setup, play, record, pause and teardown are derived from the RTSP, while the event methods were added later. The pause method was extended so that it can handle pausing separate streams, otherwise the methods work in the same way as RTSP methods.

Using and configuring the MSS is straightforward, as you will see in the following paragraphs where we describe the basic functionality of the interface.

The setup function is used to create a session from a predefined configuration. The configurations are identified by a path and several configurations can exist at the same time. The initial configuration is read from a local file, but can be altered afterwards with the announce function. The announce function can take a new local SDP as an argument. The SDP containing the active configuration can be retrieved from MSS with a describe function. The local configuration can include mss-specific SDP parameters. These parameters are usually removed from the SDP as it is retrieved with the describe function, so the active configuration can directly be used as an SDP offer.

A media session is created by the setup function. The function returns a session pointer, which is used in the subsequent calls. If the remote SDP is known, it is included in the setup function. The describe function is used to get the current local SDP from MSS. If the remote SDP has been passed to MSS, the local SDP is matched to it following the offer/answer model rules.

Mapping SIP to MSS

The following message sequence depicts how an incoming sip call is mapped to MSS. An asterisk (*) signifies a return-value parameter, that is, a parameter returned by the call.

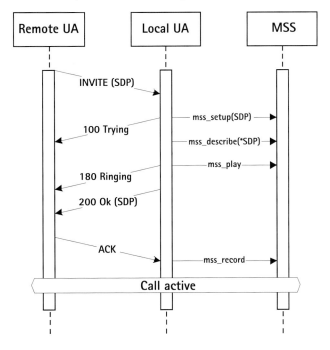

Inbound call

The inbound INVITE includes an SDP offer. This offer is passed to the MSS as the media session is created with the setup function. The answer is retrieved from the MSS with the describe function. The play function can be issued right away since it should be prepared to receive a media stream. The record function is called when an ACK is received from the other party.

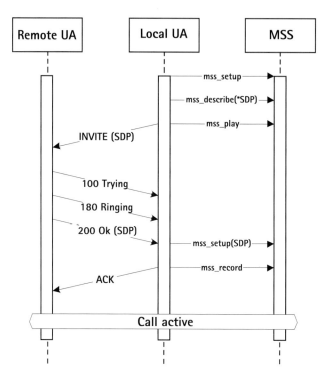

Outbound call

In the case of an outbound call, the setup function is called without a remote SDP. The SDP offer is retrieved with the describe function and the play function can also be called at this point. The offer is sent to the callee in the INVITE. The other party responds with some provisional responses and a 200 OK with the SDP answer. The answer is conveyed to the MSS with another setup function call. The record function can be issued after this.

Session Description Protocol

The SDP module implements an SDP protocol parser. This module is also utilized in the Sofia signaling subsystem.

The SDP is a text-based protocol. This makes the parsing straightforward and considerably helps debugging and development. SDP is very simple: full implementation requires less than 2000 lines of C.

The SDP is used in conjunction with signaling protocols (e.g., SIP, RTSP [RTSP], Session Announcement Protocol (SAP) [sap], and Megaco/H.248 [megaco]).

SDP session descriptions consist of lines of text in the format *<type>=<value>*. A session description is divided into a session level description and, optionally, media-level descriptions. Session-level descriptions apply to media level descriptions unless they are defined in the media description. The session level description starts with a *v=* line and continues to the first media level section, which starts with an *m=* line. There can be several media level sections.

An example of a SDP session description with minimum mandatory elements is presented in the figure below.

```
v=0
o=UserA 2890844526 2890844526 IN IP4 here.com
s=Session SDP
c=IN IP4 100.101.102.103
t=0 0
m=audio 49172 RTP/AVP 0
a=rtpmap:0 PCMU/8000
```

Example of SDP session description

The lines in the session description are as follows:

v=   version (zero currently)

o=   origin of the session (timestamps and an address)

s=   subject (must have at least one character, space recommended)

c=   connection (the actual IP address where media is sent)

t=   time the session is active (0 0 if other signaling is used to indicate this)

m=   description of the media: port to which this media is sent, protocol name, and payload type(s) to use

The SDP can also be used to negotiate dynamic binding from media encoding to dynamic RTP payload types. For this the *a=rtpmap:* attribute is used:

```
a=rtpmap:<payload type> <encoding name>/<clock rate>[/<encoding parameters>]
```

An example of this would be:

```
m=audio 49230 RTP/AVP 0 96 97 98
a=rtpmap: 0 PCMU/8000
a=rtpmap:96 L8/8000
a=rtpmap:97 L16/8000
a=rtpmap:98 AMR/8000
```

Example of rtpmap

IV Implementations

Static payload types should be mapped, though this is not mandatory. Static payload type mappings are defined in the RTP profile, and up to one rtpmap can be defined for each of the payload types. Experimental encoding formats which are not registered must be preceded by X-. An encoding format can be registered with the Internet Assigned Numbers Authority (IANA).

MSS Audio

Audio processing is provided by three MSS modules: AD, AC and RTP.

End-to-end delay has been considered the single most critical obstacle for VoIP deployment. Therefore, the most important design criteria with MSS audio has been low delay. A mouth-to-ear delay of 45 ms has been measured between two laptops running Surf terminal software. The measurement was made using an AMR speech codec, which has an algorithmic delay of 25 ms. [selin]

Overview of the Audio Transmission Process

The media handling process seems like it ought to be straightforward, but as normally happens in such cases, it proved otherwise. The media handling process covers the data flow from the network device to the audio device in both directions.

A flow diagram of an end-to-end media transmission is depicted in the figure below.

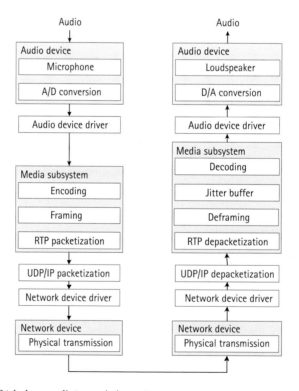

Overview of an IP telephony media transmission system

The analog signal is converted to a digital format by the audio device. The audio device driver works as an interface between the media subsystem and the device. The media subsystem encodes, frames and packetizes the audio data. The Real-time Transport Protocol (RTP) packet is then given to the network device for transmission.

The other end receives the RTP packet from the network device. The audio frames are extracted from the RTP packet and queued to the jitter buffer. When the audio device needs more data to play out, the next frame is fetched from the jitter buffer, decoded, and given to the audio device driver. The audio device then converts the digital data to analog format.

AC Module

Speech coding is the process of transforming digitized speech into a form that can be effectively transported over the network. The reverse function for encoding is decoding. A decoder tries to reproduce the original waveform as closely as possible. The combination of an encoder and a decoder is often called a codec.

Framing defines the actual frame structure for the encoded media. Framing is a separate process from encoding as it may be done in a variety of ways for the same encoded data. Frame-based codecs usually include some information on the frame besides the actual encoded data. This information can, for example, contain the type of the encoded data if the codec supports multiple bit-rates and silence suppression. Some framing schemes introduce redundant data from the previous frame to cope with packet loss. Framing also defines how multiple channels are presented.

The AC module abstracts codec implementations. At the moment, it supports the following codecs: Adaptive Multi-Rate Narrowband (AMR-NB) [amr] and Wideband (AMR-WB) [amr-wb], Global System for Mobile Communications (GSM) Enhanced Full Rate (EFR) [gsm-efr], G.723.1 [g723] and G.711 [g711]. Adding new codecs is straightforward. The AC interface is virtualized so that adding new codecs does not require any changes in the calling application nor in the interface itself.

The AC interface separates the encoding/decoding process from the framing process. For example, both AMR codecs use the same framing algorithm but separate codec engines.

AD Module

An audio device provides the interface from the computer to the real world. Analog-to-digital (A/D), and digital-to-analog (D/A), conversions are done in the audio device. In a PC, the device is usually a sound card, which is an add-on card inside the PC chassis. It is also possible that the device is integrated into the PC motherboard. In mobile devices, the audio circuitry is integrated inside the device, where the device driver for the audio device is the link to the operating system.

The quality of the audio device is essential to the overall quality of IP telephony. In mobile devices, a great deal of effort has been put into the quality of sound devices. In the PC world, the quality of these devices has proven inadequate: very few devices are well suited to real-time communications.

The AD module abstracts the audio device implementation. Audio devices can be physical devices (e.g., sound cards or Integrated Services Digital Network (ISDN) line cards) or logical devices

IV

Implementations

(e.g., software mixers or file interfaces). The interface is virtualized so that adding a device does not require changes in the interface nor in the application. Since audio device drivers are implemented in various ways in different operating systems, the AD module allows operating system dependent implementations.

Special care has been taken to ensure that the delay introduced by the audio device is minimized. The application can have precise control over the buffering done in the audio device. The amount of buffering needed depends on the processing power and load of the system and scheduling algorithm in the operating system. The basic case is a double buffering scheme where one buffer is being read by the audio device and the other is being filled by the application.

RTP Module

The RTP was first published by the IETF Audio/Video Transport (AVT) working group in January 1996. A revised version of the document was published in May 2002 [rtp].

The RTP module implements the RTP protocol as a reusable library. The RTP follows the principles of Application Level Framing (ALF) and Integrated Layer Processing (ILP). This means that the protocol can be adapted to different types of applications and that the protocol will often be implemented as part of the application. The RTP defines those functions which arc cxpcctcd to be common to all applications. To complete the protocol, at least the profile and the payload format specifications have to be defined.

A complete specification of the RTP for a given application requires a companion document called a profile. Typically, an application operates under a single profile so the profile itself is not explicitly indicated. The most commonly used profile for audio and video applications is defined in RFC 1890 [avp]. The document describes how audio and video data may be carried within the RTP.

The RTP can be transported over any suitable transport layer. Applications usually run the RTP over the UDP as it provides a low overhead best effort service. As the TCP provides sequencing and retransmissions of lost packets, it causes unnecessary delays and is not an optimal solution for the RTP.

Note that for quality-of-service (e.g. timely delivery of packets), the RTP relies on lower level protocols. The RTP does not guarantee the delivery or order of packets, nor does it assume that the underlying network is reliable or that it provides the in-order delivery of packets.

When packets are transmitted over the network, variable delay is introduced. Packets can also be dropped or duplicated. This unpredictable behavior of the network forces the receiving end to compensate in a process known as playout reconstruction. It is usually realized using a playout buffer (also known as the jitter buffer) where packets are added as they arrive and played out periodically after a delay. If the packets were to be played out as they arrive, the speech would be unintelligible.

When packets are received, they are marked with a playout time and added to the jitter buffer. When the audio device requests a new frame to be played, the jitter buffer is checked for available packets. If the playout time marked in the packet has passed, the packet can be played. The packet is then decoded and transferred to the audio device. The basic playout synchronization is demonstrated in the following figure.

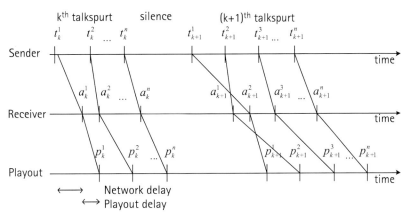

RTP playout reconstruction

The playout delay is calculated from a reference point which is usually set in the first packet of a talk-spurt. If the delay changes considerably from spurt to spurt, the quality of the speech degrades since the silent parts of the speech are not of their original length. Hearing is not very sensitive to errors in the length of silent periods, so some variation can be allowed.

RTP Control Protocol

The Real-time Transport Control Protocol (RTCP) is defined in the same document as the RTP [rtp]. The purpose of the RTCP is to monitor the quality of service and to convey information about participants in an on-going session by periodic transmission of control packets to all participants in the session. The distribution of participation information is not intended to replace call signaling, but rather to inform session members about the identities of the participants. A separate session control protocol (e.g., SIP) is needed for call control.

The primary function of the RTCP is to provide feedback on the quality of data distribution. This information may be useful for controlling adaptive encoders, and can also be used to detect network faults. Third parties (e.g., carriers) can monitor the RTCP traffic to determine the state of the network.

The RTCP provides a convenient way to reach all participants in a session. This can be used to convey information on the participants to be displayed on the user interface. Applications can also use the RTCP for application-specific purposes by defining an APP packet.

The RTP module implements the RTCP as a separate reusable component. It has separate encoding and decoding functions as well as RTP integration in the protocol engine section. The protocol engine takes care of calculating quality-of-service related parameters (e.g., round-trip-delay, jitter and packet loss). The protocol engine calculates the RTCP transmission interval based on the session bandwidth.

Video Modules

Video is included in the MSS to enable video telephony over IP applications. The video service can operate with a fixed image size of 176x144 pixels at a maximum of 30 frames per second (Quarter-Common Intermediate Format (QCIF) as in [BT601-5]) at any defined transmission bitrate up to 512 kbps. The supported video formats are H.263+ Profile 3 [h263], [h263x] and Moving Picture Experts Group Visual Simple Profile 4 [MPEG4]. The coded video is transmitted over RTP/UDP/IP, similar to audio. The corresponding RTP payload formats for H.263+ [RFC2429] and MPEG-4 Visual media [RFC3016] are used.

The modules providing the video telephony service include the video capture module (which reads directly from the video source), the video encoder and decoder, the video display module (which directly accesses the screen) and an integrated RTP module (which directly accesses the UDP network sockets for packet transfer). The internal architecture of the video telephony engine is depicted in the figure below. The video telephony modules run as a separate set of threads and are merely controlled by the MSS through the Video Telephony API.

The target transmission bitrate and other quality-of-service parameters of the encoding and decoding paths can be set at the Video Telephony API before startup or also after startup dynamically. These parameters could be included in the SDP description of video.

Through the Video Telephony API, the encoding and decoding paths can be started and stopped separately as requested by the related MSS functions. Once the paths are started, they operate without interaction with the MSS.

The video encoder is responsible for retrieving its input and forwarding its output. The video encoder frame input rate and the bitstream output bitrate is also controlled by the encoder. The target video frame rate and target transmission bitrate is communicated to the video encoder from the video manager through the Codec API. In the encoding path, a blocking buffer between the encoder and the RTP transmitter is implemented to guarantee a Constant BitRate (CBR) transmission. The encoding path implements TMN5 video rate control [TMN5], which efficiently smoothes the output bitrate of a video encoder to a constant rate and also minimizes the buffering delay required at the transmitter and receiver. It selects for encoding only certain video frames from the video source such that before a new video frame is encoded all bits of a previously encoded video frame have been transmitted at the target transmission bitrate. Receivers are able to decode a TMN5 encoded video bitstream without pre-decoder buffering.

A video frame is encoded into a number of video slices. These slices are then sent in individual RTP packets. In order to reduce end-to-end delay, slices output by the video encoder are sent immediately, even before the encoder finishes encoding the whole video frame. Similarly, on the receiver side, individual slices arriving at the RTP receiver are decoded even before all the slices of a video frame arrive. Slice-based encapsulation of the video payload into RTP packets also increases the system's packet loss robustness.

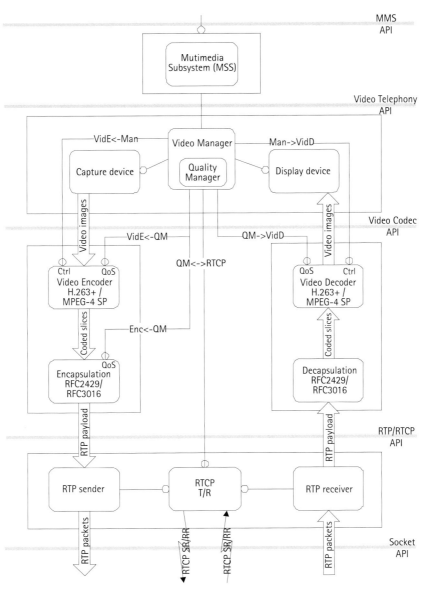

Modules of the Video Telephony Engine

Video is transmitted in its own RTP session. No explicit synchronization of the audio and video RTP sessions is done before transmission. It is assumed that both media operate real-time, without added pre-transmission buffering, thus with an implicit synchronization. In the receiver, however, lip-synchronization has to be performed to compensate for the different capture, encoding, transmission, decoding and display delay of the two media. Video has an inherently longer delay than audio due to the more complex compression scheme which requires a longer encoding time and a longer transmission time for the number of bits associated with a video frame. If the delay difference is greater than 100 to 150 ms, lip-synchronization is achieved by introducing a buffering delay before audio decoding. The calculation of this buffering delay involves estimating the audio and video decoding and playback/display times. The timing information required to perform lip-synchronization is conveyed from the transmitter to the receiver through RTCP Sender Reports.

The video manager module includes a general level *transport intelligence* sub-module, the Quality Manager (QM). The QM adaptively chooses the video codec operating point which is optimal at the target transmission bitrate and the dynamically changing error conditions of the RTP transport. It aims at achieving the best decoded video quality at the RTP receiver, while ensuring that the allowed application and link limitations (e.g., transmission bitrate and allowed end-to-end delay) are not exceeded. The QM receives input about the RTP transport statistics (e.g., packet loss rate, delay jitter) from the RTCP module which is processing the outgoing and incoming RTCP reports. The QM informs the video encoder/decoder about the channel error conditions and instructs them to use less or more robust video bitstream embedded error protection and/or error concealment. It is also responsible for monitoring the available bandwidth and, if necessary, overriding the MSS requested target transmission bitrate.

SURF

SURF [surf] is a Linux SIP UA application designed to demonstrate the rich call capabilities of Internet protocols and SIP network elements. In addition to basic SIP voice over IP calls on an IPv6 or IPv4 network, a user can, for example, exchange instant messages with other users, provide presence information with registration and subscribe to the presence state of his buddies, or obtain his watcherinfo.

SIP operations are implemented using the Sofia SIP stack. The Sofia Media Subsystem is used to provide real-time multimedia. The signaling and media subsystems run as a separate thread within the Surf process.

The Surf Graphical User Interface (GUI) was implemented with the aid of a wxWindows [wxwindows] application framework. It is a cross-platform C++ toolkit targeted mainly for GUI development, for which it provides a fairly good collection of graphical user-interface elements, widgets. The wxWindows library provides a good basis for even larger projects, as it provides a good set of classes (e.g., inter-process communications, networking, printing, and threading).

Settings can be loaded either from the local repository or remotely from the network. Smart cards have been tested to save the most vital data, (e.g., user identity and passwords). All settings are stored in eXtensible Markup Language (XML) formatted text files. Surf supports multiple profiles, which are distinct sets of configuration information. A different test environment can easily be changed by selecting another Surf profile.

Basic calls are initiated with the INVITE method. The callee can answer the call or decline it with different options. A call can be declined altogether or rejected so that it can still be forwarded to other destinations, (e.g., a voice mail server). It can also be redirected to a target selected by the user. Simultaneous multiple audio calls with automatic call-on-hold are also possible. Media types and parameters can be modified during the call simply by re-inviting.

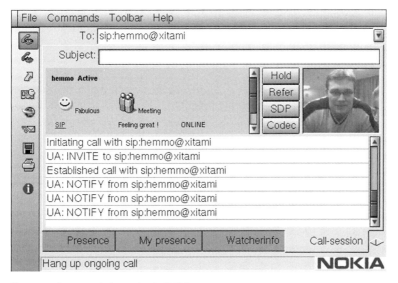

Basic call setup and presence information in SURF

Surf obtains call peer picture information using the Uniform Resource Locator (URL) found in the Call-Info headers. Call-Info headers can be included in the call setup messages (e.g., INVITE or 200 Ok). A peer's image is downloaded automatically and rendered in Surf's call window alongside the peer's current presence information.

The contact database (e.g., a phonebook or a buddy list) is usually stored locally. It can also be downloaded from the network. A user can select a contact from the phonebook for close inspection of presence status, calling or sending instant messages.

The SIP REFER method can be used to redirect the recipient to a new location by using the Refer-To header. The URI in the Refer-To header can be a SIP address, resulting in call transfer, or some other URI, such as the URL.

Shared Web browsing has been implemented using the REFER [sip-refer] method. In the shared browsing mode, each URL a user clicks on her Web browser is sent to the other participants in a shared Web session. Co-operation with the Galeon Web browser [galeon] is done through the browser's Common Object Request Broker Architecture (CORBA) interface.

IV Implementations

Push services have been demonstrated with the following scenario. A SIP client is connected to a Wireless Local Area Network and is monitoring the identifier of the access point it is connected to. When the client detects that the access point has changed, it will fetch a corresponding eXtensible Markup Language (XML) description file from a predefined Web-server. This description file contains a subscription address of an event server providing location-based information. After the client subscribes to the event server, the server will notify the client continuously with documents containing URI lists. Surf will show the contents of these URLs externally.

Event types are used to distinguish between different kinds of services (e.g., the status of your coffee maker or an advertisement push). A location-based push is only one example of the versatile possibilities of SUBSCRIBE/NOTIFY pair to be used in creating new services.

References

[amr]   3GPP, "Mandatory speech codec speech processing functions. AMR speech codec; transcoding functions," 3GPP Technical specification Group Services and System Aspects, 3G TS 26.090 V3.0.1, September 1999, 61 p.

[amr-wb]   3GPP, "AMR Wideband Speech Codec; General Description," 3GPP Technical specification Group Services and System Aspects, TS 26.171, v5.0.0, May 2001.

[avp]   H. Schulzrinne, RTP Profile for Audio and Video Conferences with Minimal Control, IETF Network Working Group RFC 1890, Standards Track, January 1996, 18 p.

[BT601-5]   ITU-R Recommendation BT.601-5 (1995): "Studio Encoding Parameters of Digital Television for Standard 4:3 and Wide-Screen 16:9 Aspect Ratios."

[g711]   ITU-T., Pulse code modulation (PCM) of voice frequencies, ITU-T Recommendation G.711, 1972, 18 p.

[g723]   ITU-T., Dual rate speech coder for multimedia communications transmitting at 5.3 and 6.3 kbit/s, ITU-T Recommendation G.723.1, March 1996, 27 p.

[galeon]   Galeon. Web Browser based on Mozilla. (GPL), http://galeon.sourceforge.net/

[h263]   ITU-T, "Recommendation H.263 - Video coding for low bit rate communication," Geneva, Switzerland, March 1996.

[h263Xx]   ITU-T, "ITU-T Recommendation H.263 Annex X, Profiles and levels definition," Geneva, Switzerland, April 2001.

[megaco]   F. Cuervo, N. Greene, C. Huitema, A. Rayhan, B. Rosen and J. Segers, Megaco Protocol version 0.8, IETF Network Working Group RFC 2885, Proposed Internet Standard, August 2000, 170 p.

[message]   Rosenberg, J., et al, "SIP Extensions for Instant Messaging," Internet Draft, draft-ietf-sip-message-01, work in progress, March 2002.

[MPEG4]   International Organization for Standardization, "ISO/IEC 14496-2:1999: Information technology - Coding of audio-visual objects - Part 2: Visual," p. 330, International Organization for Standardization, 1999.

[nua]	Pessi, P., Sofia SIP Implementation for Mobile IPv6, Nokia Research Center, 2001.
[o-a]	Rosenberg, J. and H. Schulzrinne, "An Offer/Answer Model with SDP," RFC 3264, March 2002.
[RFC2429]	C. Bormann et. al., "RTP Payload Format for the 1998 Version of ITU-T Rec. H.263 Video (H.263+)," IETF Network Working Group, RFC 2429, Proposed Internet Standard, October 1998, 17 p.
[RFC3016]	Y. Kikuchi et. al., "RTP Payload Format for MPEG-4 Audio/Visual Streams," IETF Network Working Group, RFC 3016, Proposed Internet Standard, November 2000, 21p.
[rtp]	H. Schulzrinne, S. Casner, R. Frederick and V. Jacobson, "RTP: a transport protocol for real-time applications," IETF Network Working Group, RFC 1889, Proposed Internet Standard, January 1996, 75 p.
[rtsp]	H. Schulzrinne, A. Rao, R. Lanphier, "Real Time Streaming Protocol (RTSP)," IETF Network Working Group, RFC 2326, Proposed Internet Standard, April 1998, 92 p.
[sap]	M. Handley, C. Perkins, E. Whelan, "Session Announcement Protocol," IETF Network Working Group, RFC 2974, Experimental, October 2000, 18 p.
[sdp]	M. Handley and V. Jacobson, "SDP: session description protocol," IETF Network Working Group RFC 2327, Proposed Internet Standard, April 1998, 42 p.
[selin]	Selin, J., "Media Management in IP Telephony Systems," Master's Thesis, Helsinki University of Technology, Department of Electrical and Communications Engineering, February 2001, 94 p.
[sip-bis]	Rosenberg, J., et al, "SIP: Session Initiation Protocol," RFC 3261, Proposed Internet Standard, March 2002.
[sip-refer]	Sparks, R., "The REFER Method," draft-ietf-sip-refer-00 (work in progress), July 2001.
[surf]	Urpalainen, J., Surf, SIP User-Agent Application for Mobile IPv6, Nokia Research Center, 2001.
	SIP application by the Nokia NRC Research Center.
[TMN5]	ITU-T, "Video Codec Test model near-term, Version 5 (TMN5)," H.263 Ad Hoc Group, 1996.
[wxwindows]	wxWindows. A free C++ cross-platform framework. (LGPL) http://www.wxwindows.org/

IV   Implementations

Presence and Messaging

This section provides an overview of the Sofia and Java-based implementations of SIMPLE, SIP-based instant messaging and presence. SIMPLE extends the SIP in order to provide a means of exchanging instant messages and obtaining the online presence status of other people.

Surf Messaging

SIP instant messaging uses a SIP extension method, MESSAGE [sip-im]. The contents of the instant message are delivered as a payload in the MESSAGE requests. SIP instant messages can be simple text or multimedia messages packaged in Multipurpose Internet Mail Extension (MIME) format. MESSAGE requests are transmitted like any other SIP request.

MIME [mime] provides primitives for including different types of media along with the message. For example, say you are on vacation and catch a huge pike, and you want to send a picture of it to your colleagues toiling away back at work. The picture is stored using the JPEG format and the terminal can include a Content-Type header with the value "image/jpeg" along with the message containing the image data.

Maybe the picture is not enough, and you want an even more complex multimedia document. Regarding your fish, for example, you will probably want to include some strategic measurements along with the picture, so your instant message would be composed of two parts, text and an image. MIME supports this in the form of multipart messages, where each message fragment can have its own Content-Type header along with the other relevant information required to render the message correctly.

With the Surf terminal application it is possible to enter the message subject, body text and attach images to the message. A multi-line text control widget handles the body text and the `wxListCtrl` class handles attached image names.

Surf uses the GMime library [gmime] in order to support MIME multipart messages, which are used when multiple media fragments are included in a single instant message. GMime is a Gnome MIME library used for creating and parsing multimedia messages. The GMime library targets e-mail-clients, since e-mail has been the main application for MIME. Internally, GMime uses GLib [glib], a standard GTK utility library found on most Linux distributions.

The fundamental concept in the GMime library is streams, which are used for reading and writing multimedia objects. When creating a message consisting of multiple parts (e.g., the message body text and an attached image) the application writes each part into a stream of its own, which are then used when the message is sent. A multipart message can contain elements with different content types and varying lengths. The GMIME library also supports several character encoding formats. All supported header settings have clean APIs.

Parsing a received multipart message with GMime is fairly simple. After the received data is attached to a stream, the message body and other parts can be parsed and processed according to their content type.

Presenting Instant Message Content

With multimedia messaging, there is an additional problem: how to render such a message to the user. In order to avoid the need for extensive knowledge of different multimedia formats, Surf renders both sent and received instant messages into a chat log formatted using ordinary Hyper-Text Markup Language (HTML), which already provides such functionality.

The HTML format was an easy choice, as wxWindows, the application framework Surf uses, has very versatile HTML-rendering support using wxWindows' wxHTML classes. The look and feel of the message log could be configured with, e.g., style sheets [xslt]. Configuration support needs to be studied further, however.

The chat log contains an HTML table with three columns. The first column contains the sender's and receiver's SIP-addresses and the optional message subject. The second column consists of the actual text message and images possibly included in the message. The last column shows some status information (e.g., the delivery status of the sent messages). It would be possible to add support for other content types as well. The chat log is stored in Surf as a hashed linked list with a fixed upper size forming a ring buffer. If the body text contains URLs, Surf renders the text fragments recognized as URIs as links which can be clicked and (e.g., shown externally in a Web browser). SIP URIs within body text are treated as click-to-talk links, while the user-specified Web browser handles other types of URIs.

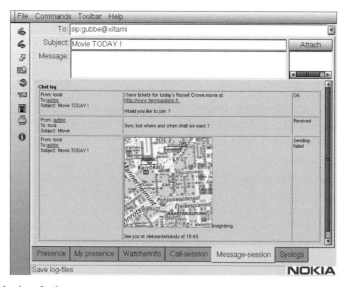

A message dialog from Surf

Surf Presence

In SIMPLE, subscribing to presence information and delivering the presence document is done with the SUBSCRIBE and NOTIFY methods. The presence data is published with the REGISTER method using the experimental extension [reg-pl]. The NUA module handles the logic required to publish and refresh presence data, set up and refresh subscriptions with SUBSCRIBE transactions and accept the presence documents with NOTIFY transactions. The main task left to the Surf application itself is generating properly formatted presence documents and rendering the presence data in a readable and friendly format.

The current presence information data format, defined by the Common Profile for Instant Messaging (CPIM) [cpim], requires parsing an XML-formatted document and representing the resulting data to the user. In SURF, XML processing is handled with the libxml2 library [libxml2], which is used to parse and generate XML documents. The libxml2 has a clean interface and supports namespaces, compression and validation, i.e., checking that documents are formed according to Document Type Definitions (DTDs).

Within the CPIM, each contact address for the consumer is presented using a so-called tuple. A tuple contains the consumer's presence information (e.g., the URI used as a contact address, the online status of the address, and a freely-formatted note). For example, a consumer who can be currently reached with instant messages and phone calls may list two tuples, one with an instant message URI and another with an ordinary SIP URI. The CPIM document does not specify how more detailed presence information might be included, but fortunately extensions of the CPIM format can be used relatively easily. With such extensions, new presence attributes can be added as long as a globally unique namespace identifier is provided. Below, consumer attributes (e.g., mood, activity, and photographic) were added using the Sofia extension which uses the sofia namespace identifier.

```
<?xml version="1.0" encoding="ISO-8859-1"?>
<impp:presence xmlns:impp="urn:ietf:params:cpim-presence:"
               xmlns:sofia="http://voipstd.research.nokia.com/sofia">
<impp:presentity id="pres:ju@research.nokia.com"/>
  <impp:tuple id="sip-im">
    <impp:status>
      <impp:value>open</impp:value>
    </impp:status>
    <impp:contact>sip:ju@ju.nrc.nokia.com</impp:contact>
    <impp:note>Future is bright !</impp:note>
    <sofia:NokiaPresence>
      <sofia:Version>0.2</sofia:Version>
      <sofia:Language>en</sofia:Language>
      <sofia:Mood Mood="Fabulous"/>
      <sofia:Activity Activity="Meeting"/>
      <sofia:PHOTO>http://www.nrc.nokia.com/~ju/face.jpg</sofia:PHOTO>
    </sofia:NokiaPresence>
  </impp:tuple>
  <impp:tuple id="web">
    <impp:status>
      <impp:value>open</impp:value>
    </impp:status>
    <impp:contact>http://lwn.net</impp:contact>
    <impp:note/>
  </impp:tuple>
</impp:presence>
```

Example of an XML-formatted presence document

IV   Implementations

The XML-library uses the Universal Transfer Format 8 (UTF-8) character encoding of Unicode. Since wxWindows is not yet fully capable of handling Unicode, the strings have to be converted from the local character set to UTF-8 and vice versa. The libxml2 library provides character set conversions.

Sofia Presence Server

The presence server is a functional element defined in the SIMPLE presence specification [presence]. This server is responsible for delivering the presence documents to watchers. Watchers, in turn, are consumers who are interested in the presence information of a presentity, an object having presence attributes (e.g., a consumer who can be online and reachable or offline and unreachable).

Watchers have to subscribe to a presence server in order to obtain a presentity's presence information. The presence server can obtain the presence documents by subscribing to a presence agent, or act as a presence agent itself and generate its own presence document. The presence agent relies on yet more logical elements called presence user agents to produce and publish the presence information.

According to the classification presented above, the Sofia presence server is also a presence agent. It can be used as a stand-alone presence server, or as part of a Sofia proxy. In both cases, it uses the registrar module and its database to obtain the presence data. The presence server module is closely linked with the registrar module, and both the presence server and the registrar are run in the same process. The close relationship enables efficient authentication of presentity and access to the location database.

Presence server functionality has been layered. The top layer takes care of generating presence state events while the underlying layer processes events in a generic way, managing watcher subscriptions and delivering event contents to watchers. The upper layer is implemented in the presence module, the bottom layer in the NEA server module.

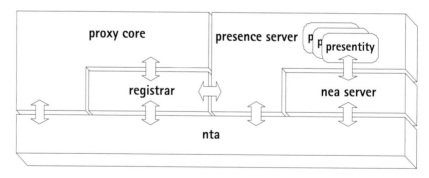

The presence server module uses the registrar and the nea server module.

Initializing the Presence Server Module

When the presence server module is instantiated, it first registers suitable SUBSCRIBE URIs with the NTA module in order to catch new subscription requests. If necessary, the presence server module can initialize the authentication module which is used to properly authenticate the incoming requests. Finally, the presence server binds itself with the registrar and is ready for incoming subscriptions.

Processing Subscriptions

The presence server forwards all incoming SUBSCRIBE requests to presentity objects. If the presentity does not exist, it will be created. Each presentity object represents the reachability status of a particular user uniquely identified by a presentity URI.

For each presentity, there is a separate notifier server object which processes all SUBSCRIBE requests destined to the presentity URI. A single presentity object may contain a number of different events or different views of the same event.

Event Views and the Notifier Server

A NEA server object typically processes multiple event views. Each event view contains the event type, the content type and the actual content describing the event state. There can be several event views with the same event and content types, for example, a presence event view with complete information for trusted consumers and another view containing minimal information for others. By default, only the minimal view exists, and all new subscribers are assigned to it.

When the subscription is established the notifier server object determines which event view the subscriber is associated with. The NEA server executes the basic selection based on the event name and content types acceptable to the subscriber. If no acceptable view is found, the NEA server rejects the subscription.

When a NEA server has determined that a new subscription can be accepted, it passes the subscriber identity on to the presentity object. The presentity object is responsible for access control: the presence server could assign the watcher to different views based on the access control lists. The server itself does not have access control lists, however, though every watcher has full access to all presence information. So, the presentity only updates the watcherinfo event, which contains information about current subscribers and their status.

When the subscription has been accepted and an event view assigned to it, the NEA server sends the current contents of the event view to the subscriber.

Updating Presence Information

Whenever the state of any active registration is changed, the registrar informs the presence server. In addition to genuine registrations, the registrar also receives the presence documents published by user agents.

When the presence server receives updated registration information it searches for the presentity object corresponding to the address-of-record URI given by the registrar. The presence server creates such a presentity object if needed. Then it lets the presentity generate new presence documents and pass them on to the notifier server object.

The presentity object can either take a presence document published by a presentity UA as such, generate a new presence document based on registration bindings, or augment the UA-published presence document with data generated from bindings. Currently, the presentity can generate or augment presence documents of the type "application/xpidf+xml" [xpidf]. For other presence formats, it depends on the presentity UA to provide the complete presence document.

After updating the presence document and corresponding event views, the presence server calls the notification function, causing the NEA server to notify the subscribers associated with the updated event views.

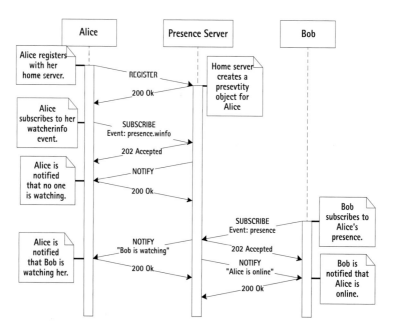

Subscribing to presence and presence.winfo events

In the figure above, Alice registers with her home server and subscribes to her watcherinfo event. When Bob subscribes to Alice's network presence, she is sent a notification of Bob's action, and he is sent Alice's current presence status.

Push Service Example

The presence server also contains an alternative data event used to implement location-based push services. When receiving a suitable update from the registrar module, the presentity object updates the alternative data event. A SIP UA can get its location from a local server. The UA can then subscribe to an *advertisement* event using a location-specific URL, for instance, `sip:60098N25349E@locserver.helina.net`. Updated advertisement contents are sent whenever the advertisement server publishes new advertisement content.

Updates are handled using the service data publishing feature [reg-pl] of the registrar; the advertisement server sends the new content as the payload of a REGISTER request.

SIP Instant Message Adaptation Server

Interoperability is of paramount importance in messaging. Users expect that messages will reach their destination and will be handled properly by the recipient's mobile device. But emerging mobile devices have made this requirement more challenging due to the wide diversity of mobile device characteristics (e.g., display size and resolution, available memory, and supported formats).

Content adaptation proxies will play an important role in maintaining interoperability and improving user experience in many domains of applications including messaging. These proxies, commonly referred to as transcoding proxies, transform content to make it suitable for the destination mobile device. For example, one such transformation is format conversion (e.g., Portable Network Graphics (PNG) to the Graphics Interchange Format (GIF)).

This section provides an overview of how SIP proxies and registrars can be extended to provide SIP message adaptation services. It also presents the Sofia Message Adaptation service.

IV

Implementations

Operations of the Message Adaptation Proxy

A message adaptation proxy is a proxy as defined in the SIP protocol specification, which can perform transformation of SIP messages on-the-fly. This is illustrated in steps 2 and 3 of the following figure. Such transformations are usually limited to the message body and include the following:

o   **Format conversion:** Conversion to a media content format supported by the mobile device. For instance, PNG images could be converted to GIF if not supported by the recipient's device. This category includes conversion of layout formats (e.g., from the Extensible HyperText Markup Language (XHTML) to the Wireless Markup Language (WML)) and conversion of modality (e.g., speech to text).

o   **Media characteristics adaptation:** This involves any modification of the media characteristics, including resolution reduction of images for small displays, reducing the quality of Joint Photographic Experts Group (JPEG) images or the number of colors in GIF images.

o   **Presentation or layout adaptation:** This involves making the content presentation suitable for the recipient's device display characteristics. For instance, the best presentation of a message (e.g., how the images are organized on the display) is different for a landscape orientation display compared to a portrait one.

o   **Message size adaptation:** Reducing the overall message size by reducing the size of the media parts it contains (or removing some of them in the worst case), is usually achieved through media characteristics or format conversion. For instance, JPEG images can be reduced in size by reducing their quality factor. This can often be done without significant reduction in the perceived quality, and is required when the original message's size is too large to be supported by the destination device (e.g., a 72 kB message is sent to a mobile device which supports only 30 kB messages as in the figure below).

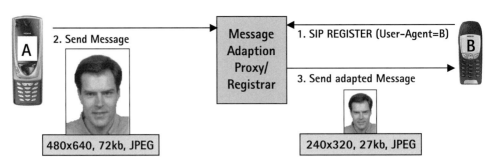

Adaptation of a message containing a JPEG image

The adaptation performed on the message is a function of the recipient's preferences and device capabilities. These capabilities can be obtained from a SIP registrar.

Capability Negotiation During Registration

The registrar can be responsible for managing the device capabilities for each consumer. Many methods may be used to obtain these capabilities. Using the first method, the device provides its capabilities (and the consumer's preferences) explicitly in the body of the registration message. The registration message may also contain the User-Agent, Accept, Accept-Encoding, and Accept-Charset header fields. The User-Agent header field describes the device type and software version. The Accept header field lists the media formats supported (e.g., image/jpeg and text/plain). This method requires further standardization work to define a device capability format and vocabulary.

The second method involves using the User-Agent header field as a key to a device capability database which contains, for every known user agent, the associated device capabilities.

In the third method, the mobile device sends a list of URLs from which the proxy retrieves device profile documents.

Regardless of the method used, the obtained device capability information (including User-Agent and Accept header fields and other relevant ones) is stored along with the standard registration information for each consumer.

The previous figure shows the mobile device providing its User-Agent to the registrar. What is not shown is that the proxy uses the device's capabilities, provided by a device capability database, to perform message adaptation.

Each method has its advantages and shortcomings. For instance, the first method does not require the creation and maintenance of a device capability database, and provides support for user preferences. On the other hand, the second solution does not require the standardization of a device capability format and vocabulary.

Implementation

This section describes the extensions made to the Sofia proxy and registrar to support SIP message adaptation. Some changes were also made to the user agent.

First, the user agent was modified to provide device capabilities in the message body when registering. The capabilities included the formats supported (Accept header), the maximum resolution supported for images (MaxImageRes), and the maximum size supported for multipart messages conveyed within SIP messages (MaxMsgSize). The device can also choose to send only the User-Agent header field to identify itself.

The registrar has been modified to search for a message body part containing device capabilities upon receiving a registration request. If none is provided, it will search in its device capability database for capabilities corresponding to the received User-Agent field. The created database contains a list of device capabilities organized in a name-value pair (e.g., MaxImageRes with 640x480). The capability information, if available, is then stored with the consumer's registration information.

The proxy has been modified to send a request to the registrar for the device capabilities associated with the recipient's address when receiving a new SIP message. If such capabilities are not

IV

Implementations

present in the registration, the message will be forwarded to the recipient without adaptation. Otherwise, it will analyze the message content to establish the transformations that are required (e.g., format conversion and image resolution reduction). If the message is too large, it will allocate a budget for each component, taking into account whether or not it can be reduced in size (for instance, text cannot be size reduced while JPEG and GIF can). The proxy supports Multipurpose Internet Mail Extensions (MIME) multipart components. The adaptation is performed on each component, and the adapted message is finally sent to the recipient.

A key feature of transcoding proxies is performance. In order to ensure top performance, novel transcoding algorithms have been developed which, by avoiding full decoding of the content at the proxy, greatly reduce the processing time taken for each message part.

Example of SIP Message Adaptation

The next figure provides an example of SIP message adaptation performed by the Sofia proxy. The original message is shown on the left. Its total size is 43 kB and it is composed of four components:

- o A small text message (41 bytes)
- o A GIF image illustrating a phone (195x195, 16 kB)
- o Two JPEG images (224x220, 15 kB and 250x187, 11 kB)

The original message is sent to two recipients. The capabilities of the middle terminal include:

- o MaxImageRes=160x120
- o Accept=text/plain;image/jpeg
- o MaxMsgSize=25 kB

The capabilities of the terminal on the right include:

- o MaxImageRes=640x480
- o Accept=text/plain;image/jpeg
- o MaxMsgSize=30 kB

The figure shows the message received for each terminal after adaptation by the Sofia proxy. The middle terminal received a 16 kB message composed of:

o   A small text message (41 bytes)

o   A JPEG image illustrating a phone (97x97, 7 kB)

o   Two JPEG images (112x110, 5.6 kB and 125x93, 3.5 kB)

The terminal on the right received a 29 kB message composed of:

o   A small text message (41 bytes)

o   A JPEG image illustrating a phone (195x195, 8.8 kB)

o   Two JPEG images (224x220, 9 kB and 250x187, 11 kB)

It is worth noting that message size reduction for the device in the middle was achieved as a side effect of the required resolution reduction. For the device on the right, no resolution reduction was required. However, the message size required reduction. Some size reduction was achieved during the conversion of the first image to JPEG, but a quality reduction of the second image was still required in order to meet the size target.

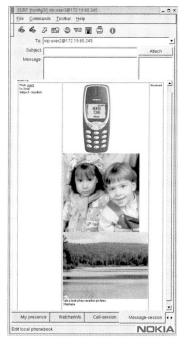

Example of message adaptation performed by the Sofia proxy

IV   Implementations

Alternative Solutions

Message adaptation can also be performed even if the recipient has not registered with the message adaptation server. In this case, the OPTIONS method can be used. Such a solution can be used at the sender's discretion simply by including the address of the message adaptation proxy in the preloaded route of the MESSAGE request. When the message adaptation proxy receives a new message, it sends an OPTIONS request message to the recipient in order to obtain its capabilities. As before, the user agent may provide these capabilities explicitly in the response; otherwise, the proxy uses the User-Agent header to retrieve the capabilities from a capability database. As before, other headers such as Accept, Accept-Encoding and Accept-Charset can be considered.

The solution is therefore very similar to the one considered so far, except that the proxy needs to do more work, since it is now also responsible for capability negotiation. The drawback of this solution is that the proxy needs to request the mobile device capabilities for each transaction, which creates more traffic. Of course, the proxy can cache the information but it runs a risk that the device capabilities change before the cache is updated with a new OPTIONS request. It is more efficient to assign to the device the responsibility of updating its registration information if its location, capabilities or preferences change.

SMS Gateway

In addition to the normal PSTN–IP Telephony gateway described above, a special gateway for instant messaging and presence between the GSM and IPT network was implemented for the MITA Reference Implementation Environment.

The SIP–SMS Gateway (SMSGW) makes it possible to access SIP-based instant messaging and presence services from an ordinary GSM terminal. In addition, an IPT call transfer to a GSM phone can be controlled via the SMSGW. The SMSGW enables an IP telephony subscriber to roam into the GSM network. While roaming, the consumer can receive phone calls and Instant Messages (IMs) directed to her SIP URI.

An IPT subscriber may register as being available in the GSM network by sending a specially constructed SMS message to the SMSGW. In this message, the consumer may request forwarding of her phone calls, instant messages or previously subscribed presence notifications to her current GSM number. Phone calls are forwarded to the consumer via a normal SIP/PSTN gateway, whereas messages and notifications are forwarded via the SMSGW. The registration may be permanent or valid only for some specified time. Similarly, the consumer may unregister from being available in the GSM network.

A consumer in the GSM network may also send SIP based instant messages and subscribe or unsubscribe the presence status of other IPT network consumers from the GSM network, using her mobile device and its SMS client.

The SMSGW plays a UAC or UAS role towards the IPT network. In the Reference Implementation, the SMSGW does not contain a consumer database and does not even keep state of the registrations. These functionalities are handled by the SIP registrar and SIP proxy in the IPT network.

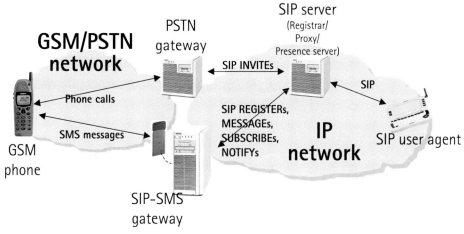

SIP-SMS gateway

General Operation

A SMS-SIP gateway operates as follows:

A Message from the GSM Network

1. The SMSGW receives an SMS message from a consumer in the GSM network.

2. The SMSGW decodes the message, converts it to a suitable SIP message and sends it to the local SIP proxy, which routes the request to the intended recipient.

3. The SMSGW receives a reply to the SIP message and interprets it.

4. Optionally, the SMSGW sends an SMS message to the sender in the GSM network, telling the status of the requested action (e.g., registration, presence subscription, or instant message sending)

A Request from the IPT Network

1. The SMSGW receives a SIP request from a consumer in the IPT network. The SMSGW processes only MESSAGE or NOTIFY requests.

2. The SMSGW decodes and interprets the request message, converts it to a suitable SMS message and sends it to the intended recipient in the GSM network.

3. The SMSGW replies to the SIP request with the appropriate response code (e.g., 200 OK, if SMS sending was successful).

Registering, Re-Registering and Unregistering

A consumer should register with the SMSGW before using its services. However, the reference implementation does not require registration for all services.

Registration enables the consumer to receive voice calls and instant messages from the IPT network.

IV Implementations

As a result of this registration procedure, the contact information of the consumer is recorded in the consumer's home registrar. This contact information points to a tel-URL for voice calls and to the SMSGW for instant messages.

As in SIP, the registration has a default lifetime, typically one hour, which will expire automatically if it is not repeated on time.

The registration procedure takes place as follows:

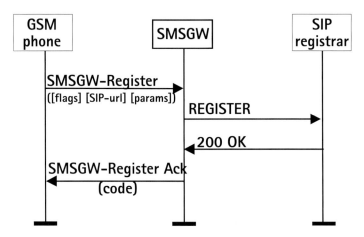

Registration via the SMSGW

1. A consumer (e.g., user1@example.net) sends an SMSGW Register message to the SMSGW, as illustrated in the four SMSGW messages below:

```
r sip:user1@example.net
r M user1@example.net
r
register IM jack@shining.com:mysecretpassword all work, no fun
```

The letters *I* and *M* denote INVITE and MESSAGE SIP methods respectively, so it is possible to forward only phone calls or instant messages. Omitting the flags entirely, sets flags to *IM* (i.e., both, calls and messages are forwarded).

The SIP URI may be omitted from the message if the SIP Registrar is able to map the originating phone number onto the consumer's actual SIP URI.

In the last example, there is also a password for SIP authentication. Additionally, it includes a presence note field for the SIP presence description.

2. The SMSGW receives a SMS and notices that it is a registration request.

3. The SMSGW sends a SIP REGISTER message to the correct SIP registrar.

For example:

```
REGISTER sip:example.com SIP/2.0
From: <sip:smsgw@smsgw.example.com>
To: <sip:user1@example.com>
Contact: <tel:0504836592>
Contact: <sip:0504836592@smsgw.example.com;method=MESSAGE>
Expires: 3600
Content-Type: application/xpidf+xml
Content-Disposition: presence; action=store
Content-Length: ...
Call-ID: 76fb28e4-1c87-11d6-6481-a3.29.e7.6c.66.dd
CSeq: 1 REGISTER
Via: SIP/2.0/UDP 10.21.60.14;branch=BtUwsFkyyxTz


<?xml version="1.0"?>
<presence>
<presentity uri="sip:user1@example.com"/>
<atom atomid="0504836592" expires=3600>
<address uri="sip:user1@example.com">
<status status="open"/>
<note>all work, no fun</note>
</address>
</atom>
</presence>
```

If the SMS registration message did not contain a SIP URI, the SMSGW will use the phone number that originated the SMS message as the destination for the SIP REGISTER. If the consumer's GSM number together with the corresponding SIP URI has been stored in the consumer database of the Registrar, it can recognize that this registration is actually for that corresponding SIP URI. The Registrar/Proxy is then able to forward SIP messages directed to the SIP URI of the consumer to the correct contact address in the GSM network.

If the GSM number is preconfigured, the SIP registrar may trust that this registration actually came from the GSM number specified and not require any further authentication.

4. The SMSGW receives a *200 OK* or some error reply from the SIP registrar. The reply may also indicate the need for authentication (*407 Unauthorized*), in which case the SMSGW may retry SIP registration using the password information it got in the SMS message.

IV

Implementations

5. The SMSGW sends the user a SMSGW Register Ack message describing the result (OK or not-OK). For example:

```
SMSGW SIP Registration OK
SMSGW SIP Registration failed (Unknown user)
```

Sending and Receiving Instant Messages

SMS messages can be sent to consumers in the IPT network.

1. The consumer in the GSM network sends an Instant Message to the SMSGW. For example:

```
m sip:user2@there.com Fancy a pint? reg.Jukka
```

2. The SMSGW receives a SMS message and notices that it is an instant message request.
3. The SMSGW sends a SIP MESSAGE to the specified destination. For example:

```
MESSAGE sip:user2@there.com SIP/2.0
To: sip:user2@there.com
From: sip:0504836592@smsgw.example.net
CSeq: …
…
Content-type:text/plain

Fancy a pint? reg.Jukka
```

4. The SMSGW receives a *200 OK* or some error reply from the SIP network.
5. Optionally, the SMSGW sends the consumer in the GSM network an SMSGW Message describing the result of the transaction. For example:

```
SMSGW SIP Message sending failed (User not found)
```

The procedure for receiving instant messages via the SMSGW is:

1. The consumer (e.g., user2@there.com) sends an instant message to another consumer (e.g., jukka@example.net) roaming in the GSM network. Based on the registration info, the SIP-registrar/proxy sends a MESSAGE to the SMSGW. For example.

```
MESSAGE sip:0504836592@smsgw.example.net SIP/2.0
To: sip:jukka@example.net
```

```
From: sip:jaska@there.com
CSeq...
Content-type: text/plain


Let's meet at the Half Pint pub! //Jaska
```

2.   The SMSGW receives a SIP message and notices that it is an instant message request.

3.   The SMSGW sends an SMS message to the current GSM number of the intended recipient. For example:

```
jaska@there.com:Let's meet at the Half Pint pub! //Jaska
```

   If the whole message content does not fit into one SMS, it will be split into parts and several SMS messages will be sent.

4.   The SMSGW sends a *200 OK* or some error reply to the SIP network.

Subscribing to Presence Events

A consumer in the GSM network can subscribe to a consumer's presence information in the IPT network via the SMSGW.

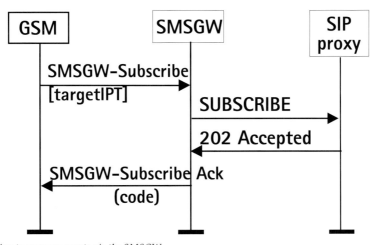

Subscribing to presence events via the SMSGW

1. A consumer in the GSM network (e.g., user1@example.net) sends a SMSGW Subscribe message to the SMSGW:

```
s user2@there.com
```

2. The SMSGW receives a SMS message and notices that it is a subscription request. It then sends a SIP SUBSCRIBE message to the specified destination. For example:

```
SUBSCRIBE sip:user2@there.com SIP/2.0
To: <sip:user2@there.com>
From: <sip:0504836592@smsgw.example.net>
Event: presence
Accept: application/xpidf+xml
Contact: <sip:0504836592@smsgw.example.net>
Expires: 3600
```

3. The SMSGW receives a *202 OK* or some error reply from the SIP network.

4. Optionally, the SMSGW may then send a confirmation or an error message to the consumer in the GSM network.

Receiving Event Notifications

After subscribing to the presence status of a consumer in the IPT network, the SMSGW will start receiving presence notifications from the presence server which are then forwarded to the consumer in the GSM network.

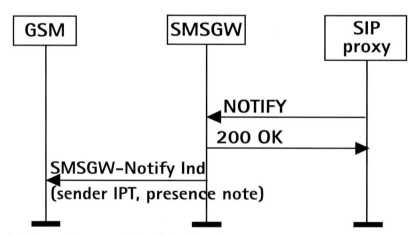

Receiving (presence) event notifications via the SMSGW

1. When a consumer's (e.g., user2@there.com) presence status changes, all subscribed consumers in the GSM network (e.g., user1@example.net) are notified:

Based on this registration info, the presence server sends a NOTIFY message to the SMSGW.

```
NOTIFY sip:0504836592@smsgw.example.net SIP/2.0
From: <sip:user2@there.com>
To: <sip:0504836592@smsgw.example.net
Event: presence
Content-Type: application/xpidf+xml
...

<?xml version="1.0"?>
<presence>
  <presentity uri="sip:user2@there.com"/>
  <atom atomid="ka6dPfQnL78a+" expires="3222163567">
    <address uri="sip:user2@there.com">
      <status status="open"/>
      <note>Feeling good!</note>
    </address>
  </atom>
</presence>
```

2. The SMSGW receives a SIP message and notices that it is an event notification. The SMSGW sends a *200 OK* or some error reply to the SIP network.

3. The SMSGW sends a SMS message to the current GSM number of the subscribing consumer in the GSM network:

```
N:user2@there.com:Online:Feeling good!
```

Since it is not possible to send all the information contained in a SIP presence description, only two items are included: the user's online/offline status and the <Note> field, if this is available.

Implementation

The SMS-SIP gateway was implemented on a standard PC platform running Linux. In addition to a basic low-end Linux-based server, the required hardware consisted of a standard Nokia Card Phone 2.0 adapter.

IV Implementations

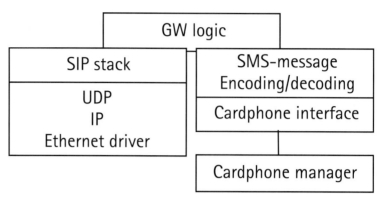

Software architecture of the SMSGW

The software components of the SMSGW are:

o   The SIP stack, which handles sending and receiving SIP messages.

o   GW logic, which implements the conversion between SIP and SMS messages.

o   The SMS message encoding and decoding part.

o   Cardphone interface controls and interfaces with a separate Cardphone manager process.

o   The Cardphone manager handles the low-level logic of sending and receiving SMS messages with a Nokia Card Phone.

Java™ Client Implementation

The purpose of the Java™ 2 Micro Edition platform (J2ME™) implementation of Instant Messaging and Presence is to provide an example application for the J2ME SIP API specification and development. It gives a practical example of how to use the API and can be used as a test bed. The J2ME client is divided into three parts as follows:

o   **Client MIDlet**

User interface, service logic, and SIP User Agent (UA)

o   **J2ME SIP API**

Definition and reference implementation of the SIP API for the J2ME platform, which is integrated into the MIDP/CLDC platform.

o **SIP stack**

Reference implementation of the SIP stack in the J2ME platform, implements SIP API interfaces, integrated in the Mobile Information Device Profile/Connected Limited Data Configuration (MIDP/CLDC) platform.

Architectural Overview

The Instant Messaging and Presence (IM/P) client for MIDP is available as one downloadable MIDlet. The MIDlet includes the SIP UA and the service logic for IM/P. It also contains the graphical user interface with MIDP Liquid Crystal Display (LCD) user interface components. The following figure shows the components of the reference implementation in the system. The MIDlet, above the core platform libraries, is divided into the model, view and controller parts. The model utilizes an XML parser for decoding presence information. The lower box shows the networking components included in the J2ME core platform.

The client was designed following the Model-View-Controller (MVC) architecture. This allows the view to be implemented separately for devices with different kinds of capabilities (e.g., screen size and various layouts for the input buttons). Re-designing the view is easier this way, since communication with the model is already defined in the interfaces between the model and the controller. This way, the model is totally isolated from GUI functionality.

The GUI components in the implementation consist of standard MIDP components. Some custom-made views are designed in order to display presence information with pictures and other graphics. Also, due to the memory limitations in small devices, instances of text fields, areas and other components are reused as much as possible.

The pictures in the Portable Network Graphics (PNG) format of the presence view are downloaded using the Hypertext Transfer Protocol (HTTP). Before drawing the screen, the presence view object checks if a picture defined in the consumer's presence info is to be displayed. If there is no such image, a thread for downloading the image is started. When the image has been downloaded, a notification is sent to the view object to re-draw itself.

The reference implementation of the J2ME SIP API (SipConnection) is implemented in Java and is integrated into the CLDC Generic Connection Framework. The SIP stack uses DatagramConnection, which is supported in the SUN MIDP/CLDC reference implementation. The HTTP protocol (*HttpConnection*) is used for downloading files and updating presence information.

IV   Implementations

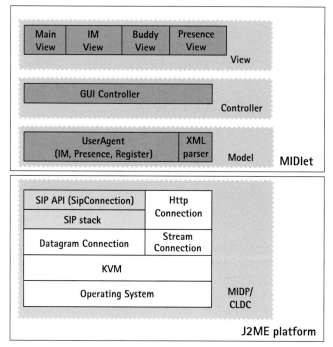

MIDP implementation of Instant Messaging and Presence

The following figure shows the main classes and most important methods of the J2ME SIP API.

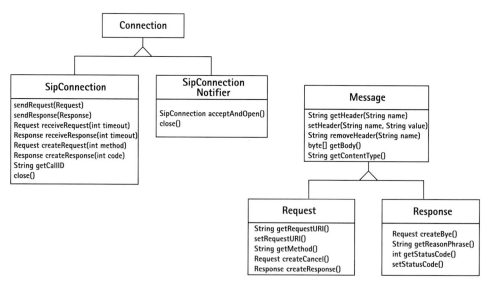

Main classes of the J2ME SIP API

The following code example shows the usage of the J2ME SIP API (SipConnection interface). The MessageAgent class is a simplified instant messenger, which uses the SipConnection interface to send MESSAGE requests and receive responses. It is not a complete MIDlet, but rather a service logic component which could be used inside a MIDlet. The internal MessageListener class uses the SipConnectionNotifier interface, which returns a new SipConnection when a new request is received. This example uses the paging mode, which does not require a SIP session for sending messages.

```
public class MessageAgent {
    MessageListener listener;

    /**
     * Initialize message agent and listener Thread
     */
    public void MessageAgent() {
listener = new MessageListener();
      listener.start();
    }

    /**
     * Send one shot textual instant message.
     * Invoked from GUI event Thread
     */
    public void sendMessage(String toAddress, String message) {
      SipConnection sc = (SipConnection) Connector.open(toAddress, WRITE);
      Request req = sc.createRequest(Request.MESSAGE);
      Response resp = null;
      try {
          req.setBody(message.getByes(), "text/plain");
          sc.sendRequest(req);
          // blocking until response received (or timeout)
          resp = sc.receiveResponse();
      } catch(Exception ex) {
          // handle I/O error
      }
      if(resp.StatusCode() == 200) {
          // message sent ok
      } else {
          // handle error or provisional response
      }
    }

    /**
```

```
      * Check if the received request was a MESSAGE
      */
    public void processRequest(SipConnection sc) {
      // The request is already in the receive queue
      Request req = sc.receiveRequest();
      if(req.getMethod() == Request.MESSAGE) {
          try {
            Response resp = req.createResponse(200); // OK
            sc.sendResponse(resp);
          }catch(Exception ex) {
            // handle error
          }
          // Show message to the user in GUI
          guiController.showMessage(req);
      } else {
          // unexpected method
          try {
            // Method Not Allowed
            Response resp = req.createResponse(405);
            sc.sendResponse(resp);
          }catch(Exception ex) {
            // handle error
          }
      }
    }


    /**
     * Listener Thread for incoming unsolicited
     * requests
     */
    public class MessageListener extends Thread {
      private boolean alive = true;
      public void run() {
          SipConnection sc;
          SipConnectionNotifier scn =
            (SipConnectionNotifier) Connector.open("sip:localhost:5060",
READ);
          while(alive) {
            sc = null;
            try {
                // blocking until request received (or timeout)
                // SipConnectionNotifier returns a new SipConnection
                // which includes the received Request
                sc = scn.acceptAndOpen();
```

```
        } catch(Exception ex) {
            // handle I/O error
        }
        if(sc != null) {
            processRequest(sc);
        }
      }
    }
  public void stop() {
      alive = false;
    }
  }
}
```

Instant Messaging and Presence MIDlet Functionality

The reference application using the J2ME SIP API is a simple Instant Messaging and Presence client with a dynamic buddy list. The buddy list can be updated from the consumer's home domain. The buddy list will show user names and their current presence info, (e.g., offline/online, availability, free format textual note, picture and contact capabilities). Since it is not possible to initiate a voice call in the MIDP platform, the client will include only messaging and presence. The following features are included:

o   Register user on MIDlet startup to SIP registrar. Refresh the registration at regular intervals.

o   Upload the user's presence information onto the SIP presence server

o   Download the user's buddy list from the home domain

o   Subscribe to the buddy list on the SIP presence server

o   Update the buddy list (e.g., online/offline) and presence screen according to changes in the buddy's presence status

o   Use HTTP to download PNG buddy pictures

o   Send and receive instant messages to a specified address or buddy list member

o   Collect messages in a chat screen

o   Unregister and update (offline) presence information upon MIDlet shutdown

IV   Implementations

Presence view and chat view screenshots

Servlet Server Implementation

Presence Server Implementation

The application server handles presence with three different components. The main component is the presence dispatcher, which takes care of distributing and storing presence documents, as well as storing subscriptions and sending notify messages to subscribed consumers. Other components are the RegisterServlet and SubscribeServlet, taking care of REGISTER and SUBCSRIBE SIP methods respectively.

The presence and contact information are stored in a database. At a lower level, the contact database uses a Java Database Connectivity (JDBC™) connection pool to manage connections to the underlying database server. All database classes are provided to applications in a Java archive (JAR) formatted library, which is included in the application Servlet Archive (SAR) file.

Incoming requests and responses are handled by servlets. There is a RegisterServlet for handling REGISTER requests, and a SubscribeServlet handling SUBSCRIBE requests. NOTIFY messages are sent directly by the presence dispatcher, although the subscribe servlet is called when notify responses arrive. The high-level presence architecture is depicted on the following page:

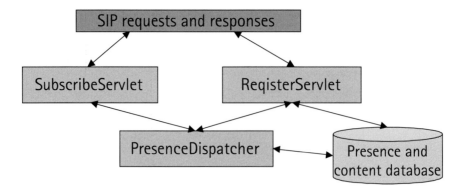

Presence Service architecture

The RegisterServlet, which handles all incoming REGISTER messages, can look like the code in the figure below. When a servlet is initialized it obtains all the resources it needs. The RegisterServlet needs to access some databases and a reference to a SipFactory object in order to create new SIP objects. When initialization is finished, all incoming REGISTER messages are passed to the servlet through the doRegister() method. The servlet obtains new contact information from the request and updates the database with that information. As a final step, the servlet responds to the received request.

```
public class ReqisterServlet extends javax.servlet.sip.SipServlet {

    private ContactDatabase contactDatabase = null;
    private PresenceDispatcher presenceDispatcher = null;
    private ServletContext servletContext = null;
    private SipFactory sipFactory = null;

    // Servlet contructor must be empty
    public ReqisterServlet() {
    }

    // Initialize servlet. Here we can create and retriev servlet specific resources
    public void init(ServletConfig config) throws ServletException {
        super.init(config);
        servletContect = config.getServletContext();
        sipFactory = (SipFactory)servletContext.getAttribute("javax.servlet.sip.SipFactory");
        ....
    }

    // Process REGISTER request
    public void doRegister(SipServletRequest req) throws SipServletException {

        SipServletResponse response = null;
        SipAddress to = req.getTo();
        long defaultExpires = getDefaultExpiresAsSeconds(req);
        List contactList = req.getContacts();

         // Update new contact information to database
        Iterator iter = contactList.iterator();
        while(iter.hasNext()) {
            updateContacts(to, contactList, req);
        }

         // Create and reponse response
        response = req.createResponse(200);
        response.setContacts(getContacts(to));
        response.send();
    }

}
```

Listing of a simple SIP REGISTER servlet

IM Service Implementation

The IM service implementation serves as an example of an application server acting as a proxy for Instant Messages (IM), using the MESSAGE SIP method. All MESSAGE requests are passed to the IM servlet through the doMessage() method. The servlet checks to whom the received message is addressed, retrieves the target address from the database and proxies the message to that address. Before starting the proxy operation, the servlet sets the record-route and recursive flags, meaning that the proxy should insert a Record-Route header into requests and retry the request when receiving a 3XX series redirect response.

References

[sip-im]   Rosenberg, J., et al, "SIP Extensions for Instant Messaging," draft-ietf-sip-message-01 (work in progress), March 2002.

[mime]   Freed, N., N. Borenstein, "Multipurpose Internet Mail Extensions (MIME) Part One: Format of Internet Message Bodies," RFC 2045 (Draft Internet Standard),November 1996.

[events]   Roach A., "SIP-Specific Event Notification," RFC 3nnn (Proposed Internet Standard), March 2002.

[presence]   Rosenberg, J., et al, "SIP Extensions for Presence," Internet-Draft, draft-ietf-simple-presence-05 (work in progress), March 2002.

[reg-pl]   Lennox J., H. Schulzrinne, " Transporting User Control Information in SIP REGISTER Payloads," draft-lennox-sip-reg-payload-01 (expired Internet-Draft), October 2000.

[gmime]   Gmime by Jeffrey Stedfast <fejj@helixcode.com>. (GPL)

             http://spruce.sourceforge.net/gmime/

[glib]   GLib. C-library for strings, memory etc. (LGPL)

             http://www.gtk.org/

[xslt]   The XSLT C library for Gnome.(MIT)

             http://xmlsoft.org/XSLT/

[cpim]   Sugano H., et al, "CPIM Presence Information Data Format," draft-ietf-impp-cpim-pidf-02.txt (work in progress), March 2002.

[libxml2]   The XML C library for Gnome. (MIT)

             http://xmlsoft.org/

[xpidf]   Rosenberg, J., et al, "Data Format for Presence Using XML," draft-rosenberg-impp-pidf-00 (expired Internet-draft), June 2000.

Mobile DRM

The Mobile DRM demonstrator studies the feasibility of secure content distribution focusing on supporting:

o   Downloading of content and rights from public kiosks to mobile devices using local networks,

o   Superdistribution of content and rights from one device to another, and

o   Accurate and timely metering mechanisms on which revenue sharing schemes can be based.

The motivation behind these objectives is to enable the legal spreading of content in and via portable devices to the greatest possible extent: allowing copies to be made while still retaining the ability to properly meter and report new copies. The target was to develop a potential architecture and build a reference implementation.

The primary requirements for the reference implementation were:

1.   Only compliant devices must be allowed to acquire and redistribute rights.

2.   It must be possible to track and report any new creation of rights.

3.   Creation and transfer of rights must be possible even when there is no on-line connection to a network server.

4.   When rights are exchanged for payment, it must be possible to use any payment scheme, both electronic and traditional. The system must not be limited to one or a few schemes only.

The first requirement is applicable to any Digital Rights Management (DRM) system based on the notion of compliant devices, while the last requirement is required for flexibility and is also generally applicable. Requirement 2 is necessary for the distribution of rights and can be easily solved if there is always a connection to an online server. But this may not always be possible for consumers, hence requirement 3. Requirements 2 and 3 can therefore be seen as specific to DRM for mobile scenarios.

Basic Concepts and Design

The mobile DRM architecture is shown in the following figure. Each consumer device is required to have at least the following two parts:

o   A tamper-resistant hardware module (called the DRM device), and

o   A protocol engine implementing the mobile DRM protocols (including a user interface)

The reason for separating these two parts is the underlying assumption of trust: the mobile DRM client, called *TranSec* node, is responsible for protecting the interests not only of the owner, but also of other parties (e.g., authors and publishers of content). This part of the node must be certifiable. It is therefore useful to identify the minimal certifiable functionality as a separate part: this is the DRM device. This separation also allows the DRM device to be used with different protocol engines, possibly implementing the Transec protocols over different transports. The implementation of DRM functionality requires some support from the underlying operating platform; this functionality is defined by the Transec platform API.

In addition, there may be additional entities such as:

o   Rendering applications that receive content from the DRM device and render it, and

o   Authorization plug-ins (e.g., for a payment system).

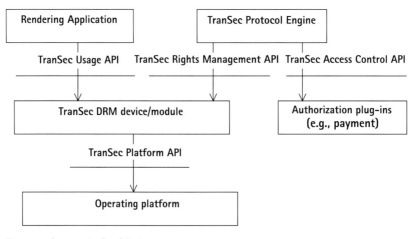

Transec node conceptual architecture

Securing Rights Transfer

A compliant device is one that behaves according to the Transec specifications. Every compliant device will have an encryption key pair and a digital signature key pair for suitable asymmetric cryptographic schemes. Each device will also have a device certificate issued by the device manufacturer, certifying the public keys of the device as belonging to a compliant device. Every device will also have the public signature verification key of the device manufacturer so that it can verify the device certificates of other devices. For the sake of simplicity, only a single manufacturer is considered. But devices of multiple manufacturers can inter-operate using certificate chains and the cross-certification of manufacturers.

A piece of content is associated with two types of rights: usage rights, which specify policies governing the local use of content, and transfer rights, which specify policies for creating new rights for another device. Our design supports several types of transfers including:

o   **Give:** A device can give away its rights to a content to another device. Once the right is transferred, the sending device will not be able to use the content anymore. Note that the receiving device may pay the sender, but such sales are not the concern of the rights management system.

o   **Copy:** Copying creates a new right. This is used when content is sold by a kiosk or superdistributed by ordinary consumers.

The rights for a piece of content are embodied in a voucher. Each piece of content is encrypted with a content key (symmetric key). The voucher contains the content key encrypted using the public key of the target device. It also contains policies specifying how this copy of the content is to be used. Compliant devices obey the policy restrictions specified in a voucher. When a right is transferred, the sending device creates a voucher targeting the receiving device. A sending device must verify that the receiving device is a compliant device before creating a voucher for it. A receiving device will accept a voucher if it can verify its correctness. A voucher being transferred contains, among other things:

o   Description of the content,

o   Description of rights,

o   Content encryption key encrypted using the public encryption key of the receiver,

o   Sequence numbers used to ensure freshness, and

o   A message authentication code on all other fields, using the content encryption key.

When a compliant receiving device is asked to import a voucher, it verifies the validity of the voucher by first extracting the content encryption key, and then checking the message authentication code. With these mechanisms, the first requirement is met.

Typically, verifying compliance alone is not enough for a sender to make an access control decision about a receiver. For example, in the case of a sale, the sender may ask the receiver to securely bind his device certificate to a payment transaction (e.g., open a secure channel, and send a credit card number and device certificate through the same channel). To enable such

IV

Implementations

access control decisions, other authorization certificates may be used. For example, a consumer may issue certificates to each of his devices so that they can recognize each other. A device can then automatically approve a give transfer if the request came from another device belonging to the same consumer.

Metering and Reporting New Rights

Requirements 2 and 3 deal with the distribution of rights by copying. Creation of a new right for a piece of content must be metered and reported so that the resulting revenue can be effectively collected and shared.

When the protocol engine asks its compliant device to create a new right by copying, it can indicate whether it should be sender-reported or receiver-reported. In the former case, the compliant device records it locally as an unreported transaction. In the latter case, it issues a voucher which is marked as report-pending. A special case of a receiver-reported voucher is a preview voucher, which comes with a specified number of free previews. By default, these vouchers need not be reported, and will disappear once the free previews are used, but the consumer can convert it into a real receiver-reported voucher by committing to report it. Such a voucher will be marked as report-pending. If proof of reporting is imported into the device, the report-pending voucher will be converted to an unconstrained voucher. When the number of report-pending vouchers reaches a specified limit, the device may be disabled in some fashion. In other words, compliant devices enforce policies on rights. Unconstrained and preview vouchers can be deleted by the consumer. If the consumer deletes a report-pending voucher, it will be marked as locked, and will be really removed only after it has been reported.

The main intent behind the reporting feature is that the copyright owner will be able to receive payment from the owner of the device reporting the transactions. This implies that sender-reported transactions will be typically of the pay-now type where the transfer is accompanied by a payment from the receiver to the sender. Receiver-reported transactions are typically of the pay-later type because the receiver should eventually pay the copyright owner.

In both types of payment scenarios, any payment scheme can be used for value transfer. Hence requirement 4 is satisfied.

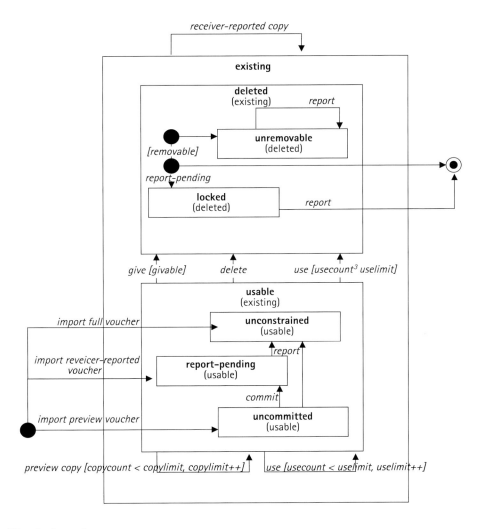

Lifecycle of a voucher

The previous figure shows the lifecycle of a voucher as a state transition diagram.

In the reference implementation, metering and reporting of new vouchers is done as follows: for transactions between mobile devices (i.e., superdistibution), only receiver-reported vouchers are supported. Kiosks sell unconstrained vouchers, so the reporting of vouchers is done implicitly by purchasing an unconstrained voucher from any kiosk. When an unconstrained voucher is imported, if there is already a corresponding report-pending voucher then instead of creating a new voucher, the old one will be marked as unconstrained.

Rights Transfer Protocol

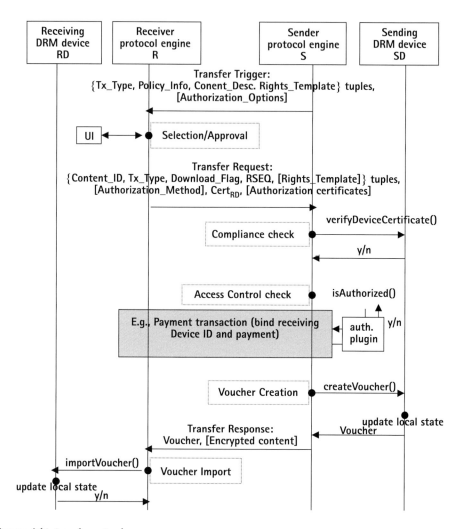

Transec rights transfer protocol

The previous figure illustrates the Transec rights transfer protocol. It consists of three message flows, but does not show any service location or browsing activity that may have preceded the actual transfer transaction. The participants are:

o   The sender is the player sending a right and/or the encrypted content. The sender's device is SD.

o   The receiver is the other player participating in the protocol. The receiving device (RD) is the recipient of the transferred right. The receiving device may belong to R, but this is not mandatory; the protocols can be used to buy a right on behalf of someone else's device.

The optional transfer trigger is sent by the sender. This message contains the proposed transaction type (e.g., copy), policy information (e.g., price requested) which can be displayed to the recipient, description of the content, and a description of the proposed voucher. It may also explicitly list the acceptable authorization options (e.g., payment methods).

The transfer request is sent by the receiver. Among other things, it should include a compliance certificate for the receiving device, and a sequence number to be used by the receiving device to guard against the replaying of old vouchers. On receiving the request, the sender should first check if the device certificate is acceptable to the sender's device. It may then do an access control check via an access control plug-in (e.g., a payment plug-in). This access control check is orthogonal to the rights transfer system. Then the sender asks the sender's device to create a voucher for the receiving device, which it will do only if the receiving device has an acceptable compliance certificate. Creation of a voucher may change the state information maintained by the sender's device, so it is important that the integrity of this state information is protected.

The transfer reply contains the newly-created voucher. The receiver may also get the encrypted content along with this reply, or separately. To use the voucher, it must be imported into a receiving device. A receiving device will also check if the voucher is acceptable, as explained earlier. In particular, it would check if RSEQ is an acceptable sequence number. If the receiving device was not consulted before sending the request, a special RSEQ value may be used. Such vouchers are marked unremovable to prevent an attack where the receiver gives this right to another device, and then replays an old voucher back into his own device, thus ending with a free voucher.

Platform Support

A compliant DRM device enforces the management of rights. Rather than design a special-purpose device, a minimal set of changes that would allow a commonly used operating system platform to be adapted as a DRM device was designed. We also list the type of typical hardware support needed.

This approach is based on authenticating processes at run-time when needed. This sets at least the following requirements on the way the operating system is operated and how it handles its processes:

1. The consumer cannot make modifications to the OS kernel. This implies that the OS can be loaded/started in a secure and reliable manner. Note that integrity only is required; the kernel source code need not contain any secrets.

2. OS processes cannot access each other's memory areas without explicit permission.

3. Disk swapping or other kinds of temporary storage that may leave traces of critical data can be disabled for processes requiring this feature.

4. The system hardware can be set to enable some secure storage in the kernel.

IV Implementations

If these requirements hold, it is easy to see that the kernel can get unique access to the secure data, enabling it to:

a)   Form a secret by which secure storage for vouchers can be implemented (and equivalently a secret protecting the private key of the device when stored). These secrets may or may not be separate.

b)   Authenticate a process claiming to be the DRM engine.

We implemented a means of authenticating processes by calculating a message digest over the text segment of the process, verifying that there is a signed and appropriate certificate matching this digest and checking the position of the program counter. If we assume that the program is statically linked, the following should hold: The text segment uniquely identifies the program, and provided that the program counter actually points to the text segment, no viral program could replicate this identity.

Based on this functionality, the kernel provides the following services to processes:

a)   A system call by which a process can claim to be the DRM engine and insert a certificate to prove this fact. Upon this request, the kernel will check the process in accordance with the method described above, and if all things match this process is given the necessary secret to maintain secure storage.

b)   A system call by which a process may register an easy-to-remember name (or some other identity) for itself.

c)   A system call by which a process may retrieve the digest and identifier Program Identifier (PID) of a process (that has registered some name).

d)   A system call by which a process may send a secret to another process identified by a specific (e.g., PID, name, digest) tuple.

e)   A system call by which a process may retrieve a secret sent to it by another process.

We need two kinds of tamper-resistant secure storage on the device: a small amount (e.g., 128 bits) secret storage which can be used to bootstrap larger amounts of secret storage for private keys and an equally small amount (128-160 bits) of integrity-protected storage, which can be used to bootstrap additional integrity-protected storage for state information. The former can be read-only, while the latter is necessarily mutable over time.

Prototype Implementation

A music player prototype with the above-mentioned features and a UI was done on Linux with X-windows and WLAN access on a Personal Digital Assistant (PDA). Several additional building blocks were needed to put together the final demonstrator. The elements in the following picture are described in more detail to show the functionality of the demonstrator.

Conceptual architecture

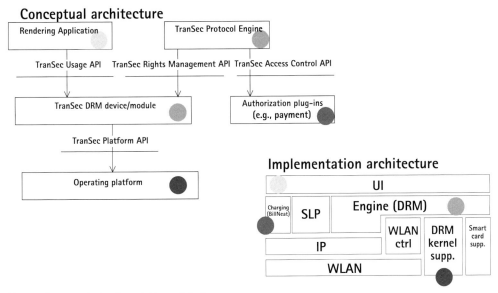

Transec demonstrator implementation architecture

a) Operating platform support has been coded into the Linux kernel as described in the previous chapter. No hardware support or support for secure kernel loading is available, so the necessary security elements have been hard-wired into the kernel. Minimal hardware support for secure kernel loading and secure storage is absolutely essential for this approach to be secure.

b) The kernel at start-up will authenticate the DRM engine. The kernel has hardcoded information of the expected message digest of the DRM engine. If the digest of the engine matches, a key is given to the DRM engine for generation of integrity-protected storage for the vouchers it handles. In this implementation, the DRM engine also owns the device secret key, which it uses to sign outgoing messages. The engine also includes the actual protocol engine for receiving, sending and verifying messages between DRM engines. Additionally, it keeps track of global device parameters (e.g., the number of unreported vouchers currently stored in the device) and maintains voucher state (e.g., the number of preview copies, and whether a specific voucher has been reported or not).

In the reference implementation, the DRM engine additionally keeps track of data essentially irrelevant to it (e.g., the position of actual encrypted content in the device, and which voucher the content relates to), some nice textual information regarding the content (originally received by the Service Location Protocol) and some additional state information needed by the user interface). In a real implementation, this functionality would not belong in the engine itself, but was included now for convenience.

c) The User Interface and Rendering application (e.g., MP3 player) are both authenticated by the DRM-engine before being taken into use. When the consumer wants to play some music the DRM-engine will send the content key to the rendering application through the kernel. We have implemented an ad-hoc encryption method where each MP3 block is encrypted separately using RC4, the purpose geared more towards ease of demonstration than actual security. The basic point, however, is that the music will be decoded and sent to the audio driver only on demand, and the plain text music will never be stored or kept in the device in decrypted form.

d)   The Service Location Protocol [2] is used to inform consumers of music available at a certain kiosk, and in consumer transactions what content is available for copying in the sender's device. Essentially, these records are used to transmit user-readable information of the music, its author, price and other textual information, as well as identification information for the related encrypted content and voucher ID. Retrieval of encrypted content is done as a non-authorized bulk transfer either directly from the kiosk or between consumers. There are no enforced restrictions on this activity (a consumer is allowed to download encrypted content without a valid voucher for it; she just cannot play it).

e)   We are using the BillNeat charging system [1] as an authorization plug-in for purchasing content vouchers at kiosks. BillNeat is a 3rd party charging solution based on a three-tier structure: the buyer, the seller and a distributed network platform containing the core of BillNeat's functionality. The authentication mechanism used in Billneat is based on asymmetric cryptography and x.509 certificates, making the billing records uncontestable.

The consumer's mobile device will tune in to kiosks and automatically show the available music; it is up to the consumer to select the music pieces he wants, download the content and pay for the vouchers. In a distribution between consumers, the consumer can turn her device into an access point which other consumers can browse as though it were a kiosk, with the difference that a kiosk only sells *pay-now* vouchers, whereas other consumers only distribute pay-later ones. Music playing is similar to any MP3-player on the market.

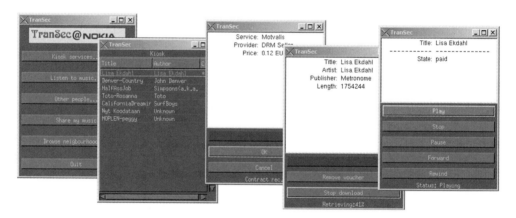

Some pictures of the user interface

References

[1] P. Ginzboorg, J-E Ekberg and A. Ylä-Jääski: "A Charging and Billing Mechanism for the Public Internet," Proceedings of Telecom Interactive 97, ITU, Geneva.

[2] Service Location Protocol, v.2, RFC 2608, June 1999.

IV

Implementations

V EPILOGUE

o Epilogue

Epilogue

The Mobile Internet does not simply refer to accessing the conventional Internet from a mobile device. We will not spend our time browsing Internet pages for content as we do today, although this will still be possible. Instead, we will use services and applications to access content, make transactions, do business, link up with friends and family, play games, watch videos and listen to and download music. More importantly, we will use the Mobile Internet to help manage our lives and give us more time to do the things we choose to, regardless of our location.

The new environment is about enabling people to shape their own Mobile World through personalized communication technology. It is also a place where companies do business by matching consumer needs with their service portfolio or product offering. To ensure the success of services in the Mobile World, they must be highly user-friendly. The consumer should be able to ignore the underlying technologies and enjoy the richness of the services regardless of the access method.

Three success factors for enabling service consumption are:

o   Consumer acceptance of the services,

o   A healthy business system, and

o   Understanding technology life cycles and maturity levels.

Nokia has a good understanding of the mobile device consumer segments, the general attitudes and needs of these segments and the characteristics of technology adoption in each of them. This knowledge is applied to new services and, through product and user interface categorization, enables an optimal consumer experience and ease of use in each of the segments.

Understanding the profit-making logic of the Mobile and Web domains, and applying this knowledge to the innovation possibilities in the Mobile World will combine the best of these domains. It is important for all constituents of the Mobile World to unlock innovation potential through solid business models, so that the flow of new services and evolving consumer needs match. This consumption of new services benefits carriers through volume and through higher average revenue per user.

All technology choices should emphasize service enabling; technical architectures can be perceived as end-to-end service enablers. These technical architectures should lead technology evolution and the related selections, establish a framework for standardization efforts, and enable early system verifications with reference implementations.

Having a common framework for services and understanding this technical foundation will be important when companies interact with each other and consider introducing new services to consumers. To facilitate this, Nokia is active in open global standardization fora, such as Open Mobile Alliance, to develop a comprehensive application and service architecture for the Mobile Internet. The ultimate objective of Nokia is to create a user-friendly Mobile Internet experience for everyone.

The Mobile Internet Technical Architecture aims to provide seamless interoperability between all interaction modes, any network environment and with any type of access. Identifying the relevant communication modes, defining the required supporting key technologies and driving industry participation to develop a common Mobile Internet platform are steps towards the needed solutions. MITA is a common Mobile Internet platform for applications, a technical framework for Mobile services, and a technical foundation for an evolution path to the Mobile World.

Customer acceptance of services is a fundamental factor for success in the Mobile World. The functionalities of the Mobile Internet need to be defined to address consumer needs in various areas. While the needs are anticipated to be versatile, the critical success factors for the creation and provisioning of services are value for the consumer, a sense of security and ease of use. These requirements should be addressed by taking a holistic view of the underlying architecture, to identify the key building blocks and strive to minimize complexity for the consumer. These considerations were investigated in the Visions section.

The Implementations section introduced the MITA Reference Implementation Environment and the reference implementations of various technologies. The real significance of reference implementations is that they provide us with a glimpse of the future, making it possible to modify and improve technologies on time. Thus, reference implementations act as a reality check for the industry. They speed up the introduction of new technologies, for example, through providing the basis for open source distributions, standardization efforts or interoperability tests.

We are in middle of an IP Convergence-driven technology evolution from three network environments: mobile networks, the Internet and Intranets towards a unified Mobile Internet. The role of end-to-end solutions, new technologies, such as SIP and Web services, together with increasing programmability in mobile devices will lead us to a personalized Mobile World where the requirements of consumers drive the development of the Mobile Internet. To achieve this goal, mobile devices, networks and service solutions must work together as one and developers must have access to develop new services. An open solution benefits all (e.g., profitable business scenarios call for interoperability, short development cycles, large volumes and, most of all, global reach). Unless there is a commonly accepted architectural solution, markets will be fragmented and require separate parameters, and be much smaller than a single global market.

As part of the open architecture development, Nokia invites all developers, service providers, carriers and other industry players to participate in further clarifying and specifying the market requirements and technical solutions required to provide the Mobile Internet needed for superior end-to-end services.

V Epilogue

VI   APPENDIX

o   Glossary

Appendix A: Glossary

2G	Second Generation
3DES	Triple DES
3G	Third generation
3GPP	Third Generation Partnership Project
3GPP2	Third Generation Partnership Project 2
A/D	Analog-to-digital
AAA	Authentication, Authorization, and Accounting
AAC	Advanced Audio Coding
AAP	Alternative Approval Process
ABNF	Advanced Backus-Naur Form
AC	Admission Control
ACID	Atomicity, Consistency, Isolation and Durability
ACIF	Australian Communications Industry Forum
AD	Area Director
ADI	Application Development Interface
ADPCM	Adaptive Differential Pulse Code Modulation
AES	Advanced Encryption Standard
A-GPS	Assisted Global Positioning System
AH	Authentication Header
AIC	Access Independent Connectivity
AII	Access Independent Interface
AKA	Authentication and Key Agreement
All-IP RAN	All-IP Radio Access Network
ALF	Application Level Framing
ALG	Application Level Gateway
AMR	Adaptive Multi-rate
AMR-NB	AMR Narrowband
AMR-WB	AMR Wideband
AMS	Application Management Software
ANSI	American National Standards Institute
AO	Application Originated
AOA	Angle Of Arrival
AP	Access Point
API	Application Programming Interface

ARIB	Association of Radio Industries and Businesses
ARL	Authority Revocation List
ARP	Address Resolution Protocol
ARPU	Average Revenue Per User
ARQ	Automatic Repeat Request
AS	Announcement Server
AS	Application Server
AS	Authentication Server
ASCII	American Standard Code for Information Interchange
ASN.1	Abstract Syntax Notation One
ASP	Application Service Provider
AT	Access and Terminals
AT	Application Terminated
ATM	Asynchronous Transfer Mode
ATM	Automatic Teller Machine
ATM-F	ATM Forum
AtoM	Any Transport over MPLS
AVT	Audio/Video Transport
AWT	Abstract Windowing Toolkit
B2B	Business-to-Business
B2BUA	Back-to-Back User Agent
B2C	Business-to-Consumer
BARB	Bluetooth Architecture and Review Board
BBTAG	BroadBand Technical Advisory Group
BCH	Basic Call Handling
BCP	Best Current Practices
BDT	Telecommunication Development Bureau
BE	Best Effort
BEC	Backward Error Correction
BEP	Bit Error Probability
BG	Border Gateway
BGCF	Breakout Gateway Control Function
BGP	Border Gateway Protocol
BizCom	Business Committee
BLER	Block Error Ratio
BMP	Windows Bitmap
BNEP	Bluetooth Network Encapsulation Protocol

BOF	Birds of a Feather
BOV	Business Operational View
BPF	Berkeley-Packet-Filter
BPSK	Binary Phase Shift Keying
BQA	Bluetooth Qualification Administrator
BQB	Bluetooth Qualification Bodies
BQRB	Bluetooth Qualification Review Board
BQTF	Bluetooth Qualification Test Facility
BR	Radiocommunication Bureau
BRAN	Broadband Radio Access Networks
BS	Base Station
BSA	Binding Security Association
BSC	Base Station Controller
BSD	Berkeley Software Distribution
BSS	Base Station System
BSS	Basic Service Set
BSSGP	Base Station System GPRS Protocol
BTAB	Bluetooth Technical Advisory Board
BTI	Bluetooth Test and Interoperability Committee
BTP	Business Transaction Protocol
BTS	Base Station
BWA	Broadband Wireless Access
CA	Certification Authority
CA	Collision Avoidance
CAMEL	Customized Applications for Mobile Network Enhanced Logic
CAR	Candidate Access Router
CBA	Command Button Area
CBR	Constant BitRate
CC	Call Control
CCK	Complementary Code Keying
CC/PP	Composite Capability/Preference Profiles
CCIF	International Telephone Consultative Committee
CCIR	International Radio Consultative Committee
CCIT	International Telegraph Consultative Committee
CCITT	International Telegraph and Telephone Consultative Committee
CCS	Cascading Style Sheets
CCU	Channel Codec Unit

VI

Glossary

CD	Collision Detection
CD	Compact Disc
CDC	Connected Device Configuration
CDMA	Code Division Multiple Access
CDR	Call Detail Record
CDR	Common Data Representation
CEK	Content Encryption Key
Cell-ID	Cell Identity
CENELEC	European Committee for Electrotechnical Standardization
CEPT	Conference of European Postal and Telecommunications Administrations
CGI	Common Gateway Interface
CGL-WG	OSDL Carrier Linux Work Group
cHTML	Compact HTML
CIDR	Classless Inter-Domain Routing
CIF	Common Intermediate Format
CIR	Carrier-to-Interference Ratio
CL	Convergence Layer
CLDC	Connected Limited Device Configuration
CLI	Command-Line Interface
CLIP	Classical IP
CLP	Common Line Protocol
CLR	Certificate Revocation List
CMT	Cellular Mobile Telephone
CN	Core Network
CoA	Care-of Address
COD	Content Object Descriptor
COFDM	Coded Orthogonal Frequency Division Multiplex
COPS	Common Open Policy Service
CORBA	Common Object Request Broker Architecture
CoT	Care-of Address Test
CoTI	Care-of Address Test Initiate
CPA	Collaboration Protocol Agreement
CPCS	Common Part Convergence Sublayer
CPIM	Common Profile for Instant Messaging
CPL	Call Processing Language
CPP	Collaboration Protocol Profile
CPS	Connection Processing Server

CPU	Central Processing Unit
CR	Change Request
CRC	Cyclic Redundancy Check
CRL	Certificate Revocation List
CRM	Customer Relationship Management
CS	Circuit Switched
CSCF	Call State Control Function
CSD	Circuit Switched Data
CSMA	Carrier Sense Multiple Access
CSP	Client-Server Protocol
CSS	Cascading Style Sheets
CTP	Cordless Telephony Profile
CTS	Clear To Send
CWM	Common Warehouse Metamodel
CVM	Java™ virtual machine supporting CDC
CVOPS	C Virtual Operating System
CWTS	China Wireless Telecommunication Standard Group
D/A	Digital-to-Analog
DAB	Digital Audio Broadcasting
DAD	Duplicate Address Detection
DAML	DARPA Agent Markup Language
DCF	Distributed Coordination Function
DCOM	Distributed Component Object Model
DECT	Digital European Cordless Telecommunications
DER	Distinguished Encoding Rules
DES	Data Encryption Standard
DFRD	Device Family Reference Design
D-G	Director-General
DHCP	Dynamic Host Configuration Protocol
DiffServ	Differentiated Services
DIFS	Distributed InterFrame Space
DLC	Data Link Control
DLPI	Data Link Provider Interface
DM	Device Management
DMCA	Digital Millennium Copyright Act
DNS	Domain Name System
DNS-Sec	DNS Security

DoD	Department of Defense
DPIT	Designated Profile Interoperability Test platform
DPSCH	Dedicated Physical SubChannel
DRM	Digital Rights Management
DS	Distribution System
DSA	Digital Signature Algorithm
DSCP	Differentiated Services Code Point
DSL	Digital Subscriber Line
DSP	Digital Signal Processor
DSUI	Differentiated Services Urgency/Importance
DSS	Distribution System Services
DSSS	Direct Sequence Spread Spectrum
DTC	Domain Technology Committee
DTD	Document Type Definition
DTMF	Dial Tone Multi-Frequency
DUNP	Dial-Up Networking Profile
DVB	Digital Video Broadcasting
DVB-T	Digital Video Broadcasting Terrestrial
DVD	Digital Versatile Disc
E.164	International public telecommunication numbers for ISDN, ITU-T
E2E	Enterprise-to-Enterprise
EAIF	External Application Interface
EAP	Extensible Authentication Protocol
EBU	European Broadcasting Union
ebXML	Electronic Business XML
EC	Executive Committee
ECDSA	Elliptic Curve DSA
ECMA TC32	Communication, Networks and Systems Interconnection
ECML	Electronic Commerce Modeling Language
ECN	Encoding Control Notation
ECN	Explicit Congestion Notification
ECSD	Enhanced Circuit Switched Data
EDGE	Enhanced Data Rates for Global Evolution
EDI	Electronic Data Interchange
EE	Environmental Engineering
EEMA	European Forum for Electronic Business
EFI	External Functionality Interface

EFR	Enhanced Full Rate
EFTA	European Free Trade Association
EGW	Multimedia E-mail Gateway
EGPRS	Enhanced GPRS
EIRP	Effective Isotropic Radiated Power
EIS	Enterprise Information System
EJB	Enterprise JavaBeans™
EMC	Electromagnetic Compatibility
EMS	Enhanced Messaging Service
EMV	EuropayMastercardVisa payment protocol
ENUM	E.164 Number Mapping
E-OTD	Enhanced Observed Time Difference
EP	ETSI Project
EP BRAN	ETSI Project Broadband Radio Access Networks
EP TIPHON	ETSI Project TIPHON
EPC	Enhanced Power Control
ERC	European Radiocommunications Committee
ERM	EMC and Radio Spectrum Matters
ESMTP	Extended Simple Mail Transfer Protocol
ESO	European Standards Organization
ESP	Encapsulating Security Payload
ESS	Extended Service Set
E-TCH	Enhanced Traffic Channel
ETIS	E- and Telecommunication Information Services
ETSI	European Telecommunications Standards Institute
EU	European Union
FACCH	Fast Associated Control Channel
FAX	Facsimile
FaxP	Fax Profile
FBWA	Fixed Broadband Wireless Access
FC	Finance Committee
FCC	Federal Communication Commission
FDD	Frequency Division Duplex
FH	Frequency Hopping
FHSS	Frequency Hopping Spread Spectrum
FOTAG	Fiber Optics Technical Advisory Group
FP	File Transfer Profile

FR	Full Rate
FRF	Frame Relay Forum
FSG	Free Standards Group
FSV	Functional Service View
FTP	File Transfer Protocol
GA	General Assembly
GAP	Generic Access Profile
GCC	GNU C Compiler
GERAN	GSM/EDGE Radio Access Network
GFSK	Gaussian Frequency Shift Keying
GGSN	Gateway GPRS Support Node
GIF	Graphics Interchange Format
GIOP	Generic Inter-Object Request Protocol
GMA	Gateway Mobility Agent
GMM	GPRS Mobility Management
GMPCS	Global Mobile Personal Communications by Satellite
GMSK	Gaussian Minimum Shift Keying
GMT	Greenwich Mean Time
GOEP	Generic Object Exchange Profile
GPL	General Public License
GPRS	General Packet Radio Service
GPS	Global Positioning System
GRA	GERAN Registration Area
GRX	GPRS Roaming Exchange
GSA	Global Mobile Suppliers Association
GSC	Global Standards Collaboration
GSM	Global System for Mobile Communications
GT	Generic Technology
GTD	Geometric Time Difference
GTP	GPRS Tunneling Protocol
GTP-U	GTP for the user plane
GUI	Graphical User Interface
GUP	Generic User Profile
GW	Gateway
HA	Home Agent
HAck	Handover Acknowledgement
HC	Handover Control

HF	Human Factors
HI	Handover Interface
HILI	High Level Interface
HIPERACCESS	High Performance Radio Access
HIPERLAN	High Performance Radio Local Area Network
HIPERLAN2	High Performance Radio Local Area Network type 2
HIPERMAN	High Performance Radio Metropolitan Area Network
HLR	Home Location Register
HoT	Home Address Test
HoTI	Home Address Test Initiate
HR	Half Rate
HSCSD	High Speed Circuit Switched Data
HSDPA	High Speed Downlink Packet Access
HSP	Handset Profile
HSS	Home Subscriber Server
HTML	HyperText Markup Language
HTTP	HyperText Transfer Protocol
IAB	Internet Architecture Board
IACC	In-Advance Credit Check
IANA	Internet Assigned Numbers Authority
IAP	Internet Access Provider
IAPP	Inter Access Point Protocol
IC	Integrated Circuit
ICL	Interoperability Certification Lab
ICMP	Internet Control Message Protocol
I-CSCF	Interrogating CSCF
ICTSB	Information and Communications Technologies Standards Board
ID	Internet Draft
ID	User Identification
IDE	Integrated Development Environment
IDL	Interactive Data Language
IDL	Interface Definition Language
IEC	International Electrotechnical Commission
IEEE	The Institute Of Electrical And Electronics Engineers
IEEE-ISTO	IEEE Industry Standards and Technology Organization
IEEE-SA	IEEE Standards Association
IETF	Internet Engineering Task Force

VI Glossary

IESG	Internet Engineering Steering Group
IFH	Intelligent Frequency Hopping
IFRB	International Frequency Registration Board
IGMP	Internet Group Multicast Protocol
IIOP	Internet Inter-Object Request Broker Protocol
IKE	Internet Key Exchange
ILP	Integrated Layer Processing
IM	Instant Messaging
IM/P	Instant Messaging and Presence
IMAP	Internet Message Access Protocol
IMEI	International Mobile Station Equipment Identity
IMPACT	International Marketing and Promotional Activities
IMPP	Instant Messaging and Presence Protocol
IMPS	Instant Messaging and Presence
IMR	IP Multimedia Register
IMS	IP Multimedia Subsystem
IMSI	International Mobile Subscriber Identity
IMT-2000	International Mobile Telecommunications 2000
IMTC	International Multimedia Telecommunications Consortium
IN	Intelligent Network
IntP	Intercom Profile
IntServ	Integrated Services
IOPCom	Interoperability Committee
IOT	Interoperability Testing
IP	Internet Protocol
IPDC	IP Datacasting
IPDL	Idle Period Down Link
IPDR.org	Internet Protocol Detail Record Organization
IPNG	Internet Protocol Next Generation
IPR	Intellectual Property Right
IPSec	IP Security
IPv4	Internet Protocol, version 4
IPv6	Internet Protocol, version 6
IR	Incremental Redundancy
IR	Infrared
IRC	Internet Relay Chat
IrDA	Infrared Data Association

IRTF	Internet Research Task Force
ISDN	Integrated Services Digital Network
ISLAN	Integrated Services LAN
ISM	Industrial, Scientific and Medical
ISO	International Organization for Standardization
ISOC	Internet Society
ISP	Internet Service Provider
ISV	Independent Software Vendor
IT	Information Technology
ITU	International Telecommunication Union
ITU-D	ITU Telecommunication Development Sector
ITU-R	ITU Radiocommunication Sector
ITU-T	ITU Telecommunication Standardization Sector
IWE	Interworking Element
IWF	Interworking Function
IVR	Interactive Voice Response
J2EE™	Java™ 2 Platform, Enterprise Edition
J2ME™	Java™ 2 Platform, Micro Edition
J2SE™	Java™ 2 Platform, Standard Edition
JAD	Java™ Application Descriptor
JAIN	Java™ APIs for Integrated Networks
JAM	Java™ Application Manager
JAR	Java™ Archive file
JAXM	Java™ API for XML Messaging
JAXP	Java™ API for XML Processing
JAXR	Java™ API for XML Registries
JAX-RPC	Java™ API for XML-based RPC
JCP	Java™ Community Process
JCTA	Japan Cable Television Engineering Association
JDBC	Java™ Database Connectivity API
JDK	Java™ Development Kit
JMS	Java™ Messaging Service
JNDI	Java™ Naming and Directory Interface
JNI	Java™ Native Interface
JPEG	Joint Photographic Experts Group
JSPA	Java Specification Participation Agreement
JSP™	JavaServer™ Pages

VI Glossary

JSR	Java Specification Request
JTC	Joint Technical Committee
JTC Broadcast	Joint Technical Committee on Broadcasting
JVM	Java™ Virtual Machine
KVM	Java™ Virtual Machine supporting CLDC
L2	Layer 2
L2CAP	Logical Link Control and Adaptation Protocol
L3	Layer 3
LA	Link Adaptation
LAN	Local Area Network
LAP	LAN Access Profile
LC	Load Control
LCD	Liquid Crystal Display
LCDUI	Limited Capability Device User Interface
LDAP	Lightweight Directory Access Protocol
LGPL	Library GNU Public License
LIF	Location Interoperability Forum
LLC	Logical Link Control
LMA	Leaf Mobility Agent
LMM	Local Mobility Management
LMP	Link Manager Protocol
LMSC	IEEE 802 LAN/MAN Standards Committee
LMU	Location Measurement Unit
LSB	Linux Standards Base
LSP	Label Switched Path
LSR	Label Switched Router
M2M	Machine-to-Machine
MAC	Media Access Control
MAC	Message Authentication Code
MAN	Metropolitan Area Network
MANET	Mobile Ad Hoc Networking
MAP	Mobile Application Part Protocol
MarCom	Marketing Committee
MBM	Multi Bitmap file
MCC	Mobile Competence Center
M-COMM	Mobile Commerce
MCS	Modulation Coding Scheme

MCU	Multiparty Conferencing Unit
MCU	Multipoint Control Unit
MD5	Message Digest 5
MDA	Model Driven Architecture
MEO	Medium Earth Orbit
MESA	Public Safety Partnership Project
MeT	Mobile Electronic Transactions
MExE	Mobile Station Application Execution Environment
MFN	Multi Frequency Network
MG	Media Gateway
MGC	Media Gateway Controller
MGCF	Media Gateway Control Function
MGW	Media Gateway
MHP	Multimedia Home Platform
MIBA	Mobile Internet Business Architecture
MIDI	Musical Instrument Digital Interface
MIDP	Mobile Information Device Profile
MII	Mobile Internet Interfaces
MIME	Multi-purpose Internet Mail Extensions
MITA	Mobile Internet Technical Architecture
MLD	Multicast Listener Discovery for IPv6
MM	Mobility Management
MMA	Multimedia Message Adaptation
MMAC	Multimedia Mobile Access Communications Promotion Council
MMCTL	Mobility Management Controller
MMS	Multimedia Messaging Service
MMSC	Multimedia Messaging Service Center
MMS-IOP	MMS Interoperability Group
MMU	Multimedia Unit
MMUSIC	Multiparty Multimedia Session Control
MO	Mobile Originated
MOF	Meta-Object Facility
MOTO	Mail Order/Telephone Order
MoU	Memoranda of Understanding
MPE	Multi-Protocol Encapsulation
MPEG	Moving Pictures Experts Group
MPEG-4	MPEG version 4

MPI	Mobile Internet Protocol Interfaces
MPLS	Multi-Protocol Label Switching
MRFC	Media Resource Function Control
MRFP	Media Resource Function Processing
MRP	Market Representation Partner
MRV	Mobile Rights Voucher
MS	Mobile Station
MSC	Mobile Services Switching Center
MSDU	MAC Service Data Unit
MSF	Multiservice Switching Forum
MSG	Mobile Standards Group
MSI	Mobile Internet Software Interfaces
MSISDN	Mobile Station International ISDN Number
MSS	Media Subsystem
MSS	Mobile Satellite Services
MT	Mobile Terminated
MTP3B	Message Transfer Part 3 Broadband
MTS	Methods for Testing and Specification
MTU	Maximum Transmission Unit
MVC	Model-View-Controller
MWIF	Mobile Wireless Internet Forum
MX	Mail eXchange
N-ISDN	Narrowband Integrated Services Digital Network
NACC	Network Assisted Cell Change
NAMP	Nokia Artuse Messaging Platform
NAPTR	Naming Authority Pointer
NAR	New Access Router
NAS	Network Access Server
NAT	Network Address Translation
NATP-PT	Network Address/Port Translation - Protocol Translation
NAT-PT	NAT - Protocol Translation
NesCom	New Standards Committee
NGN	Next Generation Networks
NIST	National Institute of Standards and Technology
NLOS	Non Line Of Sight
NNA	Naming, Numbering and Addressing
NNI	Network Node Interface

NNTP	Network News Transfer Protocol
NOKOS	NOKia Open Source license
NRT	Non-Real-Time
NSIS	New Steps In Signaling
NTA	Sofia Transaction API
NTP	Network Time Protocol
NTR	Sofia Transaction API for RTSP
NUA	Sofia User Agent API
O&M	Operations and Maintenance
OBEX	Object Exchange
OCG	Operational Coordination Group
OCSP	Online Certificate Status Protocol
OFDM	Orthogonal Frequency Division Multiplexing
OID	Other Input Document
OIF	Optical Internetworking Forum
OMA	Open Mobile Alliance
OMC	Operations and Maintenance Center
OMG	Object Management Group
OP	Organizational Partner
OPP	Object Push Profile
OR	Octal Rate
ORB	Object Request Broker
OS	Operating System
OSA	Open Service Architecture
OSDL	Open Source Development Lab
OSI	Open Source Initiative
OSI	Open Systems Interconnection
OSPF	Open Shortest Path First
OSPFv6	Open Shortest Path First for IPv6
OSS	Open Source Software
OSS	Operation Support Systems
OTA	Over The Air
OTD	Observed Time Difference
OTDOA	Observed Time Difference Of Arrival
OWL	Ontology Web Language
OWLAN	Operator Wireless Local Area Network
PACCH	Packet Associated Control Channel

PAI	Platform Adaptation Interface
PAN	Personal Area Networking
PAR	Previous Access Router
PAR	Project Authorization Request
PC	Power Control
PC	Personal Computer
PCF	Point Co-ordination Function
PCG	Project Co-ordination Group
PCM	Pulse Code Modulation
PCMCIA	PC Memory Card International Association
P-CSCF	Proxy-Call State Control Function
PDA	Personal Digital Assistant
PDC	Personal Digital Communication
PDCP	Packet Data Convergence Protocol
PDH	Plesiochronous Digital Hierarchy
PDP	Packet Data Protocol
PDTCH	Packet Data Traffic Channel
PDU	Protocol Data Unit
PFC	Packet Flow Context
PGP	Pretty Good Privacy
PHB	Per Hop Behavior
PHY	Physical
PHP	Hypertext Preprocessor
PID	Program Identifier
PII	Personally Identifiable Information
PIM	Personal Information Management
PIM	Protocol Independent Multicast
PIN	Personal Identification Number
PJAE	PersonalJava™ Application Environment
pJava	PJAE, PersonalJava™ Technology
PKC	Public Key Cryptography
PKI	Public Key Infrastructure
PLCP	Physical Layer Convergence Protocol
PLMN	Public Land Mobile Network
PLT	PowerLine Telecommunications
PMD	Physical Medium Dependent
PMO	Project Management Office

PNG	Portable Network Graphics
POI	Proof Of Identity
POP	Post Office Protocol
POP3	Post Office Protocol 3
POP	Proof Of Possession
POS	Point-Of-Sale
PPP	Point-to-Point Protocol
PRD	Program Reference Document
PS	Packet Scheduler
PS	Packet Switched
PS	Presence Server
PSCH	Physical SubChannel
PSK	Phase Shift Keying
PSS	Packet Switched Streaming
PSTN	Public Switched Telephone Network
PTC	Platform Technology Committee
PTCC	Protocol and Testing Competence Center
PTD	Personal Trusted Device
PTP	Personal Transaction Protocol
QCIF	Quarter-CIF
QM	Quality Manager
QoS	Quality of Service
QPL	Bluetooth Qualified Products List
QPSK	Quadrature Phase Shift Keying
QR	Quarter Rate
R&D	Research and Development
RA	Registration Authority
RA	Radiocommunication Assembly
RAB	Radio Access Bearer
RADIUS	Remote Authentication Dial-In User Service
RAG	Radiocommunication Advisory Group
RAN	Radio Access Network
RANAP	RAN Application Protocol
RAST	Global Radio Standardization
RB	Radio Bearer
RC	Roadmap Coordinator
RC5	Rivest Cipher 5

RDF	Resource Description Framework
RED	Random Early Deletion
REL	Rights Expression Language
RevCom	Review Committee
RF	Radio Frequency
RFC	Request For Comments
RFID	Radio Frequency ID
RFP	Request For Proposal
RI	Reference Implementation
RIP	Routing Information Protocol
RIPng	Routing Information Protocol for IPv6
RLC	Radio Link Control
RM	Resource Management
RMI	Remote Method Invocation
RMS	Record Management Store
RNC	Radio Network Controller
RNIF	RosettaNet Implementation Framework
RNSAP	Radio Network Subsystem Application Part
ROA	Recognized Operating Agencies
ROHC	Robust Header Compression
RPC	Remote Procedure Call
RR	Radio Resource
RRA	Requirement Requires Applying
RRB	Radio Regulations Board
RRC	Radio Resource Control
RRC	Regional Radiocommunication Conference
RRM	Radio Resource Management
RSA	Rivest Shamir Adleman
RSVP	Resource Reservation Protocol
RT	Railway Telecommunications
RT	Real-Time
RTCP	Real-time Transport Control Protocol
RTD	Real Time Difference
RTDC	Regional Telecommunication Development Conference
RTP	Real-time Transport Protocol
RTS	Request To Send
RTSP	Real Time Streaming Protocol

RTT	Round Trip Time
S	Signaling
S/MIME	Secure/Multi-purpose Internet Mail Extensions
SA	Security Association
SA	Selective Availability
SACCH	Slow Associated Control Channel
SA Forum	Service Availability Forum
Safety	Telecommunications Equipment Safety
SAGE	Security Algorithms Group of Experts
SAI	Service Area Identifier
SAML	Security Assertion Markup Language
SAP	Service Access Point
SAP	Session Announcement Protocol
SAR	Segmentation And Re-assembly
SAR	Servlet Archive
SCCP	Signaling Connection Control Part
SCN	Switched Circuit Network
SCP	Smart Card Platform
S-CSCF	Serving CSCF
SCTE	Society of Cable Telecommunications Engineers
SCTP	Stream Control Transmission Protocol
SDAP	Service Discovery Application Profile
SDE	Service Discovery Engine
SDH	Synchronous Digital Hierarchy
SDK	Software Development Kit
SDO	Standards Development Organization
SDP	Session Description Protocol
SDP	Service Discovery Protocol
SDPng	SDP next generation
SDS	Service Discovery Service
SEC	Security
SEC	Sponsor Executive Committee
SES	Satellite Earth Stations and Systems
SFN	Single Frequency Network
SG	Signaling Gateway
SG	Study Group
SGML	Standard Generalized Markup Language

VI Glossary

SGSN	Serving GPRS Support Node
SHA-1	Secure Hash Algorithm 1
S-HTTP	Secure HyperText Transfer Protocol
SI	Service Indication
SIFS	Short InterFrame Space
SIG	Special Interest Group
SIGCOMP	Signaling compression
SIIT	Stateless IP/ICMP Translation Algorithm
SILS	Standard for Interoperable LAN Security
SIM	Subscriber Identity Module
SIMPLE	SIP for Instant Messaging and Presence Leveraging Extensions
SIO	Scientific or Industrial Organization
SIP	Session Initiation Protocol
SIP-CGI	Common Gateway Interface for SIP
SIR	Signal-to-Interference Ratio
SLF	Subscriber Locator Function
SLP	Service Location Protocol
SM	Session Management
SMIL	Synchronized Multimedia Integration Language
SMS	Short Message Service
SMSC	Short Message Service Center
SMSGW	SMS Gateway
SMTP	Simple Mail Transfer Protocol
SNAP	Subnetwork Access Protocol
SNMP	Simple Network Management Protocol
SOAP	Simple Object Access Protocol
SOAP-DSIG	SOAP Digital Signature
SP	Service Provider
SP	Synchronization Profile
SPA	Self Provided Application
SPAN	Services and Protocols for Advanced Networks
SPD	Security Policy Database
SPI	Service Provisioning Infrastructure
SPP	Serial Port Profile
SPSCH	Shared Physical SubChannel
SRES	Signed RESponse
SS	Station Services

SS	Supplementary Services
SS7	Signaling System No. 7
SSA	Subsystem Architecture
SSCF	Service Specific Co-operation Function
SSCOP	Service Specific Connection Oriented Protocol
SSG	Special Study Group
SSI	System Software Interfaces
SSL	Secure Sockets Layer
SSO	Single Sign-On
SSP	Server-to-Server Protocol
SSPI	Security Service Application Programming Interface
STA	Station
STF	Specialist Task Force
STP	Scalable Test Platform
STQ	Speech processing, Transmission and Quality aspects
SwA	SOAP with Attachments
SWA	Systems Software Architecture
SVG	Scalable Vector Graphics
SVR4	System V Release 4.x
SWT	Standardized Web Services Technologies
SyncML	Synchronization Markup Language
T1	Standards Committee T1 - Telecommunications
TA	Timing Advance
TAP	Traditional Approval Process
TC	Technical Committee
TC	Tunnel Client
TCH	Traffic Channel
TCK	Technology Compatibility Kit
TCP	Transmission Control Protocol
TCP/IP	Transmission Control Protocol/Internet Protocol
TCS	Telephony Control System
TDAG	Telecommunication Development Advisory Group
TDD	Time Division Duplex
TDMA	Time Division Multiple Access
Tdoc	Temporary Document
TE	Terminal Equipment
TechCom	Technical Committee

VI Glossary

TELNET	Terminal Emulation Protocol
TETRA	Terrestrial Trunked Radio
TF	Transport Format
TGW	Terminal Gateway
TIA	Telecommunications Industry Association
TIPHON	Telecommunications and Internet Protocol Harmonization Over Networks
TLS	Transport Layer Security
TM	Transmission and Multiplexing
TM Forum	TeleManagement Forum
TMN	Telecommunication Management Network
TOA	Time Of Arrival
TR	Technical Reports
TRAU	Transcoder and Rate Adaptation Unit
TRX	Transceiver
TS	TimeSlot
TS	Technical Specification
TSACC	Telecommunications Standards Advisory Council of Canada
TSAG	Telecommunication Standardization Advisory Group
TSB	Telecommunication Standardization Bureau
TSG	Technical Specification Group
TSG CN	Technical Specification Group Core Network
TSG GERAN	Technical Specification Group GSM/EDGE Radio Access Network
TSG RAN	Technical Specification Group Radio Access Network
TSG SA	Technical Specification Group System Aspects
TSG T	Technical Specification Group Terminals
TTA	Telecommunications Technology Association
TTC	Telecommunication Technology Committee
TTCN	Tree and Tabular Combined Notation
TTI	Transmission Time Interval
TTP	Trusted Third Party
TU	Transaction User
TU3	Typical Urban 3 km/h
UA	User Agent
UAC	User Agent Client
UAProf	User Agent Profile
UAS	User Agent Server
UDDI	Universal Description, Discovery and Integration

UDP	User Datagram Protocol
UDP	Unacknowledged Data Protocol
UDVM	Universal Decompressor Virtual Machine
UE	User Equipment
UHF	Ultrahigh Frequency
UI	User Interface
UID	Unique Identification code
UML	Unified Modeling Language
UMTS	Universal Mobile Telecommunication System
UNI	User-Network Interface
U-NII	Unlicensed National Information Infrastructure
URI	Uniform Resource Identifier
URL	Uniform Resource Locator
USB	Universal Serial Bus
USER	Special Committee User Group
USIM	UMTS Subscriber Identity Module
USSD	Unstructured Supplementary Service Data
UTC	Universal Time Co-ordinates
UTF-8	Unicode Transformation Format 8
UTRA	UMTS Terrestrial Radio Access
UTRAN	UMTS Terrestrial Radio Access Network
UWCC	Universal Wireless Communications Consortium
VAS	Value Added Service
VASP	Value Added Service Provider
VC	Virtual Cursor
VGA	Video Graphics Array
VHF	Very High Frequency
VLAN	Virtual Local Area Network
VM	Virtual Machine
VoiceXML	Voice Extensible Markup Language
VoIP	Voice over IP
VPN	Virtual Private Network
W3C	World Wide Web Consortium
WAE	Wireless Application Environment
WAI	Web Accessibility Initiative
WAP	Wireless Application Protocol
WARC	World Administrative Radio Conference

VI

Glossary

WAV	Windows Audio File
WBMP	Wireless BitMap
WCDMA	Wideband Code Division Multiple Access
WCIT	World Conference on International Telecommunication
WDCTL	WLAN Device Controller
WECA	Wireless Ethernet Compatibility Alliance
Web-Ont	W3C Web Ontology Working Group
WEP	Wired Equivalent Privacy
WG	Working Group
WGR	Working Group on ITU Reform
WI	Work Item
WIM	Wireless Identity Module
WIM	WAP Identity Module
WINS	Windows Internet Name Service
WIP	WLAN Interworking Protocol
WLAN	Wireless Local Area Network
WMF	Wireless Multimedia Forum
WML	Wireless Markup Language
WMLS	Wireless Markup Language Script
WPAN	Wireless Personal Area Network
WP8F	ITU-R Working Party 8F
WPKI	Wireless Public Key Infrastructure
WRC	World Radiocommunication Conference
WSCL	Web Services Conversation Language
WSDL	Web Services Description Language
WSFL	Web Services Flow Language
WS-I	Web Services Interoperability Organization
WSIA	Web Services Interactive Applications
WSIL	Web Services Inspection Language
WSIS	World Summit on the Information Society
WS-License	Web Service License Language
WSP	Wireless Session Protocol
WS-Security	Web Service Security Language
WTA	Wireless Telephony Applications
WTAI	Wireless Telephony Applications Interface
WTDC	World Telecommunication Development Conference
WTLS	Wireless Transport Layer Security

WTP	Wireless Transport Protocol
WTPF	World Telecommunication Policy Forum
WTSA	World Telecommunication Standardization Assembly
WV	Wireless Village
WWW	World Wide Web
XACML	eXtensible Access Control Markup Language
xDSL	any Digital Subscription Line
XHTML	eXtensible HyperText Markup Language
XHTML MP	XHTML Mobile Profile
XKMS	XML Key Management Specification
XLANG	Web Services for Business Process Design
XMI	XML Metadata Interchange
XML	eXtensible Markup Language
XML-DSIG	XML Digital Signature
XMLP	XML Protocol
XMLP-WG	XML Protocol Working Protocol
XSD	XML Schema Definition
XSL	eXtensible Stylesheet Language
XSLT	eXtensible Stylesheet Language Transformations
xSP	any Service Provider

Index

MORE TITLES FROM IT PRESS

ile Internet Technical itecture – The Complete age

bile Internet will be much more than simply f accessing the Internet with a mobile device. e about integrating communication services everyday life. We will be able to use the Internet to help control our lives and to give e time to do the things we enjoy. The Mobile t will eventually change our way of life as e seen with the introduction of the telephone vision.

y and the Internet will be smoothly unified Mobile World. This means solid integration y existing technologies by using a thorough tanding of mobility and the unique character- of mobile business. It is also necessary to a range of completely new technologies to t new services and to meet the new challenges Mobile World. This must be done without cessive complexity for Mobile Internet service ers.

kia solution for covering these demands is bile Internet Technical Architecture (MITA).

ages, CD-ROMs, ISBN 951-826-671-9

Technologies and Standardization

Nokia

The Technologies section describes the existing technologies that will form a solid basis for future innovations, development work and the products of the Mobile Internet. The reader will learn about the technologies that already exist either in research, in the product development phase or in actual products.

The Standardization section introduces a set of standardization organizations. It also discusses the role and challenges of standardization in the new Mobile World.

520 pages, CD, ISBN 951-826-668-9

Solutions and Tools

Nokia

The Solutions section gives insight into current Nokia solutions. It provides information on how various technologies are combined to produce systems and services today.

The Tools section addresses one of the corner stones of MITA: tools for application and service development. The section describes some examples on how applications and services can be developed with Nokia tools for the Mobile Internet.

510 pages, CD, ISBN 951-826-669-7

Visions and Implementations

Nokia

The Visions section describes a set of key functions that will be essential for the Mobile Internet. The reader is given a more future oriented view on how technologies will evolve. This includes topics,such as browsing, messaging, rich call, QoS and security.

The Implementations section gives a view on MITA Reference Implementations that are used to validate new concepts, to gain experience and to smoothen the way for products based on the latest technologies.

520 pages, CD, ISBN 951-826-670-0

Professional Mobile Java with J2ME

Kontio

J2ME provides embedded software application developers the platform and operating system independence of Java programming language and thereby makes programmers' work easier. This book teaches how to develop applications using the hottest future technology: J2ME. Professional Mobile Java with J2ME covers J2ME architecture and explains in detail the functions of CLDC and MIDP. The book contains numerous practical examples of every topic covered and complete sample applications.

300 pages, CD, ISBN 951-826-554-2

Order IT Press books:
www.itpress.biz **IT Press**